Chapter and Unit Tests

Prentice Hall
Physical Science

Concepts in Action
With Earth and Space Science

PEARSON

Prentice
Hall

Needham, Massachusetts
Upper Saddle River, New Jersey

Chapter and Unit Tests

Prentice Hall
Physical Science
Concepts in Action
With Earth and Space Science

FIELD TESTERS

Robert W. Arts
Pikeville College
Pikeville, Kentucky

Peggy Lynn Bondurant
Mesquite High School
Gilbert, Arizona

Teresa Casal
Felix Varela Senior High School
Miami, Florida

Richelle Lee Dull
Vance High School
Charlotte, North Carolina

Yvonne Favaro
Englewood Cliffs, New Jersey

Mary Louise Freitas
Peoria High School
Peoria, Arizona

Karen S. Garner
Rutherford County Schools
Murfreesboro, Tennessee

Margaret A. Holzer
Chatham High School
Somerset, New Jersey

Susan McCullen
Big Rapids High School
Big Rapids, Michigan

David Petro
Cardinal Carter Secondary
 School
Leamington, Ontario, Canada

A. Marie Pool
Clinton High School
Clinton, Oklahoma

Alan Seidman
Margaretville Central School
Margaretville, New York

Evan P. Silberstein
Spring Valley High School
Spring Valley, New York

Lesia Thaisz
Gloversville High School
Gloversville, New York

James R. White
Southside High School
Chocowinity, North Carolina

John P. Wilbur
Caledonia-Mumford Schools
Caledonia, New York

SAFETY REVIEWER
Dr. Kenneth R. Roy
Glastonbury Public Schools
Glastonbury, Connecticut

ISBN 0-13-069987-X

1 2 3 4 5 6 7 8 9 10   07 06 05 04 03

● Contents

Magnetism

Physics Unit

Earth's Interior

Earth's Surface

Weather and Climate

The Solar System

Exploring the Universe

Earth and Space Science Unit

Chapter 1   Science Skills   **Chapter Test A**

Multiple Choice

Write the letter that best answers the question or completes the statement on the line provided.

_____ **1.** How are science and technology related?
   a. Technology is a branch of natural science.
   b. Science is a branch of technology.
   c. Advances in science may lead to advances in technology and vice versa.
   d. Science and technology are not related.

_____ **2.** How does Earth science overlap with life science?
   a. Earth science involves the study of Earth's rocks.
   b. Earth science involves the study of systems that may include living organisms.
   c. Earth science involves the study of the composition of matter.
   d. Earth science does not overlap with life science.

_____ **3.** What are the building blocks of all matter?
   a. forces   **b.** atoms
   c. magnetic fields   **d.** kinetic and potential energy

_____ **4.** What happens when the data in an investigation do not support the original hypothesis?
   a. The scientist gives up and starts an investigation on a new topic.
   b. The data must be incorrect and are thrown out.
   c. The hypothesis will be revised.
   d. The data are altered so that they support the original hypothesis.

_____ **5.** Which of the following statements is true about scientific theories?
   a. Scientific theories become scientific laws.
   b. Scientific theories are never proven.
   c. Scientific theories become hypotheses.
   d. Scientific theories summarize patterns found in nature.

_____ **6.** Why are scientific models important?
   a. They prove scientific theories.
   b. They help visualize things that are very complex, very large, or very small.
   c. They make it harder to understand things.
   d. They never change.

_____ **7.** Which of the following is an example of a safe laboratory procedure?
  a. tying back long hair and loose clothing
  b. eating or drinking from laboratory glassware
  c. touching hot objects with your bare hands
  d. testing an odor by directly inhaling the vapor

_____ **8.** Which of the following conversion factors would you use to change 18 kilometers to meters?
  a. 1000 m/1 km   **b.** 1 km/1000 m
  c. 100 m/1 km   **d.** 1 km/100 m

_____ **9.** There are 1660 megawatts of wind-generated electricity produced globally every year. This amount is equivalent to
  a. 1,660,000 watts   **b.** 1,660,000 kilowatts
  c. 16,600,000 watts   **d.** 166,000 kilowatts

_____ **10.** Which of the following clocks offers the most precision?
  a. a clock that measures time to the nearest hour
  b. a clock that measures time to the nearest minute
  c. a clock that measures time to the nearest second
  d. a clock that measures time to the nearest tenth of a second

_____ **11.** Approximately how many kelvins are equal to 60°F?
  a. 439   **b.** 212   **c.** 902   **d.** 289

_____ **12.** The type of graph used to show how a part of something relates to the whole is a
  a. circle graph   **b.** bar graph
  c. line graph   **d.** direct proportion

_____ **13.** How do scientists who speak different languages make their data understandable to one another?
  a. They all use different systems of measurement.
  b. They all use SI.
  c. They communicate through a universal translator.
  d. They all must speak French.

_____ **14.** Why are peer reviews important?
  a. Scientists receive questions and criticism from their peers.
  b. Data are checked for accuracy.
  c. Scientists receive comments and suggestions from other scientists.
  d. all of the above

_____ **15.** If the relationship between the manipulated variable and the responding variable is a direct proportion, what will a line graph of this relationship look like?
  a. a straight line   **b.** a curved line
  c. a jagged line   **d.** none of the above

Completion

Complete each statement on the line provided.

1. A measurement must include both a number and a(an)

   _____.

2. An experiment in which only one variable, the manipulated
   variable, is changed at a time is called a(an) _____.

3. The two main areas of physical science are physics and

   _____.

4. In an experiment, if doubling the manipulated variable results in a
   doubling of the responding variable, the relationship between the
   variables is a(an) _____.

5. The three values—10.714 m, 12.821 m, and 13.646 m—have the
   same number of _____.

Short Answer

*In complete sentences, write the answers to the questions on
the lines provided.*

1. Explain how technology and science are related.

   _____

   _____

   _____

2. What type of graph would be the best to use to compare the levels
   of lead contamination in six water wells?

   _____

   _____

3. What is the relationship between two variables if the product of
   the variables is constant?

   _____

   _____

4. What happens to the number in a measurement that is converted
   from kilometers to meters?

   _____

5. Describe a main idea of physical science that deals with space and
   time.

   _____

   _____

   _____

Using Science Skills

Use the diagram to answer each question. Write the answers on a separate sheet of paper.

1. **Analyzing Data** What is the slope of the line shown in Figure 1-1?

2. **Controlling Variables** In Figure 1-1, what is the responding variable?

3. **Analyzing Data** In Figure 1-1, what is the relationship between mass and volume?

4. **Using Graphs** In Figure 1-1, what quantity does the slope represent?

5. **Analyzing Data** In Figure 1-1, what metric units are represented by points on the plotted line?

Figure 1-1

Essay

Write the answers to each question on a separate sheet of paper.

1. Use Figure 1-2 to describe how the steel ball moved during the experiment. Average speed is calculated by dividing total distance by time. Did the steel ball speed up, slow down, or remain at the same speed throughout the experiment?

2. What is the difference between a scientific law and a scientific theory?

3. Describe some of the main ideas of physical science.

4. Describe a possible order of steps of a scientific method used in an investigation.

5. Explain how peer reviews are important in either supporting a hypothesis or revising a hypothesis.

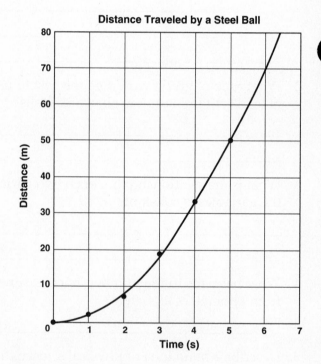

Figure 1-2

Name _____ Class _____ Date _____

Multiple Choice

Write the letter that best answers the question or completes the statement on the line provided.

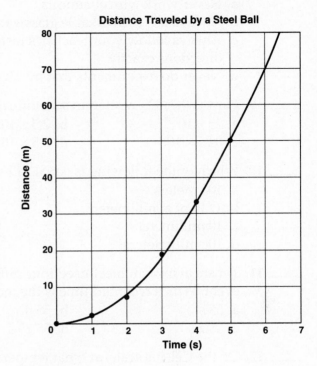

Figure 1-1

_____ 1. What type of graph is represented by Figure 1-1?
   a. bar graph
   b. line graph
   c. circle graph
   d. none of the above

_____ 2. What is a system of knowledge and the methods used to find that knowledge?
   a. science
   b. technology
   c. measurement
   d. curiosity

_____ 3. Which of the following is NOT a branch of natural science?
   a. life science
   b. Earth and space science
   c. physical science
   d. social science

_____ 4. Which of the following is NOT one of the main ideas of physical science?
   a. The universe is very old and very large.
   b. Forces cause changes in motion.
   c. Energy can be transferred from one form to another, but it can never be destroyed.
   d. One of the main branches of natural science is biology.

_____ 5. In which step of the scientific method is information obtained through the senses?
   a. drawing conclusions   **b.** making observations
   c. analyzing data   **d.** revising a hypothesis

_____ 6. What is a statement that summarizes a pattern found in nature?
   a. a scientific law   **b.** a fact
   c. a scientific theory   **d.** a hypothesis

_____ 7. What is a physical or mental representation of an object or an event?
   a. a theory   **b.** a hypothesis
   c. a model   **d.** a scientific law

_____ **8.** What is the most important safety rule?
   a. Never work with chemicals.
   b. Always use unbreakable glassware.
   c. Always follow your teacher's instructions and textbook directions exactly.
   d. Never do experiments that involve flames or hot objects.

_____ **9.** How is 0.00025 written in scientific notation?
   a. 25×10^{-5} **b.** 2.5×10^{4}
   c. 0.25×10^{-3} **d.** 2.5×10^{-4}

_____ **10.** Which of the following is equal to 1 centimeter?
   a. 100 meters
   b. 1/10 of a millimeter
   c. 10 millimeters
   d. 100 millimeters

_____ **11.** Timers at a swim meet used four different clocks to time an event. Which recorded time is the most precise?
   a. 55 s   **b.** 55.0 s
   c. 55.2 s   **d.** 55.25 s

_____ **12.** On the Celsius scale, at what temperature does water boil?
   a. 0°   **b.** 212°
   c. 100°   **d.** 32°

_____ **13.** What is the relationship in which the ratio of the manipulated variable and the responding variable is constant?
   a. inverse proportion
   b. direct proportion
   c. slope
   d. interdependent

_____ **14.** How do scientists communicate the results of investigations?
   a. by publishing articles in scientific journals
   b. by giving talks at scientific conferences
   c. by exchanging e-mails
   d. all of the above

_____ **15.** What is a peer review?
   a. a process in which only close friends of a scientist review the scientist's work
   b. a process in which scientists examine other scientists' work
   c. a process in which scientists copy other scientists' work
   d. a process in which scientists keep their work secret

Completion

Complete each statement on the line provided.

1. The SI base unit of mass is the _____.

2. An organized plan for gathering, organizing, and communicating information is called a(an) _____.

3. A(An) _____ is a way of plotting data to show changes that occur in related variables.

4. Computers are an example of _____ that helps people solve problems.

5. Natural science is divided into life science, Earth and space science, and _____.

6. The _____ is the variable that changes in response to the manipulated variable.

7. A(An) _____ is a statement that summarizes a pattern found in nature.

8. A(An) _____ makes it easier to understand things that are too small, too large, or too hard to observe directly.

9. The measurement 0.014 seconds equals _____ milliseconds.

10. _____ is the closeness of a measurement to the actual value being measured.

Short Answer

In complete sentences, write the answers to the questions on the lines provided.

1. What is the single most important laboratory safety rule?

_____

_____

2. Why do scientists speak at conferences and write articles in scientific journals?

_____

_____

_____

3. What is a peer review?

_____

_____

_____

4. How many significant figures will the answer to the calculation 65.25×37.4 have?

_____

5. What is the temperature at which water freezes, expressed in Fahrenheit, Celsius, and kelvins?

_____

_____

_____

Using Science Skills

Use the diagram to answer each question. Write the answers on a separate sheet of paper.

Figure 1-2

1. Using Graphs What measurements are compared in Figure 1-2?

2. Analyzing Data In Figure 1-2, which month had the highest amount of precipitation?

3. Inferring Why might the data in Figure 1-2 be important to share with a scientist studying agriculture trends in Port Hardy?

4. Using Graphs Use Figure 1-2 to determine the approximate total annual precipitation.

5. Calculating In Figure 1-2, how many meters of precipitation were recorded during January?

Chapter 2   Properties of Matter   **Chapter Test A**

Multiple Choice

Write the letter that best answers the question or completes the statement on the line provided.

_____ **1.** Which of the following is NOT a pure substance?
   a. milk   **b.** oxygen
   c. water   **d.** carbon dioxide

_____ **2.** If an unknown substance CANNOT be broken down into simpler substances, it is
   a. a compound.
   b. an element.
   c. made of one kind of atom.
   d. both b and c

_____ **3.** The symbol for gold is
   a. Au.   **b.** Al.   **c.** Gl.   **d.** Go.

_____ **4.** Water is a compound because it
   a. can be broken down into hydrogen and oxygen.
   b. has a fixed composition.
   c. is made of water atoms joined together.
   d. both a and b

_____ **5.** Which of the following is a characteristic of a mixture?
   a. can have varying properties
   b. has a fixed composition
   c. contains no pure substances
   d. both a and b

_____ **6.** Which of the following is a heterogeneous mixture?
   a. water in a swimming pool
   b. sugar water
   c. a jar of mixed nuts
   d. stainless steel

_____ **7.** You are about to open a container of soy milk but notice that there are instructions to "shake well before serving." The soy milk is most likely a
   a. solution.   **b.** pure substance.
   c. colloid.   **d.** suspension.

_____ **8.** Which of the following has the highest viscosity?
   a. corn syrup   **b.** milk
   c. water   **d.** orange juice

_____ **9.** A material that is malleable and conducts electricity is most likely
   a. wood.   **b.** ice.
   c. a metal.   **d.** motor oil.

_____10. Which of the following materials is useful for making molds because it has a low melting point?
   a. wood   **b.** metal   **c.** clay   **d.** wax

_____11. What method can be used to separate parts of a liquid mixture when the entire mixture can pass through a filter?
   a. filtration   **b.** distillation   **c.** straining   **d.** screening

_____12. Which of the following is a physical change?
   a. sawing a piece of wood in half
   b. burning a piece of wood
   c. rust forming on an iron fence
   d. a copper roof changing color from red to green

_____13. A substance that has high reactivity
   a. easily combines chemically with other substances.
   b. burns in the presence of water.
   c. displaces dissolved oxygen.
   d. has a high boiling point.

_____14. During which of the following chemical changes does a precipitate form?
   a. Vinegar is added to baking powder.
   b. Lemon juice is added to milk.
   c. Lemon juice is added to water.
   d. A banana ripens.

_____15. Which of the following is evidence of a chemical change?
   a. Iron changes color when heated.
   b. Gas bubbles form in boiling water.
   c. Balls of wax form when melted wax is poured into ice water.
   d. A gas forms when vinegar and baking soda are mixed.

Completion

Complete each statement on the line provided.

1. Pure substances are either _____ or
   _____.

2. The symbols for elements have either _____ or
   _____ letters.

3. A compound can be made from two or more elements or other
   _____ joined together in a fixed composition.

4. Rust forms because iron and oxygen are highly
   _____ elements.

5. When a metal changes color because it has been heated, a(an)
   _____ change occurred. When a metal changes
   color because it has reacted with another substance, a(an)
   _____ change occurred.

Short Answer

Use complete sentences to write the answers to the questions on the lines provided.

1. How can you change the properties of a mixture?

   _____

   _____

   _____

   _____

Melting and Boiling Points of Some Substances		
Substance	**Melting Point**	**Boiling Point**
Hydrogen	−259.3°C	−252.9°C
Nitrogen	−210.0°C	−195.8°C
Acetic acid	16.6°C	117.9°C
Gold	1064.2°C	2856°C

Figure 2-1

2. Based on the information in Figure 2-1, which substances would be solids at 10.0°C?

   _____

   _____

3. How do changes in temperature usually affect the viscosity of a liquid?

   _____

   _____

   _____

4. Give an example of a physical change that can be reversed and an example of a physical change that cannot be reversed.

   _____

   _____

   _____

5. What kind of change is taking place if you see white mold growing on a strawberry?

   _____

   _____

Using Science Skills

Use the table to answer each question. Write the answers on a separate sheet of paper.

Properties of Three Mixtures			
	Scatters Light	Separates into Layers	Can Be Separated by Filtration
Mixture A	Yes	No	No
Mixture B	No	No	No
Mixture C	Yes	Yes	Yes

Figure 2-2

1. **Classifying** Based on the data in Figure 2-2, is Mixture C a homogeneous or heterogeneous mixture? Explain your answer.

2. **Analyzing Data** Which of the mixtures in Figure 2-2 is a solution? Explain how you know.

3. **Analyzing Data** Which of the mixtures in Figure 2-2 is a colloid? Explain how you know.

4. **Classifying** Rank the mixtures in Figure 2-2 in order of the size of their largest particles, starting with the mixture with the smallest particles.

5. **Predicting** Why can't Mixture B in Figure 2-2 be separated by filtration? What method might be used to separate the substances in Mixture B?

Essay

Write the answer to each question on a separate sheet of paper.

1. Compare the properties of water to the properties of the elements it contains.

2. Explain how you could use a physical property to test the purity of a silver coin without damaging the coin.

3. Suppose you want to separate the leaves, acorns, and twigs from a pile of soil. Filtration and distillation are two processes of separating mixtures. Explain which process you would use and why.

4. Explain why rust forms in steel tanks that hold seawater in ships. How can nitrogen be used to reduce rust in these tanks?

5. Suppose you heat a liquid and then gas bubbles are produced. With no other evidence, can you tell if a physical change or chemical change is occurring? Explain your answer.

Chapter 2   Properties of Matter   **Chapter Test B**

Multiple Choice

Write the letter that best answers the question or completes the statement on the line provided.

_____ **1.** Which of the following are pure substances?
   a. solutions
   b. compounds
   c. homogeneous mixtures
   d. colloids

_____ **2.** A substance that is made up of only one kind of atom is a(an)
   a. compound.   **b.** homogeneous mixture.
   c. element.   **d.** solution.

_____ **3.** What is the symbol for aluminum?
   a. AL   **b.** Al   **c.** Au   **d.** A

_____ **4.** If a material contains three elements joined in a fixed proportion, it is a(an)
   a. mixture.   **b.** solution.
   c. atom.   **d.** compound.

_____ **5.** Which of the following is a mixture?
   a. carbon dioxide   **b.** silicon
   c. silicon dioxide   **d.** sand

_____ **6.** A mixture that appears to contain only one substance is a(an)
   a. homogeneous mixture.
   b. heterogeneous mixture.
   c. compound.
   d. element.

_____ **7.** A mixture can be classified as a solution, suspension, or colloid based on the
   a. number of particles it contains.
   b. size of its largest particles.
   c. color of its particles.
   d. size of its smallest particles.

_____ **8.** Which of the following is malleable?
   a. glass   **b.** pottery
   c. ice   **d.** gold

_____ **9.** A substance has a melting point of 0°C and a boiling point of 100°C. The substance is most likely
   a. water.   **b.** hydrogen.
   c. gold.   **d.** table salt.

_____10. What physical properties of nylon and leather make them good materials to use for shoelaces?
   a. high density and low conductivity
   b. durability and flexibility
   c. hardness and durability
   d. low viscosity and flexibility

_____11. Filtration can be used to separate mixtures based on
   a. their boiling points.
   b. their densities.
   c. their melting points.
   d. the size of their particles.

_____12. When a physical change occurs in a sample of matter which of the following does NOT change?
   a. shape   **b.** mass
   c. volume   **d.** composition

_____13. Flammability is a material's ability to burn in the presence of
   a. hydrogen.   **b.** nitrogen.
   c. oxygen.   **d.** carbon dioxide.

_____14. Which of the following is NOT a clue that a chemical change has occurred?
   a. change in color
   b. production of a gas
   c. formation of a precipitate
   d. change in shape

_____15. Which of the following is a chemical change?
   a. ice melting
   b. ice being carved
   c. water boiling
   d. water breaking down into hydrogen and oxygen

Completion

Complete each statement on the line provided.

1. Matter that always has exactly the same composition is classified as a(an) _____.

2. An element has a fixed composition because it contains only one type of _____.

3. The substances in a(an) _____ mixture are evenly distributed throughout the mixture.

4. If a spoon gets hot quickly when it is used to stir a pot of soup, it is probably made of _____.

Melting and Boiling Points of Some Substances		
Substance	Melting Point	Boiling Point
Hydrogen	−259.3°C	−252.9°C
Nitrogen	−210.0°C	−195.8°C
Acetic Acid	16.6°C	117.9°C
Gold	1064.2°C	2856°C

Figure 2-1

5. Based on the information in Figure 2-1, the _____ point of nitrogen is −210.0°C and the _____ point of nitrogen is −195.8°C.

6. _____ is a process that could be used to separated dissolved particles from the liquid in a solution.

7. A(An) _____ change occurs when a material changes shape or size but composition does not change.

8. _____ properties can be observed only when the substances in a sample of matter are changing into different substances.

9. A solid that forms and separates from a liquid mixture is a(an) _____.

10. A cake rises as it bakes because a chemical change causes _____ to be produced.

Short Answer

In complete sentences, write the answers to the questions on the lines provided.

1. How do the properties of a compound compare to the properties of the elements it contains?

   _____

   _____

2. How is the composition of a substance different from the composition of a mixture?

   _____

   _____

   _____

3. If you looked at a glass containing a solution and a glass containing a suspension, how could you tell which glass contained the suspension?

   _____

   _____

4. What are three common clues that a chemical change has occurred?

_____

_____

_____

5. How is a chemical change different from a physical change?

_____

_____

Using Science Skills

Use the table to answer each question. Write the answers on a separate sheet of paper.

Physical Properties of Four Materials Used to Make Sculptures			
	Malleability	**Hardness**	**Melting Point**
Wax	Soft enough to be carved and molded	Soft but keeps its shape at room temperature	Low melting point
Unbaked clay	Can be molded	Soft	Very high melting point
Baked clay	Brittle after being baked at a high temperature	Hard	Very high melting point
Metal (a mixture of copper, zinc, and lead)	Can be hammered without shattering	Hard	High melting point

Figure 2-2

1. **Comparing and Contrasting** Use Figure 2-2 to compare the physical properties of clay before and after it is baked at a high temperature.

2. **Using Tables and Graphs** Which of the materials in Figure 2-2 are malleable?

3. **Comparing and Contrasting** Based on the information in Figure 2-2, compare the properties of a sculpture made from metal and a sculpture made from baked clay.

4. **Inferring** An object made from a material listed in Figure 2-2 changes shape when you leave it in a sunny window. Which material is the object made from? How do you know?

5. **Inferring** Which of the materials described in Figure 2-2 would be least likely to be recycled? Explain your choice.

Chapter 3   States of Matter   **Chapter Test A**

Multiple Choice

Write the letter that best answers the question or completes the statement on the line provided.

_____ **1.** Ninety-nine percent of all the matter that can be observed in the universe exists as
     a. gases.   **b.** plasmas.
     c. liquids.   **d.** solids.

_____ **2.** If you move a substance from one container to another and its volume changes, the substance is a
     a. solid.   **b.** liquid.
     c. gas.   **d.** solution.

_____ **3.** Forces of attraction limit the motion of particles most in
     a. a solid.   **b.** a liquid.
     c. a gas.   **d.** both b and c

_____ **4.** Collisions of helium atoms and the walls of a closed container cause
     a. condensation.   **b.** gas pressure.
     c. a decrease in volume.   **d.** an overall loss of energy.

_____ **5.** Raising the temperature of a gas will increase its pressure IF the volume of the gas
     a. and the number of particles are increased.
     b. is increased, but the number of particles is constant.
     c. and the number of particles are constant.
     d. is constant, but the number of particles is increased.

_____ **6.** Which of the following will cause a decrease in gas pressure in a closed container?
     a. lowering the temperature
     b. reducing the volume
     c. adding more gas
     d. both a and b

_____ **7.** Boyle's law states that the volume of a gas is inversely proportional to its pressure if the
     a. temperature and number of particles are constant.
     b. temperature reaches absolute zero.
     c. number of particles decreases.
     d. temperature and number of particles are doubled.

_____ **8.** At a temperature of 274 K, the gas in a cylinder has a volume of 4.0 liters. If the volume of the gas is decreased to 2.0 liters, what must the temperature be for the gas pressure to remain constant?
     a. 137 K   **b.** 273 K
     c. 378 K   **d.** 556 K

_____ 9. The phase change that is the reverse of condensation is
   a. freezing.   **b.** sublimation.
   c. vaporization.   **d.** melting.

_____ 10. During a phase change, the temperature of a substance
   a. increases.   **b.** decreases.
   c. does not change.   **d.** increases or decreases.

_____ 11. If a solid piece of naphthalene is heated and remains at 80°C
   until it is completely melted, you know that 80°C is the
   a. freezing point of naphthalene.
   b. melting point of naphthalene.
   c. boiling point of naphthalene.
   d. both a and b

_____ 12. The heat of fusion for water is the amount of energy needed
   for water to
   a. freeze.   **b.** boil.
   c. melt.   **d.** evaporate.

_____ 13. Which of the following statements about ice melting is true?
   a. Energy flows from the ice to its surroundings.
   b. Water molecules move from their fixed position.
   c. Water molecules lose energy.
   d. The temperature of the ice increases as it melts.

_____ 14. The phase change in which a substance changes from a solid
   to a gas or vapor without changing to a liquid first is
   a. sublimation.   **b.** deposition.
   c. vaporization.   **d.** melting.

_____ 15. The phase change in which a substance changes from a gas
   directly to a solid is
   a. condensation.   **b.** vaporization.
   c. deposition.   **d.** sublimation.

_____ 16. Which of the following phase changes is an exothermic
   change?
   a. sublimation   **b.** deposition
   c. vaporization   **d.** melting

Completion

Complete each statement on the line provided.

1. The state of matter that exists only at extremely low temperatures
is called a Bose-Einstein _____.

2. The motion of one particle of a gas is unaffected by the motion of
other particles of the gas unless the particles _____.

3. The pascal is the SI unit for _____.

4. During vaporization, a substance changes from a(an) _____ to a(an) _____.

5. Evaporation is the process that changes a substance from a liquid to a gas at temperatures below the substance's _____ point.

Short Answer

Use complete sentences to write the answers to the questions on the lines provided.

1. Solid, liquid, and gas are three states of matter. What are two other states of matter, and under what conditions do they exist?

   _____

   _____

   _____

   _____

Substance A

Substance B

Substance C

Figure 3-1

2. What substance in Figure 3-1 is a solid? Explain how you know.

   _____

   _____

   _____

3. If a gas in a sealed container has a pressure of 50 kPa at 300 K, what will the pressure be if the temperature rises to 360 K?

   _____

4. Describe what happens to the arrangement of water molecules as ice melts.

   _____

   _____

   _____

5. How could you determine if a phase change is endothermic?

_____

_____

_____

Using Science Skills

Use the graph to answer each question. Write the answers on a separate sheet of paper.

1. **Interpreting Graphics** In Figure 3-2, what is the unit used for pressure? What is the pressure when the volume is 0.5 L? What is the pressure when the volume is 1.0 L?

2. **Interpreting Graphics** In Figure 3-2, what is the manipulated variable, and what is the responding variable?

3. **Predicting** How would the graph in Figure 3-2 change if the volume of the cylinder remained constant and temperature was the manipulated variable?

Figure 3-2

4. **Inferring** Based on Figure 3-2, compare the collisions between particles of gas and the walls of a container when the volume of gas is 1.0 L and when the volume is 2.0 L. Assume the number of particles does not change. Explain any differences in collisions.

5. **Interpreting Graphics** In Figure 3-2, if P_1 is 200 kPa and P_2 is 50 kPa, what are V_1 and V_2?

Essay

Write the answer to each question on a separate sheet of paper.

1. Use billiard balls to describe the motion of particles in a gas. Use students in a crowded hallway to describe the motion of particles in a liquid. Use an audience in a movie theater to describe the motion of particles in a solid.

2. Use breathing as an example to explain the relationship between volume and air pressure.

3. What factors affect the volume of a weather balloon as it rises through the atmosphere?

4. Why does pasta take longer to cook in boiling water at elevations above sea level?

5. Describe how water can change from a liquid to a vapor at temperatures lower than its boiling point.

Name _____ Class _____ Date _____

Multiple Choice

Write the letter that best answers the question or completes the statement on the line provided.

_____ **1.** A gas has
   a. a definite volume but no definite shape.
   b. a definite shape but no definite volume.
   c. no definite shape or definite volume.
   d. a definite volume and definite shape.

_____ **2.** Matter that has a definite volume but no definite shape is a
   a. liquid.   **b.** solid.
   c. gas.   **d.** plasma.

Substance A

Substance B

Substance C

Figure 3-1

_____ **3.** In which of the substances in Figure 3-1 are the forces of
         attraction among the particles so weak that they can be
         ignored under ordinary conditions?
   a. Substance A   **b.** Substance B
   c. Substance C   **d.** all of the above

_____ **4.** What is the result of a force distributed over an area?
   a. temperature   **b.** volume
   c. pressure   **d.** mass

_____ **5.** Which of the following factors affect the pressure of an
         enclosed gas?
   a. temperature   **b.** volume
   c. number of particles   **d.** all of the above

_____ **6.** The temperature and volume in a closed container of gas
         remain constant. If the number of particles of gas is
         increased, the gas pressure will
   a. increase.
   b. decrease.
   c. remain constant.
   d. cause a decrease in the average kinetic energy of
         the particles.

_____ **7.** The law that states that the volume of a gas is directly
proportional to its temperature in kelvins if the pressure and
the number of particles is constant is
   a. Boyle's law.
   b. Bose's law.
   c. Einstein's law.
   d. Charles's law.

_____ **8.** If the volume of a cylinder is reduced from 4.0 liters to
2.0 liters, the pressure of the gas in the cylinder will
change from 100 kilopascals to
   a. 50 kilopascals.
   b. 150 kilopascals.
   c. 200 kilopascals.
   d. 400 kilopascals.

_____ **9.** What type of change occurs when water changes from a
solid to a liquid?
   a. a phase change
   b. a physical change
   c. an irreversible change
   d. both a and b

_____ **10.** During a phase change, the temperature of a substance
   a. increases.
   b. decreases.
   c. stays the same.
   d. either increases or decreases, depending on the change.

_____ **11.** During what phase change does the arrangement of water
molecules become more orderly?
   a. melting   **b.** freezing
   c. boiling   **d.** condensing

_____ **12.** The phase change in which a substance changes from a
liquid to a gas is
   a. deposition.   **b.** sublimation.
   c. condensation.   **d.** vaporization.

_____ **13.** The phase change in which a substance changes from a solid
to a liquid is
   a. freezing.   **b.** melting.
   c. sublimation.   **d.** condensation.

_____ **14.** Which of the following phase changes is an endothermic
change?
   a. condensation   **b.** vaporization
   c. deposition   **d.** freezing

Name _____ Class _____ Date _____

Completion

Complete each statement on the line provided.

1. A(an) _____ has a definite volume and a definite shape.

2. Materials can be classified as solids, liquids, or gases based on whether their shapes and _____ are definite or variable.

3. The shape of a material remains constant when it is moved from one container to another. This material is a(an)

   _____.

4. The _____ theory of matter states that all particles of matter are in constant motion.

5. _____ between the particles of a gas and the walls of the container cause pressure in a closed container of gas.

6. Reducing the volume of a gas _____ its pressure if the _____ of the gas and the number of particles are constant.

7. A graph representing Charles's law shows that the _____ of a gas increases at the same rate as the _____ of the gas.

8. If you are using Charles's law to find the volume of a gas at a certain temperature, the temperature must be expressed in

   _____.

9. Water boils when its vapor pressure becomes equal to _____ pressure.

10. During a(an) _____ change, the system releases energy to its surroundings.

Short Answer

Use complete sentences to write the answers to the questions on the lines provided.

1. Compare the shape and volume of solids, liquids, and gases.

   _____

   _____

   _____

   _____

2. Why is the volume of a liquid constant?

   _____

   _____

   _____

3. Why does the air pressure in a car's tires increase after a long drive?

_____

_____

_____

_____

4. Describe what happens to the average kinetic energy of water molecules as water freezes.

_____

_____

_____

_____

5. Name and describe the phase change that occurs when dry ice is placed in an open container at room temperature.

_____

_____

_____

_____

_____

Using Science Skills

Use the diagram to answer each question. Write the answers on a separate sheet of paper.

1. **Interpreting Graphics** Identify the phase changes in Figure 3-2 that are labeled a, b, and c.
2. **Interpreting Graphics** Explain why the phase changes in Figure 3-2 are shown in pairs.
3. **Comparing and Contrasting** Use the terms in Figure 3-2 to compare the phase changes that occur when water vapor changes to dew or frost.
4. **Interpreting Graphics** Describe the two phase changes represented in Figure 3-2 that can happen to a liquid.
5. **Applying Concepts** What three phase changes in Figure 3-2 are endothermic?

Figure 3-2

Chapter 4   Atomic Structure

Multiple Choice

Write the letter that best answers the question or completes the statement on the line provided.

_____ **1.** Democritus thought that matter was made of tiny particles
   a. of earth, air, fire, and water.
   b. that could not be divided.
   c. that could be divided.
   d. that were all round and smooth.

_____ **2.** If 2 grams of element X combine with 4 grams of element Y to form compound XY, how many grams of element Y would combine with 12 grams of X to form the same compound?
   a. 6 grams   **b.** 12 grams
   c. 18 grams   **d.** 24 grams

_____ **3.** Which of the following most accurately represents John Dalton's model of the atom?
   a. a tiny, solid sphere with an unpredictable mass for a given element
   b. a hollow sphere with a dense nucleus
   c. a tiny, solid sphere with a predictable mass for a given element
   d. a sphere that is hollow throughout

_____ **4.** J.J. Thomson's experiments provided evidence that an atom
   a. is the smallest particle of matter.
   b. contains negatively charged particles.
   c. has a negative charge.
   d. has a positive charge.

_____ **5.** Rutherford's gold foil experiment provided evidence for which of the following statements?
   a. Negative and positive charges are spread evenly throughout an atom.
   b. Alpha particles have a positive charge.
   c. Gold is not as dense as previously thought.
   d. There is a dense, positively charged mass in the center of an atom.

_____ **6.** Which statement best describes Rutherford's model of the atom?
   a. It is like an avocado with the pit representing the nucleus.
   b. It is like an aquarium with swimming fish representing positive charges.
   c. It is like a fried egg with the yolk representing the nucleus.
   d. It is like a huge stadium with a positively charged marble at the center.

_____ **7.** Which statement about subatomic particles is true?
   a. Protons, neutrons, and electrons all have about the same mass.
   b. Unlike protons or neutrons, electrons have no mass.
   c. Neutrons have no charge and no mass.
   d. An electron has far less mass than either a proton or neutron.

_____ **8.** Which of the following is unique for any given element?
   a. the number of neutrons
   b. the charge on the electrons
   c. the number of protons
   d. the mass of a neutron

_____ **9.** Suppose an atom has a mass number of 35. Which statement is true beyond any doubt?
   a. The atom has an odd number of neutrons.
   b. The atomic number is less than 17.
   c. The atom is not an isotope.
   d. The number of protons in the nucleus does not equal the number of neutrons.

_____ **10.** Which statement is true about oxygen-17 and oxygen-18?
   a. They do not have the same number of protons.
   b. Their atoms have an identical mass.
   c. They are isotopes of oxygen.
   d. The have the same mass number.

_____ **11.** How was Bohr's atomic model similar to Rutherford's model?
   a. It assigned energy levels to electrons.
   b. It described electron position in terms of the electron cloud model.
   c. It described how electrons gain or lose energy.
   d. It described a nucleus surrounded by a large volume of space.

_____ **12.** Which statement accurately represents the arrangement of electrons in Bohr's atomic model?
   a. Electrons vibrate in fixed locations around the nucleus.
   b. Electrons travel around the nucleus in fixed energy levels with energies that vary from level to level.
   c. Electrons travel around the nucleus in fixed energy levels with equal amounts of energy.
   d. Electrons travel randomly in the relatively large space outside the nucleus.

_____ **13.** What do scientists use to predict the locations of electrons in atoms?
   a. probability   **b.** algebra
   c. geometry   **d.** ratios and proportions

_____14. Which statement about electrons and atomic orbitals
is NOT true?
a. An electron has the same amount of energy in all orbitals.
b. An orbital can contain a maximum of two electrons.
c. An electron cloud represents all the orbitals in an atom.
d. An atom's lowest energy level has only one orbital.

_____15. The glowing of a neon light is caused by electrons emitting
energy as they
a. move from lower to higher energy levels.
b. collide with other electrons.
c. move from higher to lower energy levels.
d. collide with the nucleus.

Completion

Complete each statement on the line provided.

1. Unlike Democritus, Aristotle did not believe that matter was
composed of tiny, indivisible _____.

2. John Dalton observed that elements always combine in the same
ratio to form a particular _____.

Figure 4-1

3. In Rutherford's gold foil experiment, shown in Figure 4-1, alpha
particles that bounce straight back from the foil have struck
_____ in the gold atoms.

4. The region in which an electron is most likely to be found is called
a(an) _____.

5. An atom in which an electron has moved to a higher energy level
is in a(an) _____ state.

Short Answer

*Use complete sentences to write the answers to the questions on
the lines provided.*

1. What scientific word comes from a Greek word meaning "uncut"?
   Which Greek philosopher first used the word to describe matter?

   _____

   _____

   _____

   _____

2. If an atom of an element has a mass number of 31 and 16 neutrons
   in its nucleus, what is the atomic number of the element?

   _____

   _____

3. If an atom of germanium has a mass number of 70 and an atomic
   number of 32, how many neutrons are in its nucleus?

   _____

   _____

4. What did Bohr's model of the atom do that Rutherford's model
   did not?

   _____

   _____

   _____

   _____

5. How does the electron cloud model of the atom represent the
   locations of electrons in atoms?

   _____

   _____

   _____

   _____

Using Science Skills

Use the diagram to answer each question. Write the answers on a separate sheet of paper.

Nucleus

● Proton   ● Neutron

Figure 4-2

1. **Analyzing Data** What subatomic particles are represented in Figure 4-2? Assuming all the particles in the nucleus are visible, what are the atomic and mass numbers of the atom shown?

2. **Inferring** Would Dalton have recognized the model of a nucleus shown in Figure 4-2? Explain your answer.

3. **Inferring** Would Rutherford have recognized the model of a nucleus in Figure 4-2? Explain your answer.

4. **Inferring** Why do you think the proton was discovered before the neutron? (*Hint:* Consider the properties of protons and neutrons.)

5. **Evaluating** Is Figure 4-2 a useful model of an atom? Explain your answer.

Essay

Write the answer to each question on a separate sheet of paper.

1. Why did Rutherford propose a new model of the atom after seeing the results of the gold foil experiment?

2. A sample of calcium contains calcium-40, calcium-44, calcium-42, calcium-48, calcium-43, and calcium-46 atoms. Explain why these atoms can have different mass numbers, but they must have the same atomic number.

3. Why is Bohr's model of the atom often called the planetary model?

4. What is the difference between an orbital and the electron cloud?

5. Explain what the colors in a fireworks display reveal about the movement of electrons in atoms.

Multiple Choice

Write the letter that best answers the question or completes the statement on the line provided.

_____ 1. The Greek philosopher Democritus coined what word for a tiny piece of matter that cannot be divided?
  a. element   **b.** atom
  c. electron   **d.** molecule

_____ 2. According to John Dalton's observations, when elements combine in a compound,
  a. the ratio of their masses is always the same.
  b. each element contributes an equal number of atoms.
  c. their volumes are always equal.
  d. their masses are always equal.

_____ 3. Which of the following is NOT part of John Dalton's atomic theory?
  a. All elements are composed of atoms.
  b. All atoms of the same element have the same mass.
  c. Atoms contain subatomic particles.
  d. A compound contains atoms of more than one element.

Figure 4-1

_____ 4. The diagram in Figure 4-1 shows the results of Rutherford's gold foil experiment. What caused some of the alpha particles to bounce straight back from the gold foil?
  a. electrons in the gold atoms
  b. negative charges in the gold atoms
  c. other alpha particles
  d. nuclei in the gold atoms

_____ 5. Who provided evidence for the existence of a nucleus in an
           atom?
           a. John Dalton
           b. J.J. Thomson
           c. Democritus
           d. Ernest Rutherford

_____ 6. In an atomic model that includes a nucleus, positive
           charge is
           a. concentrated in the center of an atom.
           b. spread evenly throughout an atom.
           c. concentrated at multiple sites in an atom.
           d. located in the space outside the nucleus.

_____ 7. Which subatomic particle has a negative charge?
           a. electron   b. alpha particle
           c. neutron   d. proton

_____ 8. Which statement about subatomic particles is NOT true?
           a. Protons and neutrons have almost the same mass.
           b. Protons and electrons have opposite charges.
           c. Unlike protons and electrons, neutrons have no charge.
           d. Protons and neutrons have the same charge.

_____ 9. The number of protons in one atom of an element is
           that element's
           a. mass number.   b. balanced charge.
           c. atomic number.   d. isotope.

_____10. To find the number of neutrons in an atom, you
           would subtract
           a. mass number from atomic number.
           b. atomic number from mass number.
           c. atomic number from electron number.
           d. isotope number from atomic number.

_____11. In Niels Bohr's model of the atom, electrons move
           a. like balls rolling down a hill.
           b. like planets orbiting the sun.
           c. like popcorn in a popcorn popper.
           d. like beach balls on water waves.

_____12. What can you assume has happened if an electron moves to
           a higher energy level?
           a. The atom has become more stable.
           b. The electron has lost energy.
           c. The electron has gained energy.
           d. The atom has lost an electron.

_____ **13.** What does the electron cloud model describe?
  a. the most likely locations of electrons in atoms
  b. the precise locations of electrons in atoms
  c. the number of electrons in an atom
  d. the mass of the electrons in an atom

_____ **14.** Which of the following provides the best analogy for an electron in an atomic orbital?
  a. a bee moving from flower to flower in a garden
  b. a bird resting on a tree branch
  c. an ant crawling on the surface of a leaf
  d. a bee trying to escape from a closed jar

_____ **15.** What is the difference between an atom in the ground state and an atom in an excited state?
  a. The atom in the ground state has less energy and is less stable than the atom in an excited state.
  b. The atom in an excited state has one fewer electron than the atom in the ground state.
  c. The atom in an excited state has more energy and is less stable than the atom in the ground state.
  d. The atom in an excited state has one more electron than the atom in the ground state.

Completion

Complete each statement on the line provided.

1. According to _____, all matter was made up of four elements—earth, air, fire, and water.

2. John Dalton concluded that all the atoms of a single _____ have the same mass.

3. The subatomic particle that J.J. Thomson discovered has a(an) _____ charge.

4. In Rutherford's gold foil experiment, some of the _____ aimed at gold atoms bounced back, suggesting that a solid mass was at the center of the atom.

5. Protons and _____ are found in the nucleus of an atom.

6. If element Q has 11 protons, its atomic _____ is 11.

7. The nuclei of isotopes contain different numbers of _____.

8. In Bohr's model of the atom, _____ move in fixed orbits around the nucleus.

9. The moving blades of an airplane propeller provide an analogy for the electron _____ model.

10. When all the electrons in an atom are in orbitals with the lowest possible energy, the atom is in its _____ state.

Short Answer

Use complete sentences to write the answers to the questions on the lines provided.

1. What did Democritus believe about matter?

_____

_____

_____

_____

2. How did the results of J.J. Thomson's experiments change how scientists thought about atoms?

_____

_____

_____

_____

3. What did Rutherford conclude about the location of positive charge in an atom?

_____

_____

_____

_____

4. What is the maximum number of electrons that an atomic orbital can contain?

_____

_____

_____

5. How does the state of atoms in a neon light change when light is emitted?

_____

_____

_____

_____

Name _____ Class _____ Date _____

Using Science Skills

Use the diagram to answer each question. Write the answers on a separate sheet of paper.

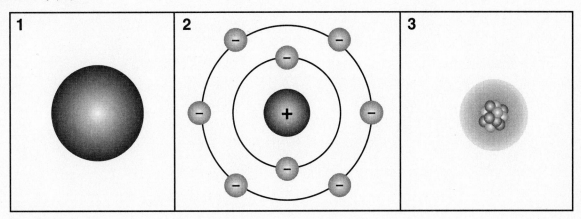

Figure 4-2

1. **Comparing and Contrasting** In Figure 4-2, what is the main difference between the atomic model in panel 1 and the model in panel 2?

2. **Comparing and Contrasting** In Figure 4-2, what is the main difference between the atomic model in panel 2 and the model in panel 3?

3. **Interpreting Graphics** Are the atomic models in Figure 4-2 arranged in the order that they were developed? Explain your answer.

4. **Using Analogies** Read the following analogy and explain how it applies to panels 1 and 2 in Figure 4-2: The atomic model in panel 1 is to the model in panel 2 as a drawing of the outside of a house is to a blueprint of the inside.

5. **Evaluating** In Figure 4-2, how is the atomic model in panel 2 helpful to your understanding of the atom? In what ways is it not helpful?

Chapter 5   The Periodic Table   **Chapter Test A**

Multiple Choice

Write the letter that best answers the question or completes the statement on the line provided.

_____ **1.** Mendeleev arranged the known chemical elements in a
table according to increasing
   a. atomic number.   **b.** number of electrons.
   c. number of protons.   **d.** mass.

_____ **2.** Mendeleev gave the name *eka-aluminum* to a(an)
   a. compound containing aluminum.
   b. mixture of aluminum and an unknown element.
   c. unknown element he predicted would have properties
      similar to those of aluminum.
   d. rare isotope of aluminum.

_____ **3.** Moving from left to right across a row of the periodic table,
which of the following values increases by exactly one from
element to element?
   a. isotope number   **b.** atomic number
   c. atomic mass unit   **d.** mass number

_____ **4.** The standard on which the atomic mass unit is based is the
mass of a
   a. proton.   **b.** neutron.
   c. chlorine-35 atom.   **d.** carbon-12 atom.

_____ **5.** The atomic mass of an element is
   a. the sum of the protons and neutrons in one atom of
      the element.
   b. twice the number of protons in one atom of the element.
   c. a ratio based on the mass of a carbon-12 atom.
   d. a weighted average of the masses of the element's
      isotopes

_____ **6.** At room temperature, none of the metals are
   a. soft.   **b.** liquids.
   c. malleable.   **d.** gases.

_____ **7.** Which general statement does NOT apply to metals?
   a. Most metals are ductile.
   b. Most metals are malleable.
   c. Most metals are brittle.
   d. Most metals are good conductors of electric current.

_____ **8.** Two highly reactive elements in Period 4 are the metal
potassium and the
   a. metalloid arsenic.   **b.** nonmetal selenium.
   c. nonmetal bromine.   **d.** nonmetal krypton.

_____ **9.** Atoms of the most reactive elements tend to have
      a one or seven valence electrons.
      b. eight valence electrons.
      c. four or five valence electrons.
      d. no valence electrons.

_____ **10.** An alkali metal has one valence electron, while an alkaline earth metal has
      a. none.   **b.** two.
      c. four.   **d.** three.

_____ **11.** Which statement is NOT true about the elements fluorine, chlorine, and iodine?
      a. They are all halogens.
      b. They react easily with metals.
      c. They are similar to noble gases.
      d. They are all nonmetals.

_____ **12.** Among the alkali metals, the tendency to react with other substances
      a. does not vary among the members of the group.
      b. increases from top to bottom within the group.
      c. varies in an unpredictable way within the group.
      d. decreases from top to bottom within the group.

_____ **13.** Which halogen is most likely to react?
      a. Br (bromine)   **b.** F (fluorine)
      c. I (iodine)   **d.** Cl (chlorine)

_____ **14.** To keep them from reacting, some highly reactive elements are stored in
      a. water.   **b.** pure oxygen.
      c. liquid mercury.   **d.** argon.

_____ **15.** Which element is found in nature only in compounds?
      a. sodium   **b.** helium
      c. oxygen   **d.** nitrogen

Completion

Complete each statement on the line provided.

1. When Mendeleev organized elements in his periodic table in order of increasing mass, elements with similar properties were in the same _____.

2. Mendeleev predicted that the undiscovered element he called *eka-aluminum* would have a(an) _____ melting point.

3. The pattern of repeating properties of elements revealed in the periodic table is known as the _____.

4. Fertilizers usually contain two elements from Group 5A, which are _____ and phosphorus.

5. One way to demonstrate reactivity among the alkaline earth metals, Group 2A, is to observe what happens when they are placed in _____.

Short Answer

Use complete sentences to write the answers to the questions on the lines provided.

1. Why did Mendeleev want to make a periodic table of the elements?

_____

_____

2. What do the whole numbers on the periodic table represent?

_____

_____

Figure 5-1

3. In which segment of Figure 5-1, A or B, will properties of the elements vary the most?

_____

_____

4. Selenium has six valence electrons, while rubidium has one valence electron. Identify each element as a metal or a nonmetal.

_____

_____

5. Silicon (atomic number 14) and chlorine (atomic number 17) are both in Period 3. Which is the more reactive element?

_____

_____

6. Sulfur is often found in nature as an element, not combined with other elements in a compound. What does this fact tell you about the reactivity of sulfur?

_____

_____

Using Science Skills

Use the chart to answer each question. Write the answers on a separate sheet of paper.

1. Classifying Classify the elements in Figure 5-2 as metals, metalloids, or nonmetals. Explain your answer.

2. Inferring Identify the most reactive element shown in Figure 5-2. Explain your answer.

3. Predicting Explain why knowing the properties of K, Ca, Sc, and Ti would allow you to predict the properties of Rb, Sr, Y, and Zr.

4. Using Tables and Graphs What do the numbers in the boxes in Figure 5-2 represent? What is the importance of these numbers?

5. Comparing and Contrasting Describe ways in which the elements in Group 1A are similar. Then describe ways in which Group 2A elements differ from elements in Group 1A.

	1A			
		2A		
	3 **Li**	4 **Be**		
	11 **Na**	12 **Mg**	3B	4B
	19 **K**	20 **Ca**	21 **Sc**	22 **Ti**
	37 **Rb**	38 **Sr**	39 **Y**	40 **Zr**

Figure 5-2

Essay

Write the answer to each question on a separate sheet of paper.

1. In a laboratory procedure, you form a highly reactive compound. How could you store the compound so that it will not react?

2. In science lab, your teacher gives you two small pieces of matter and tells you that one piece is a metal and one is a nonmetal. Without changing the size or shape of the pieces, how could you test them to determine which is the metal?

3. How are the octaves on a keyboard an analogy for the periods in a periodic table?

4. Although lithium and neon are both in Period 2 of the periodic table, they have very different properties. Explain how this is possible.

Chapter 5   The Periodic Table   **Chapter Test B**

Multiple Choice

Write the letter that best answers the question or completes the statement on the line provided.

_____ **1.** In a periodic table, a set of properties repeats from
       a. element to element.   **b.** group to group.
       c. column to column.   **d.** row to row.

_____ **2.** The usefulness of Mendeleev's periodic table was confirmed by
       a. the discovery of subatomic particles.
       b. its immediate acceptance by other scientists.
       c. the discovery of elements with predicted properties.
       d. the discovery of the nucleus.

_____ **3.** Figure 5-1 shows a portion of a blank periodic table. Identify the segments labeled A and B.
       a. A and B are both periods.
       b. A is a period and B is a group.
       c. A and B are both groups.
       d. A is a group and B is a period.

Figure 5-1

_____ **4.** One-twelfth the mass of a carbon-12 atom is used to define a(an)
       a. atomic number.   **b.** atomic mass.
       c. mass number.   **d.** atomic mass unit.

_____ **5.** How is the atomic mass of an element determined?
       a. Average the atomic masses of all its isotopes.
       b. Use the atomic mass of the most abundant isotope.
       c. Take a weighted average of the masses of the isotopes present in nature.
       d. Count the number of protons and neutrons in an atom of the element.

_____ **6.** Which list of elements contains only metals?
       a. helium, carbon, gold
       b. sodium, chromium, copper
       c. iodine, iron, nickel
       d. phosphorus, nitrogen, oxygen

_____ 7. Which statement is true about the metalloid silicon?
   a. Silicon is a better conductor of an electric current than silver is.
   b. Silicon does not conduct electric current under any conditions.
   c. Silicon's ability to conduct an electric current does not vary with temperature.
   d. Silicon is a better conductor of an electric current than sulfur is.

_____ 8. The column on the far left of the periodic table contains the
   a. most reactive metals.   **b.** most reactive nonmetals.
   c. least reactive nonmetals.   **d.** least reactive metals.

_____ 9. As you move from left to right across a period, the number of valence electrons
   a. increases.
   b. stays the same.
   c. increases and then decreases.
   d. decreases.

_____10. Compared with Group 1A elements, Group 7A elements have
   a. more atoms in ground state.
   b. more valence electrons.
   c. more isotopes.
   d. fewer valence electrons.

_____11. The tendency of an element to react chemically is closely related to
   a. its atomic mass.
   b. attractions between its atoms.
   c. the number of valence electrons in atoms of the element.
   d. the ratio of protons to neutrons in atoms of the element.

_____12. Which of these Group 1A elements is the most reactive?
   a. Cs (cesium)   **b.** Li (lithium)
   c. K (potassium)   **d.** Na (sodium)

_____13. Which of these Group 7A elements is the most reactive?
   a. Cl (chlorine)   **b.** I (iodine)
   c. F (fluorine)   **d.** Br (bromine)

_____14. Which of the following gases emit colors when an electric current is applied?
   a. hydrogen and helium   **b.** helium and neon
   c. fluorine and chlorine **d.** oxygen and nitrogen

_____15. Which element is found in most of the compounds in your body except for water?
   a. iodine   **b.** potassium   **c.** iron   **d.** carbon

Completion

Complete each statement on the line provided.

1. Mendeleev organized elements in his periodic table in order of increasing _____.

2. Mendeleev's periodic table was useful because it enabled scientists to predict properties of unknown _____.

3. Phosphorus is one block to the left of sulfur in the periodic table. The atomic number of sulfur is 16. The atomic number of phosphorus is _____.

4. The atomic mass unit (amu) is defined as one-twelfth the mass of a(an) _____-12 atom.

5. Elements can be classified as metals, nonmetals, and

   _____.

6. From left to right across a period in the periodic table, elements become less _____ and more _____ in their properties.

7. Element 3, lithium, has one valence electron, and element 4, beryllium, has two valence electrons. Element 5, boron, has _____ valence electrons.

8. In general, a(an) _____ metal will be more reactive than an alkaline earth metal in the same period.

9. Although they are called _____ lights, they can contain any noble gas.

10. Reactive elements, such as alkali metals and halogens, are found in nature only as _____.

Short Answer

Use complete sentences to write the answers to the questions on the lines provided.

1. Suppose you are looking at elements in the periodic table in this order: element 23, element 24, element 25, element 26, and so on. Are you looking across a period or down a group? Explain your answer.

   _____

   _____

2. What determines an element's chemical properties?

   _____

3. On the periodic table, there are two numbers in the block for the element krypton (Kr): 36 and 83.80. What are each of these numbers, and what do they represent?

   _____

   _____

4. Sodium chloride is a compound of sodium and chlorine. Which of these elements is the alkali metal, and which is the halogen?

_____

5. Why is argon gas used instead of air in light bulbs that contain a filament that is heated to glowing?

_____

_____

Using Science Skills

Use the chart to answer each question. Write the answers on a separate sheet of paper.

1	2	3 . . .											. . .	18
														He
	Be								C	N		F		
Na*	?													
			V											
												I		

* Atomic number = 11

Figure 5-2

1. **Using Tables and Graphs** Which of the elements shown in Figure 5-2 are in the same period?
2. **Classifying** Which element in Figure 5-2 is a transition metal? Which is a noble gas?
3. **Using Tables and Graphs** Which elements in Figure 5-2 have the same number of valence electrons? How do you know?
4. **Comparing and Contrasting** Based on what you know about elements and the periodic table, compare and contrast the elements beryllium (Be) and iodine (I).
5. **Inferring** Find the block labeled ? in Figure 5-2. Predict the properties of this element. What is its atomic number? How many valence electrons does it have? Which of the elements shown in Figure 5-2 will it most resemble?

Essay

Write the answer to the question on a separate sheet of paper.

1. Why were the elements gallium (Ga), scandium (Sc), and germanium (Ge) important to Mendeleev?

Chapter 6   Chemical Bonds   **Chapter Test A**

Multiple Choice

Write the letter that best answers the question or completes the statement on the line provided.

_____ **1.** Which of the following groups contain three elements with stable electron configurations?
   a. lithium, krypton, argon   **b.** argon, neon, barium
   c. xenon, neon, boron   **d.** helium, xenon, neon

_____ **2.** Ionization energies tend to
   a. decrease from left to right across a period.
   b. increase from the top of a group to the bottom.
   c. increase from left to right across a period.
   d. decrease from the bottom of a group to the top.

_____ **3.** The formation of an ionic bond involves the
   a. transfer of electrons.   **b.** transfer of neutrons.
   c. transfer of protons.   **d.** sharing of electrons.

_____ **4.** Which of the following statements correctly describes the substance with the formula KI?
   a. Molecules of potassium iodide contain one atom of potassium and one atom of iodine.
   b. There is a one-to-one ratio of potassium ions to iodide ions.
   c. Potassium iodide is a molecular compound.
   d. Potassium iodide is a polyatomic ion.

_____ **5.** Which statement best describes the properties of sodium chloride?
   a. Sodium chloride is a malleable solid.
   b. Solid sodium chloride is a good conductor of electric current.
   c. Sodium chloride has a low melting point.
   d. Liquid sodium chloride is a good conductor of electric current.

_____ **6.** When two atoms of the same nonmetal react, they often form a(an)
   a. ionic bond.   **b.** polyatomic ion.
   c. diatomic molecule.   **d.** polar molecule.

_____ **7.** Which of the following formulas represents a compound whose molecules contain a triple bond?
   a. $N \equiv N$ **b.** $O = O = O$ **c.** O_3 **d.** SO_3

_____ **8.** In a polar covalent bond,
   a. electrons are shared equally between atoms.
   b. a cation is bonded to an anion.
   c. electrons are transferred between atoms.
   d. electrons are not shared equally between atoms.

_____ 9. Because water molecules are polar and carbon dioxide molecules are nonpolar,
   a. water has a lower boiling point than carbon dioxide does.
   b. attractions between water molecules are weaker than attractions between carbon dioxide molecules.
   c. carbon dioxide cannot exist as a solid.
   d. water has a higher boiling point than carbon dioxide does.

_____ 10. Fluorine, F, forms a binary ionic compound with lithium, Li. What is the name of this compound?
   a. fluorine lithide   b. lithium fluoride
   c. lithium fluorine   d. fluorine lithium

_____ 11. If *copper(II)* appears in the name of a compound, it indicates that the compound contains
   a. copper ions with a 11+ charge.
   b. copper ions with a 2+ charge.
   c. copper ions with a negative charge.
   d. two types of copper ions.

_____ 12. Beryllium, Be, and chlorine, Cl, form a binary ionic compound with a one-to-two ratio of beryllium ions to chloride ions. The formula for the compound is
   a. Be_2Cl.   b. $2BeCl$.
   c. $BeCl_2$.   d. Be_2Cl_2.

_____ 13. Metallic bonding is similar to ionic bonding because
   a. electrons are transferred between atoms.
   b. electrons are shared between atoms.
   c. the lattice that forms contains anions and cations.
   d. there is an attraction between positively charged and negatively charged particles.

_____ 14. Many metals can be drawn into thin wires without breaking because
   a. cations are still surrounded by electrons when they shift their positions in the lattice.
   b. metals generally have low melting points.
   c. when a metal is struck with a hammer, the positions of the anions do not change.
   d. electrons have fixed positions in a metallic lattice.

_____ 15. How does increasing the amount of carbon in steel affect its properties?
   a. Carbon makes the lattice harder and stronger.
   b. Carbon forms an oxide that protects the steel from rusting.
   c. Carbon makes the steel light enough to use for airplane parts.
   d. Carbon makes the steel softer and easier to cut.

Name _____ Class _____ Date _____

Completion

Complete each statement on the line provided.

1. In the binary ionic compound potassium bromide, KBr, the element that forms cations is _____.

2. KBr is the formula for an ionic compound. The fact that neither symbol is followed by a subscript means that there is a(an) _____ ratio of ions in the compound.

3. You are given the melting points of three unknown substances and asked to predict which is an ionic compound. You would select the compound with the _____ melting point.

4. Among the elements potassium, lithium, and iron, the metallic bonds are likely to be strongest in _____.

5. To produce stainless steel, steelmakers add _____ to iron.

Short Answer

Use complete sentences to write the answers to the questions on the lines provided.

Figure 6-1

1. Study the electron dot diagrams in Figure 6-1. Which of the elements are most likely to react and form a compound? What type of compound are they likely to form?

_____

_____

2. In the binary ionic compound lithium iodide, LiI, which element forms anions?

_____

3. The molecules in compound AB are strongly polar, while the molecules in compound XY are nonpolar. Which substance probably has the higher boiling point?

_____

_____

4. In potassium bromide, KBr, which element forms anions?

_____

5. Why are metals good conductors of electric current?

_____

_____

_____

Using Science Skills

Use the table to answer each question. Write the answers on a separate sheet of paper.

	Substances	Compound	Remarks
A	potassium, K, and iodine, I	KI	Iodine is a member of the halogen group; potassium is an alkali metal.
B	carbon, C, and oxygen, O	CO_2	Carbon and oxygen are both nonmetals.
C	Al, O, and H	$Al(OH)_3$	OH^- (hydroxide) is a polyatomic ion.

Figure 6-2

1. **Applying Concepts** How does the saying "Opposites attract" apply to the bonding in the compound shown in row A of Figure 6-2?

2. **Comparing and Contrasting** What kind of bond forms between the elements in row B of Figure -2? How is this type of bond different from the type of bond that forms between the elements in row A?

3. **Comparing and Contrasting** How are the compounds in rows A and C of Figure 6-2 similar? How are they different?

4. **Inferring** A hydroxide ion has a charge of 1–. What is the charge on the aluminum ion? Explain your answer. Use Figure 6-2 to answer this question.

5. **Predicting** Suppose you could substitute sulfur, S, for iodine in row A in Figure 6-2. What would the formula for the resulting compound be? Explain your answer.

Essay

Write the answer to each question on a separate sheet of paper.

1. Fluorine is the most reactive nonmetal. To fluorine's immediate right in the periodic table is neon, a noble gas that does not form chemical bonds. Explain this contrast in reactivity in terms of atomic structure.

2. How is an electron dot diagram a useful model for focusing on the chemical properties of an element?

3. Water droplets tend to have a spherical, round shape. Explain this fact in terms of the polar nature of water molecules.

4. Compare and contrast the lattice in an ionic compound, such as sodium chloride, with the lattice in a metal, such as tungsten. How do any differences affect the malleability of these solids?

5. How does the ability of metals such as copper and alloys such as steel to be drawn into wires affect the possible uses of these materials?

Chapter 6   Chemical Bonds

Multiple Choice

Write the letter that best answers the question or completes the statement on the line provided.

_____ 1. Typically, atoms gain or lose electrons to achieve
 a. an exchange of energy.
 b. ionization.
 c. a stable electron configuration.
 d. vaporization.

_____ 2. In an electron dot diagram, the symbol for an element is used to represent
 a. the nucleus.
 b. the nucleus and all electrons.
 c. the nucleus and valence electrons.
 d. the nucleus and all nonvalence electrons.

_____ 3. Study the electron dot diagrams for lithium, carbon, fluorine, and neon in Figure 6-1. Choose the statement that correctly identifies the most stable of the elements.

Figure 6-1

 a. Lithium is the most stable element because it has to lose only one electron to achieve a stable configuration.
 b. Carbon is the most stable element because it can form four bonds.
 c. Fluorine is the most stable element because it has to gain only one electron to achieve a stable configuration.
 d. Neon is the most stable element because its highest occupied energy level is filled.

_____ 4. In the compound $MgCl_2$, the subscript 2 indicates that
 a. there are two magnesium ions for each ion of chlorine.
 b. the chloride ion is twice the size of the magnesium ion.
 c. magnesium and chlorine form a double covalent bond.
 d. there are two chloride ions for each magnesium ion.

_____ 5. Which of the following is a typical property of an ionic compound?
 a. low melting point
 b. poor conductor of electric current when melted
 c. tendency to shatter when struck
 d. all of the above

_____ 6. Which of the following compounds does NOT contain molecules?
 a. H_2 b. NaCl
 c. CO_2 d. H_2O

_____ 7. You see a structural formula in which the symbols for elements are connected by a long dash. You can assume that the chemical bonds in the compound are
   a. ionic.
   b. covalent.
   c. metallic.
   d. unstable.

_____ 8. The water molecule H_2O is polar because it contains two polar single bonds and
   a. its molecule has a linear shape.
   b. molecules that contain polar bonds are always polar.
   c. its molecule has a bent shape.
   d. the attractions between water molecules are strong.

_____ 9. Water has a higher boiling point than expected because
   a. there is so much water vapor in the atmosphere.
   b. water molecules are not very massive.
   c. hydrogen and oxygen form single covalent bonds.
   d. of the strong attractions between polar water molecules.

_____ 10. The elements most likely to form more than one type of ion are the
   a. transition metals.
   b. alkali metals.
   c. halogens.
   d. alkaline earth metals.

_____ 11. Which of the following statements about ions is true?
   a. All metals form more than one type of ion.
   b. Many transition metals can form more than one type of ion.
   c. Halogens form more than one type of ion.
   d. Alkali metals form more than one type of ion.

_____ 12. In the name *carbon dioxide,* the prefix of the second word indicates that a molecule of carbon dioxide contains
   a. two carbon atoms.
   b. two oxygen atoms.
   c. a polyatomic ion.
   d. an ionic bond.

_____ 13. Which phrase *best* describes a metallic bond?
   a. a bond that is formed by a metal
   b. the attraction between a metal anion and a shared pool of electrons
   c. a bond that forms between a metal and a nonmetal
   d. the attraction between a metal cation and a shared pool of electrons

_____ 14. Which statement about metals is true?
   a. A metal lattice is extremely rigid.
   b. The bonds within a metal lattice are weak.
   c. Electrons in a metal lattice are free to move.
   d. Generally, metals have a low melting point.

_____15. An alloy that contains mainly copper and tin is
  a. sterling silver.   b. stainless steel.
  c. brass.   d. bronze.

Completion

Complete each statement on the line provided.

1. In an electron dot diagram, each dot represents a(an)

   _____.

2. In an ionic compound, the attractions between cations and
   _____ hold the compound together.

3. The chemical formula for calcium chloride, $CaCl_2$, shows that the
   compound contains two _____ ions for every
   _____ ion.

4. The ions in solid sodium chloride are arranged in a structure
   called a(an) _____ lattice.

5. A polar covalent bond forms when _____ are not
   shared equally between atoms.

6. A(An) _____ ion is a covalently bonded group of
   atoms that has a positive or negative charge.

7. In ionic compounds, the sum of the charges of all the cations and
   anions must be _____.

8. The metallic bonds in a transition metal, such as tungsten, are
   stronger than the metallic bonds in a(an) _____
   metal, such as sodium.

9. In a metal lattice, _____ are surrounded by a pool
   of shared electrons.

10. In its simplest form, the alloy brass consists of zinc and

   _____.

Short Answer

*Use complete sentences to write the answers to the questions on
the lines provided.*

1. In a periodic table that included electron dot diagrams, in which
   column would the diagrams contain more dots—Group 2A (the
   alkaline metals) or Group 7A (the halogens)?

   _____

   _____

2. In an electron dot diagram of rubidium, there is one dot. In an
   electron dot diagram of silicon, there are four dots. Which element
   would you expect to be more reactive?

   _____

3. Potassium, an alkali metal, and bromine, a halogen, are both in Period 4 of the periodic table. Which element has a higher ionization energy? Explain your answer.

_____

_____

_____

_____

4. Which material is most likely to shatter if you strike it with a hammer—sodium chloride or bronze?

_____

_____

5. Mixing magnesium and aluminum together produces an excellent lightweight material from which to make airplane parts. What is this type of mixture called?

_____

_____

Using Science Skills

Use the table to answer each question. Write the answers on a separate sheet of paper.

Chemical Formula	Name	Type of Bond	Description of Bond
NaCl	(1)	ionic	(2)
CO_2	carbon dioxide	(3)	Atoms share pairs of valence electrons.
W	tungsten	(4)	Metal cations are attracted to the shared electrons that surround them.

Figure 6-2

1. **Using Tables and Graphs** Write a description to place in box (2) in Figure 6-2.

2. **Using Tables and Graphs** What compound name belongs in box (1) in Figure 6-2?

3. **Classifying** What type of bond belongs in box (3) in Figure 6-2?

4. **Classifying** What type of bond belongs in box (4) in Figure 6-2?

5. **Comparing and Contrasting** How are metallic bonds and ionic bonds similar? How are they different? Use Figure 6-2 to answer these questions.

Chapter 7   Chemical Reactions   **Chapter Test A**

Multiple Choice

Write the letter that best answers the question or completes the statement on the line provided.

_____ 1. Hydrochloric acid, HCl, is added to solid NaOH. After the reaction is complete, NaCl dissolved in water remains. What are the products of this chemical reaction?
a. NaOH and HCl   b. NaOH and H_2O
c. HCl and NaCl   d. NaCl and H2O

_____ 2. Which of the following does NOT show the law of conservation of mass?
a. 24 g of Mg burn in 32 g O_2 to produce 56 g of MgO.
b. 24 mL of Mg burn in 32 mL O_2 to produce 56 mL of MgO.
c. 2 atoms of Mg react with 1 molecule of O_2 to produce 2 units of MgO.
d. 1 atom of Mg reacts with 1 atom of O to produce a unit of MgO that contains 2 atoms.

_____ 3. Which of the following is a chemical equation that accurately represents what happens when sulfur and oxygen react to form sulfur trioxide?
a. Sulfur and oxygen react to form sulfur trioxide.
b. S and O_2 produce SO_3.
c. $S + O_2 \rightarrow SO_3$
d. $S + 3O_2 \rightarrow 2SO_3$

_____ 4. Methane, CH_4, burns in oxygen gas to form water and carbon dioxide. What is the correct balanced chemical equation for this reaction?
a. $CH_4 + O \rightarrow H_2O + CO_2$
b. $CH_4 + 4O \rightarrow 2H_2O + CO_2$
c. $CH_4 + O_2 \rightarrow H_2O + CO_2$
d. $CH_4 + 2O_2 \rightarrow 2H_2O + CO_2$

_____ 5. How many grams of HNO_3 are in 2.6 mol of the compound?
a. 24.2 g   b. 63.0 g
c. 93.0 g   d. 163.8 g

_____ 6. An industrial process makes calcium oxide by decomposing calcium carbonate. Which of the following is NOT needed to calculate the mass of calcium oxide that can be produced from 4.7 kg of calcium carbonate?
a. the balanced chemical equation
b. molar masses of the reactants
c. molar masses of the product
d. the volume of the unknown mass

_____ 7. When magnesium carbonate, $MgCO_2$, reacts with nitric acid, HNO_3, magnesium nitrate and carbonic acid form. Carbonic acid then breaks down into water and carbon dioxide. What two types of reactions take place in this process?
   a. synthesis and decomposition
   b. single-replacement and combustion
   c. double-replacement and decomposition
   d. double-replacement and combustion

_____ 8. In a chemical reaction, an iron atom became the ion Fe^{2+}. What happened to the iron atom?
   a. It lost electrons and was oxidized.
   b. It lost electrons and was reduced.
   c. It gained electrons and was oxidized.
   d. It gained electrons and was reduced.

_____ 9. Which of the following statements is true about what happens during a chemical reaction?
   a. Bonds of the reactants are broken, and bonds of the products are formed.
   b. Bonds of the reactants are formed, and bonds of the products are broken.
   c. The bonds of both the reactants and the products are broken.
   d. The bonds of both the reactants and the products are formed.

_____ 10. For the chemical reaction $C_2H_6 + 137$ kJ $\rightarrow C_2H_4 + H_2$, the chemical energy of the
   a. reactant is greater than the chemical energy of the products.
   b. products is greater than the chemical energy of the reactant.
   c. reactant and the chemical energy of the products are equal.
   d. reaction is conserved.

_____ 11. For the chemical reaction $H_2 + CO_2 \rightarrow H_2O + CO$, the energy contained in the reactants is 352 kJ, and the energy contained in the products is 394 kJ, assuming 1 mol of each substance is present. Which of the following statements is true?
   a. 42 kJ is released, and the reaction is exothermic.
   b. 42 kJ is released, and the reaction is endothermic.
   c. 42 kJ is absorbed, and the reaction is exothermic.
   d. 42 kJ is absorbed, and the reaction is endothermic.

_____12. Reaction rates do NOT tell you how fast
    a. reactants are being consumed.
    b. products are being formed.
    c. substances are changing state.
    d. energy is being absorbed or released.

_____13. What happens to the reaction $2NO_2 \rightleftharpoons N_2O_4 + 57.2$ kJ when the temperature of the reaction is increased?
    a. More reactant is formed.
    b. More product is formed.
    c. No change occurs in the amounts of reactant and product present.
    d. The effect depends on whether or not a catalyst is present.

_____14. The reaction $H_2CO_3 + H_2O \rightleftharpoons H_3O^+ + HCO_3^-$ takes place in water. What happens to the equilibrium when the pressure is increased?
    a. It favors formation of reactants.
    b. It favors formation of products.
    c. It does not change.
    d. It is conserved.

$2N_2$ + $3H_2$ $\rightleftharpoons$ $2NH_3$ + energy

Figure 7-1

_____15. The reaction in Figure 7-1 shows the formation of ammonia from nitrogen and hydrogen in the Haber process. What will be the effect on the equilibrium if the temperature is increased and some of the ammonia is removed from the system?
    a. More ammonia will definitely form.
    b. More reactants will definitely form.
    c. The changes definitely will have no overall effect on the reaction..
    d. Any effect will depend on the amount of change of temperature and concentration.

Completion

Complete each statement on the line provided.

1. In an experiment, 44 g of propane were burned, producing 132 g of carbon dioxide and 72 g of water. The mass of oxygen that was needed for the reaction was _____.

2. A sample of HBr contains 186 g of the compound. The sample contains _____ moles of HBr.

3. An iron fence is left unpainted, and it reacts with the oxygen in the air, forming rust. The formation of rust is an oxidation-reduction reaction, but it is also an example of a(an) _____ reaction.

4. A catalyst is used in a catalytic converter in vehicles to help control pollution. For example, the catalytic converter _____ the rate at which carbon monoxide is oxidized to carbon dioxide. ($2CO + O_2 \rightarrow 2CO_2$)

5. Many manufacturing processes involve chemical reactions that reach equilibrium. One way to increase the amount of product formed is to decrease the _____ of the product in the system.

Short Answer

Use complete sentences to write the answers to the questions on the lines provided.

1. A student balanced the chemical equation $Mg + O_2 \rightarrow MgO$ by writing $Mg + O_2 \rightarrow MgO_2$. Was the equation balanced correctly? Explain your answer. If the equation was not balanced correctly, write the correctly balanced equation.

_____

_____

_____

_____

_____

2. How many moles of nitrogen are contained in 1.61×10^{24} atoms of nitrogen?

_____

3. In a decomposition reaction, a compound is broken down into two or more simpler substances. Explain why the term *compound* is used to refer to the reactant and the term *substances* is used to refer to the products.

_____

_____

_____

_____

_____

4. When most fuels burn, water and carbon dioxide are the two main products. Why can't you say that water and carbon dioxide are products of all combustion reactions?

_____

_____

_____

_____

_____

_____

5. Explain why batteries and film will stay fresh longer if they are kept in a refrigerator or freezer.

_____

_____

_____

_____

_____

_____

Using Science Skills

Use the diagram to answer each question. Write the answers on a separate sheet of paper.

Figure 7-2

1. Applying Concepts In an exothermic reaction as seen in Figure 7-2, do the reactants or the products contain more chemical energy?

2. Inferring Cooking an egg white involves an endothermic reaction. Which has more chemical energy in its chemical bonds—an uncooked egg white or a cooked egg white? Use Figure 7-2 to explain your answer.

3. **Problem Solving** If the bonds in the reactants of Figure 7-2 contained 432 kJ of chemical energy and the bonds in the products contained 478 kJ of chemical energy, what would be the amount of energy change during the reaction? Would this energy be absorbed or released?

4. **Using Tables and Graphs** What do the peaks on the graphs in Figure 7-2 represent?

5. **Interpreting Graphics** Although the amount of energy involved is small enough that it is not noticed, iron rusts according to the following word equation:

$$\text{iron} + \text{oxygen} \rightarrow \text{rust} + \text{energy}$$

Which of the energy diagrams in Figure 7-2 could be applied to the formation of rust? Explain your answer.

Problem

Write the answers to each question on a separate sheet of paper.

1. Balance the following chemical equation.
$$Cu + HNO_3 \rightarrow Cu(NO_3)_2 + NO_2 + H_2O$$

2. When iron metal reacts with oxygen, the reaction can form Fe_2O_3. Write a balanced chemical equation for this reaction, and find the number of moles of oxygen that are needed to form 6 mol of Fe_2O_3.

3. Sodium reacts with chlorine gas to form sodium chloride. Write a balanced chemical equation for the reaction, and find the mass of chlorine gas that will react with 96.6 g of sodium.

Essay

Write the answers to each question on a separate sheet of paper.

1. Which two types of reactions are also always redox reactions? Explain your answer.

2. Explain the difference between a physical equilibrium and a chemical equilibrium.

Chapter 7   Chemical Reactions   **Chapter Test B**

Multiple Choice

Write the letter that best answers the question or completes the statement on the line provided.

_____ **1.** The substances that are present before a chemical reaction
takes place are called
   a. reactants.   **b.** products.
   c. coefficients.   **d.** elements.

_____ **2.** Which of the following does NOT state what the arrow
means in a chemical equation?
   a. forms   **b.** produces
   c. conserves   **d.** yields

_____ **3.** Which of the following is a balanced chemical equation for
the synthesis of NaBr from Na and Br_2?
   a. $Na + Br_2 \rightarrow NaBr$
   b. $2Na + Br_2 \rightarrow NaBr$
   c. $Na + Br_2 \rightarrow 2NaBr$
   d. $2Na + Br_2 \rightarrow 2NaBr$

_____ **4.** How many atoms are present in 2 moles of chromium?
   a. 6.02×10^{23} atoms   **b.** 1.20×10^{23} atoms
   c. 1.20×10^{24} atoms   **d.** 52.0 atoms

_____ **5.** How many moles of Cr are in 156 g of the element?
   a. 1.0 mol   **b.** 3.0 mol
   c. 6.5 mol   **d.** 156 mol

_____ **6.** The coefficients in a balanced chemical equation always can
express the ratio of
   a. moles of reactants and products.
   b. volume of reactants and products.
   c. atoms of reactants and products.
   d. mass of reactants and products.

_____ **7.** Which of the following is NOT always true about a
synthesis reaction?
   a. One product is formed.
   b. There is only one reactant.
   c. The general formula is $A + B \rightarrow C$.
   d. A reactant might be a compound, or it might be an
      element.

_____ **8.** Which of the following takes place during a redox reaction?
   a. Electrons are gained only.
   b. Electrons are lost only.
   c. Electrons are both gained and lost.
   d. Electrons are neither gained nor lost.

_____ **9.** In a compound, chemical energy is contained in the
  a. nuclei of the atoms.
  b. unbonded electrons.
  c. bonds.
  d. movement of the electrons.

_____**10.** In terms of energy, how would you classify the following chemical reaction? $2Cu + O_2 \rightarrow 2CuO + 315\ kJ$
  a. endothermic
  b. exothermic
  c. both endothermic and exothermic
  d. neither endothermic nor exothermic

_____**11.** The total amount of energy before and after a chemical reaction is the same. Thus, energy is
  a. created. **b.** destroyed.
  c. conserved. **d.** the same as mass.

_____**12.** In general, if the temperature of a chemical reaction is increased, reaction rate
  a. increases. **b.** decreases.
  c. remains the same. **d.** cannot be predicted.

_____**13.** A log is burning in a fireplace. If the amount of oxygen reaching the log is decreased, which of the following statements is true?
  a. The reaction rate increases.
  b. The reaction rate decreases.
  c. The reaction rate remains the same.
  d. The reaction rate depends only on the temperature.

_____**14.** When the forward and reverse paths of a change occur at the same rate,
  a. the system is conserved.
  b. the system is in equilibrium.
  c. he change must be physical.
  d. the change must be chemical.

_____**15.** The equation $2NO_2 \rightleftharpoons N_2O_4$ shows a system
  a. in chemical equilibrium.
  b. in physical equilibrium.
  c. that does not reach equilibrium.
  d. that does not change.

Completion

Complete each statement on the line provided.

1. The statement that in chemical reactions, the total mass of the reactants equals the total mass of the products is the law of

_____.

2. A(An) _____ is the number that appears before a formula in a chemical equation.

3. The molar mass of chlorine is _____.

4. Butane burns as shown in the balanced chemical equation $2C_4H_{10} + 13O_2 \rightarrow 10H_2O + 8CO_2$. If 6 mol of butane burn, _____ mol of carbon dioxide are produced.

5. The element _____ is always present in a combustion reaction.

6. In a double-replacement reaction, there are two reactants and _____ product(s).

7. When fluorine reacts with a metal, it forms an F^- ion. The fluorine atom has gained an electron and undergone _____

8. In terms of energy, the general chemical equation AB + CD + energy $\rightarrow$ AD + CB represents a(an) _____ reaction.

9. Measuring how quickly a reactant disappears is one way to measure the _____ of the reaction.

10. The statement that when a change is introduced to a system in equilibrium, the equilibrium shifts in the direction that relieves the stress on the system is known as _____.

Short Answer

Use complete sentences to write the answers to the questions on the lines provided.

1. How does the law of conservation of mass explain why only a bit of ash is left after burning a large sheet of paper?

_____

_____

_____

2. What is the purpose of balancing a chemical equation?

_____

_____

_____

3. How many grams of Mn are in 4.0 mol of the element?

_____

_____

4. Explain why ice in liquid water at 0°C is an example of physical equilibrium.

_____

_____

_____

5. In Figure 7-1, both the reactants and the product of the reaction are gases. In this equilibrium, the reaction that produces fewer gas molecules is favored. Explain why increasing the pressure on the reaction favors the formation of ammonia rather than the formation of the reactants.

$2N_2$ + $3H_2$ ⇌ $2NH_3$ + energy

Figure 7-1

_____

_____

_____

_____

_____

_____

Using Science Skills

Use the diagram to answer each question. Write the answers on a separate sheet of paper.

Unbalanced equation:

CH_4 + O_2 → CO_2 + H_2O

Figure 7-2

1. **Interpreting Graphics** How many of each type of atom are present on each side of the equation in Figure 7-2?

2. **Inferring** If the total number of atoms on the left side of the equation in Figure 7-2 equaled the total number of atoms on the right side of the equation, would this necessarily mean that the equation was balanced? Explain your answer.

3. **Drawing Conclusions** If there are 4 hydrogen atoms on the left side of equation in Figure 7-2, how many hydrogen atoms must there be on the right side in order to balance this reaction?

4. **Problem Solving** How do you balance the number of hydrogen atoms in the equation in Figure 7-2?

5. **Communicating Results** What is the balanced chemical equation for the reaction represented in Figure 7-2?

Chapter 8 Solutions, Acids, and Bases   Chapter Test A

Multiple Choice

Write the letter that best answers the question or completes the statement on the line provided.

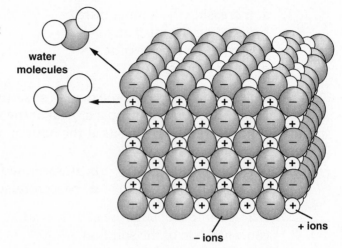

water
molecules

− ions

+ ions

Figure 8-1

_____ 1. Study Figure 8-1. When the ionic compound KI is dissolved in water, the I^- ions are pulled into solution by the attraction between
   a. the K^+ and I^- ions.
   b. the K^+ ion and the negative end of a water molecule.
   c. the I^- ion and the negative end of a water molecule.
   d. the I^- ion and the positive end of a water molecule.

_____ 2. The more particles a solute forms in solution, the greater is its effect on the freezing point of the solution. Which of the following will lower the freezing point the most if 1 mol of it is added to 1 L of water?
   a. the molecular compound propanol, C_2H_5OH
   b. the ionic compound NaCl
   c. the ionic compound $MgCl_2$
   d. the ionic compound $AlCl_3$

_____ 3. The amount of energy required to break the attractions among the solute particles and among the solvent particles is
   a. greater than the energy released as attractions form between solute and solvent particles.
   b. less than the energy released as attractions form between solute and solvent particles.
   c. equal to the energy released as attractions form between solute and solvent particles.
   d. equal to the heat of solution.

_____ 4. All materials that are considered to be insoluble will dissolve in a solvent to a very small extent. The rate of dissolving of a rock in a streambed would be increased by all of the following EXCEPT
   a. breaking the rock into smaller pieces.
   b. moving the rock to a faster-moving current.
   c. moving the rock to warmer water.
   d. reducing the exposure of the rock to the water.

_____ 5. The solubility of carbon dioxide gas in water can be increased by
   a. increasing the temperature.
   b. agitating the mixture.
   c. increasing the pressure.
   d. using more solvent.

_____ 6. One way to determine the degree of saturation of a solid-liquid solution is to drop a crystal of the solute into the solution. If the crystal sits at the bottom of the container, the solution is
   a. saturated.   b. unsaturated.
   c. supersaturated.   d. concentrated.

_____ 7. A 25-g sample of sugar was dissolved in 50 g of water. The concentration of the solution is
   a. 50 percent by mass.
   b. 33 percent by mass.
   c. 0.5 M.
   d. 50 percent by volume.

_____ 8. A girl tasted each of the following foods. Which of the following would NOT taste acidic to her?
   a. lime   b. tomato
   c. orange   d. celery

_____ 9. Which of the following is NOT a common property of bases?
   a. feels slippery
   b. tastes bitter c. reacts with metals
   d. changes colors of indicators

_____ 10. The products of the neutralization reaction between hydrochloric acid and magnesium hydroxide are
   a. $MgCl$ and H_2O.   b. $MgCl_2$ and H_2O.
   c. HCl and $MgOH$.   d. HCl and $Mg(OH)_2$.

_____ 11. Ammonia, NH3, can be classified as a base because in a chemical reaction with an acid, ammonia will
   a. produce hydroxide ions in solution.
   b. produce hydronium ions in solution.
   c. donate a proton and become NH_2^-.
   d. accept a proton and become NH_4^+.

_____ 12. Tomatoes have a hydronium ion concentration of 1×10^{-4} M. What is the pH of a tomato?
   a. 4   b. –4   c. 10   d. 1×10^{-4}

_____13. The hydroxide ion concentration in pure water at 25°C is
NOT equal to
a. the hydronium ion concentration.
b. 1×10^{-7} M.
c. the hydroxide concentration in a solution with a pH of 7.
d. 1×10^{7} M.

_____14. A compound has a pH of 1 in solution, where it has
completely ionized. The compound is a
a. strong base.   b. weak base.
c. strong acid.   d. weak acid.

_____15. Calcium hydroxide forms very few hydroxide ions in
solution, but it is still considered a strong base because
a. calcium hydroxide is insoluble.
b. all the calcium hydroxide in solution ionizes.
c. all the calcium hydroxide in solution dissociates.
d. very little of the calcium hydroxide in solution ionizes.

_____16. Which of the following would NOT form a buffer solution?
a. $NH_3 + NH_4Cl$ b. $HC_2H_3O_2 + NaC_2H_3O_2$
c. $HCl + NaCl$ d. $H_2CO_3 + NaHCO_3$

_____17. Which of the following are examples of strong electrolytes?
a. strong and weak bases
b. strong acids and strong bases
c. weak acids and weak bases
d. pure water and buffers

Completion

Complete each statement on the line provided.

1. A substance dissolves in water by breaking up into smaller pieces.
These pieces of the same substance spread throughout the water.
This process is known as _____. .

2. Antifreeze is added to a radiator because it _____
the boiling point and _____ the freezing point of
the solution contained in the radiator.

3. Stirring increases the rate of solution of a solid in a liquid because
solute particles in solution are moved _____ the
surface of the solute.

4. Many foods are acidic. These foods do not hurt you when you eat
them because they contain _____ acids.

5. Acetic acid is considered a weak _____ because it
only partially ionizes.

Name _____ Class _____ Date _____

Short Answer

*In complete sentences, write the answers to the questions on
the lines provided.*

1. Both ionization and dissociation produce ions of the solute in solution. How do the two processes differ?

   _____

   _____

   _____

   _____

2. Compare and contrast an exothermic chemical reaction and an exothermic solution formation by dissociation.

   _____

   _____

   _____

   _____

3. A solid solute is added to a liquid solvent. The solution is stirred, but it is also cooled. Can you predict whether the solution process will speed up or not? Explain your answer.

   _____

   _____

   _____

   _____

4. You place a drop of a solution on red litmus paper, and no color change occurs. Can you conclude that the solution is neutral because no color change occurred? Explain your answer.

   _____

   _____

   _____

5. Explain how water can act as either a proton donor or a proton acceptor, depending on the other reactant. Use examples.

   _____

   _____

   _____

   _____

Name _____ Class _____ Date _____

Using Science Skills

Use the diagram to answer each question. Write the answers on a separate sheet of paper.

Substance	Solubility (g/100 g H_2O, 20°C)	Substance	Solubility (g/100 g H_2O, 20°C)
Barium hydroxide	3.89	Potassium chloride	34.2
Barium nitrate	9.02	Sodium chloride	35.9
Calcium hydroxide	0.173	Sucrose (table sugar)	203.9

Figure 8-2

1. **Classifying** A 71.8-g sample of NaCl was added to 200.0 g of water at 20°C. Is the solution saturated, unsaturated, or supersaturated? Use Figure 8-2 to answer this question.

2. **Calculating** Potassium chloride was added to 40 g of water at 20°C until the solution was saturated. How much potassium chloride was used? Use Figure 8-2 to answer this question.

3. **Applying Concepts** A boy wanted to make candy from crystalized sugar. He dissolved 300.0 g of sucrose in 75 g of water at 100°C. To the nearest gram, how much sugar crystalized out of the saturated solution when it cooled to 20°C? Use Figure 8-2 to answer this question.

4. **Calculating** A sample of calcium hydroxide is placed into a jar containing water. The mass of the calcium hydroxide sample is 1.34 g. Assume the water is at 20°C and that the resulting calcium hydroxide solution is saturated. What mass of water was present in the jar? Use Figure 8-2 to answer this question.

5. **Using Tables and Graphs** A student was given a sample of either barium hydroxide or barium nitrate. How could she use the solubility information from Figure 8-2 to determine which compound she was given?

Problem

Write the answers to each question on a separate sheet of paper.

1. A sample of 54.7 g of HCl gas is dissolved to make 1 L of solution. What is the molarity of the solution?

2. Rubbing alcohol is often a 70 percent solution by volume of alcohol and water. If a bottle of rubbing alcohol contains 0.50 L, what volume of alcohol does it contain?

3. The buffer system in the blood contains HCO_3^- ions and H_2CO_3. Write a balanced chemical equation that shows what happens when a small amount of acid is added to blood and another equation that shows what happens when a small amount of base is added.

Essay

Write the answers to each question on a separate sheet of paper.

1. Compare and contrast the factors that affect rate of solution and those that affect solubility.

2. Describe how you would prepare 2.00 L of a 1.20-M solution of potassium chloride, KCl, in water.

Chapter 8   Solutions, Acids, and Bases   **Chapter Test B**

Multiple Choice

Write the letter that best answers the question or completes the statement on the line provided.

_____ **1.** In order for a solution to form,
   a. one substance must dissolve in another.
   b. a solid must dissolve in a liquid.
   c. the solvent must be water.
   d. a gas must dissolve in a liquid.

_____ **2.** A salt is dissolved in water, which has a boiling point of 100°C. The boiling point of the solution will be
   a. greater than 100°C.
   b. less than 100°C.
   c. exactly equal to 100°C.
   d. exactly equal to 0°C.

_____ **3.** During the formation of a solution, energy is
   a. either released or absorbed.
   b. neither released nor absorbed.
   c. released only.
   d. absorbed only.

_____ **4.** A student dissolved equal amounts of salt in equal amounts of warm water, room-temperature water, and ice water. Which of the following is true?
   a. The salt dissolved most quickly in the warm water.
   b. The salt dissolved most quickly in the room-temperature water.
   c. The salt dissolved most quickly in the ice water.
   d. none of the above

_____ **5.** The maximum amount of a solute that will dissolve in a certain amount of solvent at a given temperature is that solute's
   a. solubility.   **b.** concentration.
   c. degree of saturation.   **d.** rate of solution.

_____ **6.** A solution that contains more solute than it would normally hold at that temperature is said to be
   a. saturated.   **b.** unsaturated.
   c. supersaturated.   **d.** concentrated.

_____ **7.** To calculate the molarity of a solution, you need to know the moles of solute and the
   a. volume of the solvent.
   b. volume of the solution.
   c. mass of the solution.
   d. volume of the solute.

_____ 8. Which of the following is NOT a property of an acid?
   a. tastes sour
   b. usually reacts with a metal
   c. changes the color of an indicator
   d. feels slippery

_____ 9. A base is defined as a compound that produces
   a. hydroxide ions in solution.
   b. hydrogen ions in solution.
   c. hydronium ions in solution.
   d. sodium ions in solution.

_____ 10. The salt that is formed during the reaction between potassium hydroxide and hydrochloric acid is
   a. NaCl.   **b.** H_2O.   **c.** KCl.   **d.** K_2Cl.

_____ 11. An acid can be defined as
   a. a proton acceptor.
   b. a proton donor.
   c. neither a proton donor nor a proton acceptor.
   d. both a proton donor and a proton acceptor.

_____ 12. A small amount of acid is added to a buffer solution. The pH of the solution will
   a. increase.   **b.** decrease.
   c. stay about the same.   **d.** become neutral.

_____ 13. A substance that ionizes or dissociates into ions when placed in water is always a(an)
   a. conductor.   **b.** electrolyte.
   c. strong acid.   **d.** strong base.

Completion

Complete each statement on the line provided.

1. When sugar dissolves in water, water is the

   _____

   and sugar is the

   _____.

2. Study Figure 8-1. When KBr dissolves in water, the K^+ and Br^- ions are pulled into solution in a process known as

   _____.

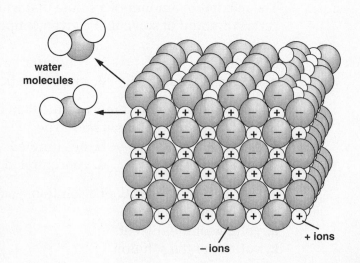

Figure 8-1

3. The physical properties of a solution that differ from those of its solute and solvent include freezing point, boiling point, and _____.

4. A food packet taken on a camping trip has a warming packet. This packet contains water and a solute that releases heat when it is dissolved. The dissolving process for this solute and solvent can be described as _____.

5. The rate that a solid solute dissolves in a liquid solvent depends on the frequency and energy of the _____ between the particles of the solute and solvent.

6. Table salt is _____ soluble in cold water than it is in hot water.

7. If a saturated solution of sugar water is heated, the solution will become _____.

8. An acid produces _____ when it is dissolved in water.

9. When a substance donates a proton during a chemical reaction, that substance can be classified as a(an) _____.

10. Acids that contain carbon are weak acids, which means that they _____ only to a small extent in solution.

Short Answer

In complete sentences, write the answers to the questions on the lines provided.

1. If a liquid dissolves in a gas, in what state will the solution be? Explain your answer.

   _____

   _____

   _____

   _____

2. Which will freeze at a higher temperature—a freshwater marsh or a saltwater marsh? Explain your answer.

   _____

   _____

   _____

3. What is the difference between a saturated solution and an unsaturated solution?

   _____

   _____

   _____

4. What is a buffer solution?

_____

_____

_____

5. What type of electrolyte is a weak acid?

_____

_____

_____

Using Science Skills

Use the diagram to answer each question. Write the answers on a separate sheet of paper.

Figure 8-2

1. **Interpreting Graphics** Detergent has a pH of about 10. Is detergent acidic or basic? Use Figure 8-2 to answer this question.

2. **Drawing Conclusions** Oven cleaner has a pH of 14, and household ammonia has a pH of about 11.2. What generalization might you make about whether most cleaners contain acids or bases? Use Figure 8-2 to answer this question.

3. **Applying Concepts** Unpolluted rain has a pH of about 6. Is this rain acidic, basic, or neutral? Why is the term *acid rain* used to refer to rain that has been polluted with oxides of nitrogen and sulfur? This rain frequently has a pH between 4 and 5 and has been found to have a pH as low as 1.8. Use Figure 8-2 to answer these questions.

4. **Problem Solving** Stomach acid has a pH of about 2. What conclusion can you reach about the pH of an antacid solution that is used to neutralize excess stomach acid? Use Figure 8-2 to answer this question.

5. **Inferring** Sea water has a pH of about 8, and pure water has a pH of 7. Would sea water change the color of red litmus paper? Explain your answer. Use Figure 8-2 to answer this question.

Chapter 9 Carbon Chemistry   **Chapter Test A**

Multiple Choice

Write the letter that best answers the question or completes the statement on the line provided.

_____ **1.** In buckminsterfullerene, carbon atoms are
  a. bonded in a network solid.
  b. bonded to three other carbon atoms in a
     widely spaced layer.
  c. bonded in alternating hexagons and pentagons on
     the surface of a hollow sphere.
  d. not bonded to each other.

_____ **2.** Which of the following statements is true?
  a. Organic compounds always contain
     carbon and hydrogen.
  b. Organic compounds contain only carbon and hydrogen.
  c. Organic compounds are produced only in organisms.
  d. About 10 percent of all known compounds are
     organic compounds.

_____ **3.** Butane has the formula C_4H_{10}. Which of the following is the
     formula of cyclobutane?
  a. C_4H_4 **b.** C_4H_6 **c.** C_4H_8 **d.** C_4H_{10}

_____ **4.** Which of the following is a saturated hydrocarbon?
  a. isopropane
  b. butene
  c. pentyne
  d. benzene

_____ **5.** The prefix *dec-* means "ten." Which of the following best
     describes the structure of decene?
  a. It contains ten carbon atoms and only single bonds.
  b. It contains ten carbon atoms and at least one
     double bond.
  c. It contains ten carbon atoms and at least one triple bond.
  d. It contains a total of ten atoms.

_____ **6.** Burning coal usually produces more soot than burning
     natural gas or petroleum products because coal
  a. formed in ancient swamps.
  b. is formed from the remains of marine organisms.
  c. contains aromatic hydrocarbons with high molar masses.
  d. contains a mixture of hydrocarbons.

_____ **7.** One of the gases released after gasoline burns in a car's engine is carbon monoxide. Which of the following statements explains why there is carbon monoxide in this mixture of gases?

    a. Not enough oxygen is present when gasoline is burned in the engine.

    b. Gasoline contains carbon monoxide.

    c. The combustion of gasoline in the engine is complete.

    d. Carbon monoxide is produced during the complete combustion of a fossil fuel.

_____ **8.** Which of the following statements explains why inhaling carbon monoxide is dangerous?

    a. Carbon monoxide reacts with oxygen to produce carbon dioxide.

    b. Carbon monoxide keeps hemoglobin in the blood from carrying oxygen to cells.

    c. Carbon monoxide is a colorless, odorless gas.

    d. all of the above

_____ **9.** The functional group in butanoic acid, which is an organic acid, is the

    a. amino group.   **b.** hydroxyl group.

    c. carboxyl group.   **d.** butane group.

_____ **10.** Propanoic acid and ethyl alcohol can react. The products of this reaction are water and an

    a. organic base.   **b.** ester.

    c. organic acid.   **d.** amine.

_____ **11.** In a polymer, monomers are linked by

    a. ionic bonds.

    b. covalent bonds.

    c. metallic bonds.

    d. polyatomic ions.

_____ **12.** Which of the following statements about natural rubber and synthetic rubber is true?

    a. Natural and synthetic rubber contain different monomers.

    b. There is an unlimited supply of both types of rubber.

    c. Both types of rubber are made from petroleum products.

    d. Natural and synthetic rubber have exactly the same properties.

_____ **13.** The monomers from which proteins are made are

    a. sugars.   **b.** amino acids.

    c. nucleic acids.   **d.** starches.

_____14. Which of the following statements is true?
  a. Photosynthesis occurs only in plants, and cellular respiration occurs only in animals.
  b. Photosynthesis occurs only in animals, and cellular respiration occurs only in plants.
  c. Both photosynthesis and cellular respiration occur in plants.
  d. Both photosynthesis and cellular respiration occur in animals.

_____15. Proteins that act as catalysts for chemical reactions that occur in cells are
  a. vitamins.
  b. enzymes.
  c. carbohydrates.
  d. amino acids.

_____16. Which of the following statements is true about enzymes?
  a. Enzymes allow a reaction to occur that would **never** occur without the enzymes.
  b. Enzymes allow reactions to proceed at temperatures near 37°C.
  c. Enzymes cannot be produced within cells.
  d. One enzyme can control all the reactions in a cell.

Completion

Complete each statement on the line provided.

1. More than 90 percent of all known compounds are organic compounds, mainly because carbon contains _____ valence electrons and can form multiple carbon-to-carbon bonds.

2. Straight-chain hydrocarbons that contain one to three carbon atoms are likely to be _____ at room temperature.

3. Suppose a saturated and unsaturated hydrocarbon both contain the same number of carbon atoms. The saturated hydrocarbon contains more of the element _____ than the unsaturated hydrocarbon does.

4. During photosynthesis, _____ energy is converted to _____ energy in the bonds of the products.

5. Some enzymes require a(an) _____ which is often a metal ion or a water-soluble _____ to function.

Name _____ Class _____ Date _____

Short Answer

Use complete sentences to write the answers to the questions on the lines provided.

1. Based on the structure of graphite shown in Figure 9-1, explain why graphite is a good lubricant.

   _____

   _____

   _____

   _____

   _____

Figure 9-1

   _____

   _____

2. How can butane and isobutane both have the formula C_4H_{10}?

   _____

   _____

   _____

   _____

   _____

   _____

3. Compare the bonding in alkenes and alkynes.

   _____

   _____

   _____

   _____

   _____

4. What two products are formed from the reaction of a halocarbon and a base?

   _____

   _____

5. One important difference between DNA and RNA is that RNA contains the base uracil instead of thymine. What base will pair with uracil in RNA—adenine, guanine, or cytosine?

_____

_____

Using Science Skills

Use the structural formulas to answer each question. Write the answers on a separate sheet of paper.

a.
```
        H   H
        |   |
   H — C — C — H
        |   |
        Br  Br
```

b.
```
        H   H   OH
        |   |   |
   H — C — C — C — H
        |   |   |
        H   H   H
```

c.
```
        H   H   H      O
        |   |   |    //
   H — C — C — C — C
        |   |   |    \
        H   H   H      OH
```

d.
```
        H
        |
   H — C — N — H
        |   |
        H   H
```

E.
```
        H   H   H   O        H   H
        |   |   |   ||       |   |
   H — C — C — C — C — O — C — C — H
        |   |   |            |   |
        H   H   H            H   H
```

Figure 9-2

1. **Inferring** The ester ethyl butanoate provides the taste and smell to pineapple. Identify the structural formula in Figure 9-2 for ethyl butanoate.

2. **Interpreting Graphics** Amines are formed during the breakdown of proteins in animal cells. Identify the structural formula in Figure 9-2 for an amine, and name the functional group.

3. **Interpreting Graphics** Which of the structures in Figure 9-2 is the formula for propanol? What is the functional group in this compound?

4. **Applying Concepts** Which diagram in Figure 9-2 shows the structural formula of a halocarbon? Why is the prefix *halo-* used?

5. **Using Models** Butanoic acid is found in rancid butter. Which of the structural formulas in Figure 9-2 is butanoic acid? What is the functional group in an organic acid?

Problem

Write the answer to each question on a separate sheet of paper.

1. Write a balanced chemical equation for the complete combustion of methane, CH_4, and one for the incomplete combustion of methane.

2. Write a balanced chemical equation for the formation of carbonic acid from carbon dioxide and water.

Essay

Write the answer to each question on a separate sheet of paper.

1. In terms of their structures, explain why diamond is so much harder than graphite.

2. Suppose a gas furnace is producing a large amount of carbon monoxide. What process is causing carbon monoxide to be produced, and how can the amount that is produced be reduced?

3. Describe the structure of the nucleotides in DNA, and explain how two strands join to form the double helix.

Chapter 9   Carbon Chemistry   **Chapter Test B**

Multiple Choice

Write the letter that best answers the question or completes the statement on the line provided.

_____ 1. Figure 9-1 is a model of graphite. Which of the following statements is true about graphite?

   a. Within each layer, the atoms form alternating single and double bonds.
   b. Graphite is an example of a network solid.
   c. Each carbon atom in graphite is bonded to four other carbon atoms.
   d. The bonds between graphite layers are weaker than the bonds within graphite layers.

Figure 9-1

_____ 2. Which of the following statements helps explain why there are millions of carbon compounds?
   a. Carbon has four valence electrons.
   b. Carbon atoms form bonds with other carbon atoms.
   c. Carbon atoms can form single, double, and triple bonds.
   d. all of the above

_____ 3. The carbon atoms in a hydrocarbon CANNOT be arranged in
   a. straight chains.   b. branched chains
   c. rings.   d. a network solid.

_____ 4. Which of the following is another name for a saturated hydrocarbon?
   a. alkane   b. alkene
   c. alkyne   d. alkali

_____ 5. Which of the following compounds is most reactive?
   a. ethane
   b. ethene
   c. ethyne
   d. They are all equally reactive.

_____ 6. Which of the following is NOT an example of a fossil fuel?
   a. coal   b. petroleum
   c. natural gas   d. methanol

_____ 7. What are the main products of the incomplete combustion of fossil fuels?
  a. water and carbon dioxide
  b. oxygen and hydrocarbons
  c. water and carbon monoxide
  d. carbon dioxide and hydrocarbons

_____ 8. Which of the following is NOT a result of the complete combustion of fossil fuels?
  a. The amount of carbon dioxide in the atmosphere increases.
  b. The amount of carbon monoxide in the atmosphere increases.
  c. Nitrogen oxides are released into the atmosphere.
  d. Sulfur dioxide is released into the atmosphere.

_____ 9. In the compound CH_3F, the fluorine atom is a(an)
  a. functional group.   b. substituted hydrocarbon.
  c. hydroxyl group.   d. amino group.

_____ 10. The smell of rotten fish is caused by the presence of an
  a. amine.   b. alcohol.   c. ester.   d. organic acid.

_____ 11. When monomers link together, they usually form
  a. a polymer.   b. another monomer.
  c. ionic bonds.   d. a network solid.

_____ 12. Which of the following exists as both a natural and a synthetic polymer?
  a. cellulose   b. nylon   c. polyethylene   d. rubber

_____ 13. Natural polymers are produced
  a. only in plant cells.
  b. only in animal cells.
  c. in both plant and animal cells.
  d. in neither plant nor animal cells.

_____ 14. Plants convert energy from sunlight into chemical energy during
  a. cellular respiration.   b. photosynthesis.
  c. vaporization.   d. depolymerization.

Completion

Complete each statement on the line provided.

1. Diamond is an example of a(an) _____ in which all the carbon atoms are linked by covalent bonds.

2. Compounds with the same molecular formula but different structural formulas are _____.

3. In a saturated hydrocarbon, all the bonds are _____ bonds.

4. The primary products of the complete combustion of fossil fuels are _____ and _____.

5. Some products of the combustion of fossil fuels cause the _____ of rain to increase.

6. The manufacture of chlorofluorocarbons has been restricted because they deplete Earth's _____ layer.

7. Glucose is the monomer in the natural polymers _____ and _____.

8. The strands of DNA are held together in the double helix by _____ between hydrogen atoms on one strand and nitrogen or oxygen atoms on the other strand.

9. The energy that your body needs is released by the process of _____.

10. Vitamins B and C are examples of vitamins that can dissolve in _____.

Short Answer

Use complete sentences to write the answers to the questions on the lines provided.

1. What elements do organic compounds always contain?

   _____

   _____

2. Classify the compounds ethyne, heptane, and benzene.

   _____

   _____

   _____

3. What fossil fuel formed from the remains of buried plants in ancient swamps?

   _____

4. Why can't people survive without plants?

   _____

   _____

5. Why might it be harmful for a person to take large quantities of many vitamins each day?

   _____

Using Science Skills

Use the diagram to answer each question. Write the answers on a separate sheet of paper.

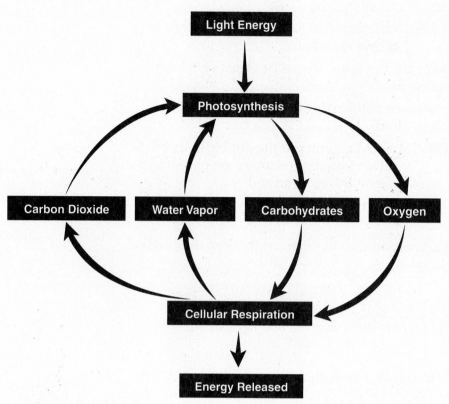

Figure 9-2

1. **Interpreting Graphics** Water is a product of which process described in Figure 9-2? In which process is water a reactant?

2. **Interpreting Graphics** Which process described in Figure 9-2 produces carbohydrates? In which process are carbohydrates reactants?

3. **Inferring** What role does energy play in the cycle of photosynthesis and cellular respiration? Use Figure 9-2 to answer this question.

4. **Predicting** Predict how reducing the number of plants grown worldwide might affect the composition of the atmosphere. Use Figure 9-2 to answer this question.

5. **Drawing Conclusions** What elements are cycled through the processes of photosynthesis and cellular respiration? Use Figure 9-2 to answer this question.

Chapter 10   Nuclear Chemistry   Chapter Test A

Multiple Choice

Write the letter that best answers the question or completes the statement on the line provided.

_____ 1. Uranium-238 undergoes nuclear decay. Therefore, uranium-238 will
   a. remain stable.
   b. change into a different element altogether.
   c. emit neutral particles and no energy.
   d. none of the above

_____ 2. When radium-226 decays to form radon-222, the radium nucleus emits a(an)
   a. alpha particle.   b. beta particle.
   c. gamma ray.   d. electron.

_____ 3. Carbon-14 forms nitrogen-14 by
   a. alpha decay.   b. beta decay.
   c. gamma decay.   d. none of the above

_____ 4. Alpha-emitting substances, such as radon gas, can be a serious health hazard only if
   a. they are inhaled or eaten.
   b. their radiation strikes the skin.
   c. exposure to them is external.
   d. none of the above

_____ 5. Which of the following is NOT a step in the operation of a Geiger counter?
   a. Nuclear radiation ionizes gas in a tube.
   b. Ionized gas produces an electric current.
   c. Magnets cause the ions to conduct electricity.
   d. The electric current is detected and measured.

_____ 6. The half-life of tritium, or hydrogen-3, is 12.32 years. After about 37 years, how much of a sample of tritium will be left?
   a. $\frac{1}{8}$ b. $\frac{1}{4}$ c. $\frac{1}{3}$ d. $\frac{1}{2}$

_____ 7. In a water solution, HCl and NaOH react to form H_2O and NaCl. Radium-226 undergoes alpha decay to form radon-222. The temperature of both of these reactions is increased. Which of the following statements is true?
   a. The rate of the chemical reaction will increase, but the rate of the nuclear reaction remains the same.
   b. The rate of the nuclear reaction will increase, but the rate of the chemical reaction remains the same.
   c. The rates of both reactions will increase.
   d. The rates of both reactions will remain the same.

_____ 8. Carbon-14 has a half-life of 5730 years. If the age of an object older than 50,000 years cannot be determined by radiocarbon dating, then
   a. carbon-14 levels in a sample are undetectable after approximately ten half-lives.
   b. carbon-14 levels in a sample are undetectable after approximately nine half-lives.
   c. the half-life of carbon-14 is too long to accurately date the object.
   d. a radioisotope with a shorter half-life should be used to date the object.

_____ 9. Which of the following is NOT an example of a transmutation?
   a. Uranium-238 emits an alpha particle and forms thorium-234.
   b. Uranium-238 is bombarded with a neutron to produce uranium-239.
   c. Potassium-38 emits a beta particle and forms argon-38.
   d. Plutonium-239 is bombarded with two neutrons to produce americium-241 and a beta particle.

_____ 10. When curium-242 is bombarded with an alpha particle, two products are formed, one of which is a neutron. What is the other product?
   a. californium-246   b. californium-245
   c. californium-247   d. plutonium-239

_____ 11. The main purpose of a particle accelerator is to
   a. magnetize small particles.
   b. speed up small particles.
   c. slow down reaction products.
   d. reproduce reaction conditions found in nature.

_____ 12. In general, the nucleus of a small atom is stable. Therefore, over very short distances, such as those in a small nucleus,
   a. the strong nuclear force is much greater than the electric force.
   b. the electric force is much greater than the strong nuclear force.
   c. the strong nuclear force equals the electric force.
   d. the strong nuclear force and the electric force are both attractive.

_____ 13. Suppose three neutrons are released when an atom in a sample of fissionable nuclei undergoes fission. Each of these neutrons has enough energy to cause another fission reaction in another nucleus of the material. If the reaction is not controlled, how many atoms will have undergone fission after a series of five additional nuclear fissions?
   a. 15   b. 18   c. 243   d. 729

_____14. Which of the following is NOT a way that water is used in
a nuclear power station?
  a. Water cools the steam in the turbine chamber.
  b. Water is changed to steam by heat released by the
     reactor core.
  c. Steam makes the turbines rotate.
  d. Running water cools the rotating turbines.

_____15. Which of the following is NOT an advantage of using a
fusion reaction instead of a fission reaction to produce
energy?
  a. Workers are not in as much danger from radiation.
  b. Hydrogen is used, and hydrogen is easily obtained
     from water.
  c. No harmful waste products are produced.
  d. Fusion reactors require less energy than fission
     reactors do.

Completion

Complete each statement on the line provided.

1. Francium has 36 isotopes, but only francium-223 occurs in nature.
   Francium-223 spontaneously emits particles and energy, so
   francium-223 is a(an) _____ of francium.

2. You want to be shielded from all three types of nuclear radiation.
   If you find shielding that blocks _____ radiation,
   then it will most likely also block the other two types.

3. A less common type of radioactive particle emitted is the positron.
   If potassium-38 forms argon-38 by positron emission, the mass
   number of a positron is _____ and the charge is
   _____.

4. The fission reaction within a nuclear reactor is kept under control
   by the use of _____ that absorb extra
   _____.

5. Although the fusion of hydrogen to produce helium is the most
   common fusion reaction occurring in the sun, several other fusion
   reactions occur. In one of these, two helium-4 nuclei fuse to form
   one unstable _____ nucleus.

Short Answer

*In complete sentences, write the answers to the questions on
the lines provided.*

1. How is an electron in a stable atom similar to a beta particle?

   _____

   _____

2. Radiation treatments are commonly used to treat cancerous tumors. Explain why the radiation for these treatments comes in many different beams from many different directions toward the body instead of just one beam aimed toward the tumor.

_____

_____

_____

_____

_____

_____

3. Americium-241 is used in smoke detectors. What two particles are used to bombard an atom of plutonium-239 to create an atom of americium-241 if a beta particle is also produced?

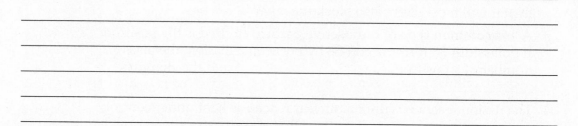

$$^{239}_{94}\text{Pu} + 2 \quad ? \rightarrow \quad ^{241}_{95}\text{Am} + \quad ^{0}_{-1}\text{e}$$

_____

_____

4. In terms of electrical attraction, why is it necessary to accelerate an alpha particle in order for it to effectively bombard a nucleus of a large atom?

_____

_____

_____

_____

_____

5. Use the equation $E = mc^2$ to explain why large amounts of energy are produced by very small amounts of mass during nuclear fission.

_____

_____

_____

_____

_____

_____

Name _____ Class _____ Date _____

Using Science Skills

Use the diagram to answer each question. Write the answers on a separate sheet of paper.

1. **Applying Concepts** What product isotope is formed by the decay of radon-222? Use Figure 10-1 to answer this question.

2. **Calculating** Assume you have a 100-g sample of iodine-131. What product isotope is formed by the decay of this radioisotope? How much iodine-131 will remain unchanged after 24.21 days? Use Figure 10-1 to answer these questions.

3. **Calculating** Study Figure 10-1. How much nitrogen-14 will be produced from a 200-g sample of carbon-14 after 17,190 years?

4. **Applying Concepts** A rock sample contains one-fourth as much radium-226 as the relatively newly formed rock around it contains. How old is the rock sample? Use Figure 10-1 to answer this question.

A Nuclear Forces Acting on a Proton of a Small Nucleus

Strong nuclear forces

Electric force

B Nuclear Forces Acting on a Proton of a Large Nucleus

Strong nuclear forces

Electric forces

Figure 10-1

5. **Using Tables and Graphs** What product isotope is produced by the decay of thorium-234? If an initial sample contains 48 g of thorium-234, how much of this product isotope will be present after 72.3 days? Use Figure 10-1 to answer these questions.

Problem

Write the answers to each question on a separate sheet of paper.

1. Astatine-218 has a half-life of 1.6 s. Suppose you have a 1.2-g sample of astatine-218. How much of the sample remains unchanged after 6.4 seconds?

2. A sample of phosphorus-32 has a half-life of 14.28 days. If 25 g of this radioisotope remain unchanged after approximately 57 days, what was the mass of the original sample?

3. After 15 minutes, 30 g of a sample of polonium-218 remain unchanged. If the original sample had a mass of 960 g, what is the half-life of polonium-218?

Essay

Write the answers to each question on a separate sheet of paper.

1. Compare and contrast the processes of fission and fusion.

2. Explain the path followed by carbon-14 atoms from when they form in the atmosphere until they are found in compounds in the human body.

Chapter 10   Nuclear Chemistry   **Chapter Test B**

Multiple Choice

Write the letter that best answers the question or completes the statement on the line provided.

_____ **1.** What is the process in which an unstable atomic nucleus emits charged particles or energy or both?
  a. radioactivity
  b. oxidation
  c. decomposition
  d. none of the above

_____ **2.** What type of nuclear decay produces energy instead of a particle?
  a. alpha decay
  b. beta decay
  c. gamma decay
  d. electron decay

_____ **3.** What type of radiation is emitted when polonium-212 forms lead-208?
  a. an alpha particle
  b. a beta particle
  c. gamma radiation
  d. all of the above

_____ **4.** Which of the following statements is NOT true?
  a. You are exposed to nuclear radiation every day.
  b. Most of the nuclear radiation you are exposed to occurs naturally in the environment.
  c. Naturally occurring nuclear radiation is called background radiation.
  d. All natural radiation is at a level low enough to be safe.

_____ **5.** Many people work near a source of nuclear radiation. To detect the amount of exposure they have to radiation, they most likely will use a
  a. Geiger counter.
  b. film badge.
  c. radon kit.
  d. lead shield.

_____ **6.** The half-life of a radioisotope is the amount of time it takes for
  a. half the sample to decay.
  b. all the sample to decay.
  c. the age of an artifact to be calculated.
  d. detectable radiation to be absorbed by a sample.

_____ **7.** Which of the following statements is true?
  a. Chemical reaction rates vary with the conditions of the change, but nuclear decay rates do not.
  b. Nuclear decay rates vary with the conditions of the change, but chemical reaction rates do not.
  c. Both chemical reaction rates and nuclear decay rates vary with the conditions of the change.
  d. Neither chemical reaction rates nor nuclear decay rates vary with the conditions of the change.

_____ 8. Which of the following is a radioisotope used to date rock formations?

    a. carbon-14   **b.** potassium-40   **c.** cobalt-60   **d.** carbon-12

_____ 9. Transmutation involves

    a. nuclear change.   **b.** chemical change.

    c. both a nuclear change and a chemical change.

    d. neither a nuclear nor chemical change.

_____ 10. Which of the following is an example of a transuranium element?

    a. samarium, Sm   **b.** uranium, U

    c. curium, Cm   **d.** thorium, Th

_____ 11. Which of the following particles is smaller than the rest?

    a. electron   **b.** proton   **c.** neutron   **d.** quark

_____ 12. Study Figure 10-1. The strong nuclear force felt by a single proton in a large nucleus

    a. is much greater than that felt by a single proton in a small nucleus.

Nuclear Radiation			
Radiation Type	**Symbol**	**Charge**	**Mass (amu)**
Alpha particle	α, ^4_2He	2+	4
Beta particle	β, $^0_{-1}\text{e}$	1−	$\frac{1}{1836}$
Gamma ray	γ	0	0

Figure 10-1

    b. is much less than that felt by a single proton in a small nucleus.

    c. is about the same as that felt by a single proton in a small nucleus.

    d. is about the same as the electric force felt by a single proton in a small nucleus.

_____ 13. During nuclear fission, great amounts of energy are produced from

    a. very small amounts of mass.   **b.** tremendous amounts of mass.

    c. a series of chemical reactions.   **d.** particle accelerators.

_____ 14. Which of the following is an advantage of using nuclear power plants to produce electricity?

    a. Nuclear power plants do not pollute the air.

    b. Nuclear power plants produce wastes that are easy to dispose.

    c. Nuclear power plants produce more stable wastes compared to fossil fuel combustion.

    d. all of the above

_____ 15. In what state must matter exist for fusion reactions to take place?

    a. solid   **b.** liquid   **c.** gas   **d.** plasma

Completion

Complete each statement on the line provided.

1. An alpha particle is the same as a(an) _____ nucleus.

2. In the symbol ^4_2He, the superscript *4* is the _____ for helium, and the subscript 2 is the _____ for helium.

3. When a human body is exposed to external nuclear radiation, the amount of tissue damage depends on the _____ power of the radiation.

4. A sample of a radioisotope had a mass of 100.0 g. After exactly 24 days, 6.25 g of the sample remained. The half-life of the isotope is _____ days.

5. In radiocarbon dating, the carbon-14 levels in the object being dated is compared to the carbon-14 levels in the _____.

6. Scientists can synthesize a transuranium element by the artificial _____ of a lighter element.

7. The particle that makes up protons and neutrons and is thought to be a basic unit of matter is a(an) _____.

8. One purpose of collision experiments is to study _____ structure.

9. In nuclear reactions, _____ is converted into energy.

10. In a(an) _____, neutrons released during a fission reaction cause a series of other fission reactions.

Short Answer

In complete sentences, write the answers to the questions on the lines provided.

1. How did the physicist Becquerel first observe the effects of nuclear decay?

   _____
   _____
   _____
   _____
   _____
   _____

2. What particle will balance the following nuclear equation?

$$^{234}_{91}Pa \rightarrow U + ?$$

   _____

3. What is one common source of background radiation?

_____

_____

_____

4. What radioisotope is used as the fuel for a nuclear reactor?

_____

5. What two problems must be overcome before fusion can be used to produce energy?

_____

_____

Using Science Skills

Use the diagram to answer each question. Write the answers on a separate sheet of paper.

1. **Drawing Conclusions** A beta particle does have mass, so why is zero the mass number for a beta particle? Use Figure 10-2 to answer this question.

2. **Calculating** Study Figure 10-2. What type of nuclear radiation completes the following decay equation?

$$^{218}_{84}Po \rightarrow {}^{214}_{82}Pb + ?$$

3. **Calculating** Study Figure 10-2. What type of nuclear radiation completes the following decay equation?

$$^{210}_{83}Bi \rightarrow {}^{204}_{84}Po + ?$$

4. **Using Tables and Graphs** Why doesn't emission of gamma radiation change either the mass number or the atomic number of the nucleus? Use Figure 10-2 to answer this question.

5. **Drawing Conclusions** Study Figure 10-2. Explain how the mass and atomic numbers of an alpha particle can be used to determine the number of neutrons in the particle.

A Nuclear Forces Acting on a Proton of a Small Nucleus

Strong nuclear forces

Electric force

B Nuclear Forces Acting on a Proton of a Large Nucleus

Strong nuclear forces

Electric forces

Figure 10-2

Unit 1   Chemistry   **Unit Test A**

Multiple Choice

Write the letter that best answers the question or completes the statement on the line provided.

_____ 1. How are science and technology related?
  a. Technology is a branch of natural science.
  b. Science is a branch of technology.
  c. Advances in science may lead to advances in technology and vice versa.
  d. Science and technology are not related.

_____ 2. Why are scientific models important?
  a. They prove scientific theories.
  b. They help visualize things that are very complex, very large, or very small.
  c. They make it harder to understand things.
  d. They never change.

_____ 3. The type of graph used to show how a part of something relates to the whole is a
  a. circle graph   b. bar graph
  c. line graph   d. direct proportion

_____ 4. Which of the following is a characteristic of a mixture?
  a. has varying properties
  b. has a fixed composition
  c. contains only pure substances
  d. both a and b

_____ 5. Which of the following has the highest viscosity?
  a. corn syrup   b. milk
  c. water   d. orange juice

_____ 6. A substance that has high reactivity
  a. easily combines chemically with other substances.
  b. burns in the presence of water.
  c. displaces dissolved oxygen.
  d. has a high boiling point.

_____ 7. Forces of attraction limit the motion of particles most in
  a. a solid.   b. a liquid.
  c. a gas.   d. both b and c

_____ 8. The phase change that is the reverse of condensation is
  a. freezing.   b. sublimation.
  c. vaporization.   d. melting.

_____ 9. The phase change in which a substance changes from a solid to a gas or vapor without changing to a liquid first is
  a. sublimation.   b. deposition.
  c. evaporation.   d. melting.

_____10. Which of the following most accurately represents John Dalton's model of the atom?
   a. a tiny, solid sphere with an unpredictable mass for a given element
   b. a hollow sphere with a dense nucleus
   c. a tiny, solid sphere with predictable mass for a given element
   d. a sphere that is hollow throughout

_____11. Which statement about subatomic particles is true?
   a. Protons, neutrons, and electrons all have about the same mass.
   b. Unlike protons or neutrons, electrons have no mass.
   c. Neutrons have no charge and no mass.
   d. An electron has far less mass than either a proton or neutron.

_____12. What do scientists use to predict the locations of electrons in atoms?
   a. probability   b. algebra
   c. geometry   d. ratios and proportions

_____13. The standard on which the atomic mass unit is based is the mass of a
   a. proton.   b. neutron.
   c. chlorine-35 atom.   d. carbon-12 atom.

_____14. Atoms of the most reactive elements tend to have
   a. one or seven valence electrons.
   b. eight valence electrons.
   c. four or five valence electrons.
   d. no valence electrons.

_____15. Which element is found in nature only in compounds?
   a. sodium   b. helium
   c. oxygen   d. nitrogen

_____16. Which of the following groups contain three elements with stable electron configurations?
   a. lithium, krypton, argon
   b. argon, neon, barium
   c. xenon, neon, boron
   d. helium, xenon, neon

_____17. Ionization energies tend to
   a. decrease from left to right across a period.
   b. increase from the top of a group to the bottom.
   c. increase from left to right across a period.
   d. decrease from the top of a group to the bottom.

_____18. The name *copper(II)* indicates that a compound contains
     a. copper ions with a 11+ charge.
     b. copper ions with a 2+ charge.
     c. copper ions with a negative charge.
     d. two types of copper ions.

_____19. An industrial process makes calcium oxide by decomposing calcium carbonate.Which of the following is NOT needed to calculate the mass of calcium oxide that can be produced from 4.7 kg of calcium carbonate?
     a. the balanced chemical equation
     b. molar masses of the reactants
     c. molar masses of the product
     d. the volume of the unknown mass

_____20. For the chemical reaction $C_2H_6 + 137 \text{ kJ} \rightarrow C_2H_4 + H_2$, the chemical energy of the
     a. reactant is greater than the chemical energy of the products.
     b. products is greater than the chemical energy of the reactant.
     c. reactant and the chemical energy of the products are equal.
     d. reaction is conserved.

_____21. The reaction $H_2CO_3 + H_2O \rightleftharpoons H_3O^+ + H_cO_3^-$ takes place in water. What happens to the equilibrium when the pressure is increased?
     a. It favors formation of reactants.
     b. It favors formation of products.
     c. It does not change.
     d. It is conserved.

_____22. The solubility of carbon dioxide gas in water can be increased by
     a. increasing the temperature.
     b. agitating the mixture.
     c. increasing the pressure.
     d. using more solvent.

_____23. Which of the following is NOT a common property of bases?
     a. feels slippery   **b.** tastes bitter
     c. reacts with metals   **d.** changes colors of indicators

_____24. The products of the neutralization reaction between hydrochloric acid and magnesium hydroxide are
     a. $MgCl$ and H_2O.   **b.** $MgCl_2$ and H_2O.
     c. HCl and $MgOH$.   **d.** HCl and $Mg(OH)_2$.

_____ 25. Butane has the formula C_4H_{10}. Which of the following is the formula of cyclobutane?

      a. C_4H_4 b. C_4H_6 c. $4H_8$ d. C_4H_{10}

_____ 26. Which of the following statements explains why inhaling carbon monoxide is dangerous?

      a. Carbon monoxide reacts with oxygen to produce carbon dioxide.

      b. Carbon monoxide keeps hemoglobin in the blood from carrying oxygen to cells.

      c. Carbon monoxide is a colorless, odorless gas.

      d. all of the above

_____ 27. Proteins that act as catalysts for chemical reactions that occur in cells are

      a. vitamins.   b. enzymes.

      c. carbohydrates.   d. amino acids.

_____ 28. Uranium-238 undergoes nuclear decay. Therefore, uranium-238 will

      a. remain stable.

      b. change into a different element altogether.

      c. emit neutral particles and no energy.

      d. none of the above

_____ 29. In a water solution, HCl and NaOH react to form H_2O and NaCl. Radium-226 undergoes alpha decay to form radon-222. The temperature of both of these reactions is increased. Which of the following statements is true?

      a. The rate of the chemical reaction will increase, but the rate of the nuclear reaction remains the same.

      b. The rate of the nuclear reaction will increase, but the rate of the chemical reaction remains the same.

      c. The rates of both reactions will increase.

      d. The rates of both reactions will remain the same.

_____ 30. Suppose three neutrons are released when an atom in a sample of fissionable nuclei undergoes fission. Each of these neutrons has enough energy to cause another fission reaction in another nucleus of the material. If the reaction is not controlled, how many atoms will have undergone fission after a series of five additional nuclear fissions?

      a. 15   b. 18   c. 243   d. 729

Completion

Complete each statement on the line provided.

1. An experiment in which only one variable, the manipulated variable, is changed at a time is called a(an) _____.

2. In scientific notation, $(8.2 \times 10^4 \text{ m}) \times (3.7 \times 10^2 \text{ m})$ equals

_____.

3. In a(an) _____ mixture, the parts of the mixture are noticeably different from one another.

4. Rust forms because iron and oxygen are highly _____ elements.

5. If you know the volume and pressure of a gas and the pressure changes, you can find the new volume by multiplying P_1 by V_1 and _____ this number by P_2.

6. During vaporization, a substance changes from a(an) _____ to a(an) _____.

7. The difference between a sample of heavy water and regular water is that a hydrogen atom in heavy water has an extra

_____.

8. An atom in which an electron has moved to a higher energy level is in a(an) _____ state.

9. The pattern of repeating properties of elements revealed in the periodic table is known as the _____.

10. Fertilizers usually contain two elements from Group 5A, which are _____ and phosphorus.

11. When cesium and fluorine react, they form an ionic compound called cesium _____.

12. The compound whose formula is SO_3 is called sulfur

_____.

13. For a certain chemical reaction, the reactants contain 362 kJ of chemical energy, and the products contain 342 kJ of chemical energy. In order for energy to be conserved, 20 kJ of energy must be _____.

14. A sample of HBr contains 186 g of the compound. The sample contains _____ moles of HBr.

15. Antifreeze is added to a radiator because it _____ the boiling point and _____. the freezing point of the solution contained in the radiator.

16. The pH of a solution is 11. The concentration of hydronium ions in the solution is _____.

17. Suppose a saturated and unsaturated hydrocarbon both contain the same number of carbon atoms. The saturated hydrocarbon contains more of the element _____ than the unsaturated hydrocarbon does.

18. High-density polyethylene (HDPE) is much harder than low-density polyethylene (LDPE). You can conclude that there are more carbon atoms in a chain of _____.

19. A less common type of radioactive particle emitted is the positron. If potassium-38 forms argon-38 by positron emission, the mass number of a positron is _____ and the charge is _____.

20. Although the fusion of hydrogen to produce helium is the most common fusion reaction occurring in the sun, several other fusion reactions occur. In one of these, two helium-4 nuclei fuse to form one unstable _____ nucleus.

Short Answer

In complete sentences, write the answers to the questions on the lines provided.

1. The study of an organism that lived 10 million years ago would most likely fall under which two branches of natural science?

_____

_____

2. How do changes in temperature usually affect the viscosity of a liquid? Explain how the viscosity of motor oil makes it a good choice for protecting an automobile engine in both hot and cold weather.

_____

_____

_____

_____

3. How could you determine if a phase change is endothermic?

_____

_____

_____

_____

4. How does the electron cloud model of the atom represent the locations of electrons in atoms?

_____

_____

_____

5. The elements silicon (atomic number 14) and chlorine (atomic number 17) are both in Period 3. Which is the more reactive element?

_____

Name _____ Class _____ Date _____

6. In potassium bromide, KBr, which element forms anions?

_____

7. A student balanced the chemical equation Mg + O$_2$ → MgO by writing Mg + O$_2$ → MgO$_2$. Was the equation balanced correctly? Explain your answer. If the equation was not balanced correctly, write the correctly balanced equation.

_____

_____

_____

_____

8. Compare and contrast an exothermic chemical reaction and an exothermic solution formation by dissociation.

_____

_____

_____

_____

9. What two products are formed from the reaction of a halocarbon and a base?

_____

10. In terms of electrical attraction, why is it necessary to accelerate an alpha particle in order for it to effectively bombard a nucleus of a large atom?

_____

_____

_____

_____

_____

_____

_____

Using Science Skills

Use the diagram to answer each question. Write the answers on a separate sheet of paper.

1. Using Tables and Graphs In Figure 1-1, what quantity does the slope represent?

Figure 1-1

Properties of Three Mixtures			
	Scatters Light	Separates into Layers	Can Be Separated by Filtration
Mixture A	Yes	No	No
Mixture B	No	No	No
Mixture C	Yes	Yes	Yes

Figure 1-2

2. **Analyzing Data** Which of the mixtures in Figure 1-2 is a colloid? Explain how you know.

3. **Interpreting Graphics** In Figure 1-3, what is the unit used for pressure? What is the pressure when the volume is 0.5 L? What is the pressure when the volume is 1.0 L?

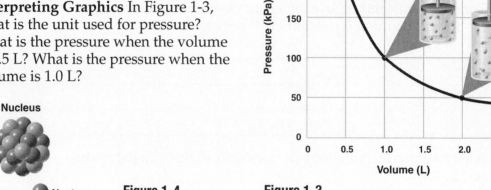

Figure 1-3

Nucleus

Proton   Neutron   Figure 1-4

4. **Evaluating** Is Figure 1-4 a useful model of an atom? Explain your answer.

5. **Inferring** Identify the most reactive element shown in Figure 1-5. Explain your answer.

6. **Comparing and Contrasting** In Figure 1-6, how are the compounds in rows A and C similar? How are they different?

Figure 1-5

Figure 1-6

	Substances	Compound	Remarks
A	potassium, K, and iodine, I	KI	Iodine is a member of the halogen group; potassium is an alkali metal.
B	carbon, C, and oxygen, O	CO_2	Carbon and oxygen are both nonmetals.
C	Al, O, and H	$Al(OH)_3$	OH^+ (hydroxide) is a polyatomic ion.

Figure 1-7

7. **Using Tables and Graphs** What do the peaks on the graphs in Figure 1-7 represent?

Substance	Solubility (g/100 g H_2O, 20°C)	Substance	Solubility (g/100 g H_2O, 20°C)
Barium hydroxide	3.89	Potassium chloride	34.2
Barium nitrate	9.02	Sodium chloride	35.9
Calcium hydroxide	0.173	Sucrose (table sugar)	203.9

Figure 1-8

8. **Applying Concepts** A boy wanted to make candy from crystallized sugar. He dissolved 300.0 g of sucrose in 75 g of water at 100°C. To the nearest gram, how much sugar crystallized out of the saturated solution when it cooled to 20°C? Use Figure 1-8 to answer this question.

a.

$$H - \underset{\underset{Br}{|}}{\overset{\overset{H}{|}}{C}} - \underset{\underset{Br}{|}}{\overset{\overset{H}{|}}{C}} - H$$

b.

$$H - \underset{\underset{H}{|}}{\overset{\overset{H}{|}}{C}} - \underset{\underset{H}{|}}{\overset{\overset{H}{|}}{C}} - \underset{\underset{H}{|}}{\overset{\overset{OH}{|}}{C}} - H$$

c.

$$H - \underset{\underset{H}{|}}{\overset{\overset{H}{|}}{C}} - \underset{\underset{H}{|}}{\overset{\overset{H}{|}}{C}} - \underset{\underset{H}{|}}{\overset{\overset{H}{|}}{C}} - C\overset{O}{\underset{OH}{}}$$

d.

$$H - \underset{\underset{H}{|}}{\overset{\overset{H}{|}}{C}} - \underset{\underset{H}{|}}{\overset{\overset{H}{|}}{C}} - \underset{\underset{H}{|}}{\overset{\overset{H}{|}}{C}} - \overset{O}{\overset{||}{C}} - O - \underset{\underset{H}{|}}{\overset{\overset{H}{|}}{C}} - \underset{\underset{H}{|}}{\overset{\overset{H}{|}}{C}} - H$$

e.

$$H - \underset{\underset{H}{|}}{\overset{\overset{H}{|}}{C}} - \underset{\underset{H}{|}}{N} - H$$

Figure 1-9

9. **Inferring** The ester ethyl butanoate provides the taste and smell to pineapple. Identify the structural formula in Figure 1-9 for ethyl butanoate.

10. Using Tables and Graphs
What product isotope is produced by the decay of thorium-234? If an initial sample contains 48 g of thorium-234, how much of this product isotope will be present after 72.3 days? Use Figure 1-10 to answer these questions.

A **Nuclear Forces Acting on a Proton of a Small Nucleus**

Strong nuclear forces

Electric force

B **Nuclear Forces Acting on a Proton of a Large Nucleus**

Strong nuclear forces

Electric forces

Figure 1-10

Problem

Write the answers to each question on a separate sheet of paper.

1. When iron metal reacts with oxygen, the reaction can form Fe_2O_3. Write a balanced chemical equation for this reaction, and find the number of moles of oxygen that are needed to form 6 mol of Fe_2O_3.

2. Write a balanced chemical equation for the formation of carbonic acid from carbon dioxide and water.

Essay

Write the answers to each question on a separate sheet of paper.

1. Explain how peer reviews are important in either supporting a hypothesis or revising a hypothesis.

2. Suppose you want to separate the leaves, acorns, and twigs from a pile of soil. Filtration and distillation are two processes of separating mixtures. Explain which process you would use and why.

3. Use breathing as an example to explain the relationship between volume and air pressure.

Multiple Choice

Write the letter that best answers the question or completes the statement on the line provided.

_____ 1. Which of the following is NOT one of the main ideas of physical science?
   a. The universe is very old and very large.
   b. Forces cause changes in motion.
   c. Energy can be transferred from one form to another, but it can never be destroyed.
   d. One of the main branches of natural science is biology.

_____ 2. What is the most important safety rule?
   a. Never work with chemicals.
   b. Always use unbreakable glassware.
   c. Always follow your teacher's instructions and textbook directions exactly.
   d. Never do experiments that involve flames or hot objects.

_____ 3. How do scientists communicate the results of investigations?
   a. by publishing articles in scientific journals
   b. by giving talks at scientific conferences
   c. by exchanging e-mails
   d. all of the above

_____ 4. A substance that is made up of only one kind of atom is a(an)
   a. compound.   b. homogeneous mixture.
   c. element.   d. solution.

_____ 5. A mixture can be classified as a solution, suspension, or colloid based on the
   a. number of particles it contains.
   b. size of its largest particles.
   c. color of its particles.
   d. size of its smallest particles.

_____ 6. Which of the following is a chemical change?
   a. ice melting
   b. ice being carved
   c. water boiling
   d. water breaking down into hydrogen and oxygen

_____ 7. A gas has
   a. a definite volume but no definite shape.
   b. a definite shape but no definite volume.
   c. no definite shape or definite volume.
   d. a definite volume and definite shape.

_____ **8.** The temperature and volume in a closed container of gas remain constant. If the number of particles of gas is increased, the gas pressure will
   a. increase.   **b.** decrease.
   c. remain constant.
   d. cause a decrease in the average kinetic energy of the particles.

_____ **9.** During what phase change does the arrangement of water molecules become more orderly?
   a. melting   **b.** freezing   **c.** boiling   **d.** condensing

_____ **10.** Which of the following is NOT part of John Dalton's atomic theory?
   a. All elements are composed of atoms.
   b. All atoms of the same element have the same mass.
   c. Atoms contain subatomic particles.
   d. A compound contains atoms of more than one element.

_____ **11.** Which subatomic particle has a negative charge?
   a. electron   **b.** alpha particle
   c. neutron   **d.** proton

_____ **12.** What does the electron cloud analogy suggest?
   a. An electron cannot be precisely located at any one moment in time.
   b. Protons move occasionally.
   c. Protons and neutrons spin around each other.
   d. Atoms do not stay still long enough to be observed.

_____ **13.** One-twelfth the mass of a carbon-12 atom is used to define a(an)
   a. atomic number.   **b.** atomic mass.
   c. mass number.   **d.** atomic mass unit.

_____ **14.** The column on the far left of the periodic table contains the
   a. most reactive metals.
   b. most reactive nonmetals.
   c. least reactive nonmetals.
   d. least reactive metals.

_____ **15.** As you move from left to right across a period, the number of valence electrons
   a. increases.   **b.** stays the same.
   c. increases and then decreases.   **d.** decreases.

_____ **16.** Typically, atoms gain or lose electrons to achieve
   a. an exchange of energy.
   b. ionization.
   c. a stable electron configuration.
   d. vaporization.

_____17. Which of the following compounds does NOT contain
molecules?
a. H_2 b. NaCl   c. CO_2 d. H_2O

_____18. Which statement about metals is true?
a. A metal lattice is extremely rigid.
b. A metal lattice has weak bonds within a metal.
c. Electrons in a metal lattice are free to move.
d. Generally, metals have a low melting point.

_____19. Which of the following is a balanced chemical equation for
the synthesis of NaBr from Na and Br2?
a. $Na + Br_2 \rightarrow NaBr$ b. $2Na + Br_2 \rightarrow NaBr$
c. $Na + Br_2 \rightarrow 2NaBr$ d. $2Na + Br_2 \rightarrow 2NaBr$

_____20. Which of the following takes place during a redox reaction?
a. Electrons are gained only.
b. Electrons are lost only.
c. Electrons are both gained and lost.
d. Electrons are neither gained nor lost.

_____21. When the forward and reverse paths of a change occur at
the same rate,
a. the system is conserved.
b. the system is in equilibrium.
c. the change must be physical.
d. the change must be chemical.

_____22. A salt is dissolved in water, which has a boiling point
of 100°C. The boiling point of the solution will be
a. greater than 100°C.   b. less than 100°C.
c. exactly equal to 100°C.   d. exactly equal to 0°C.

_____23. A base is defined as a compound that produces
a. hydroxide ions in solution.
b. hydrogen ions in solution.
c. hydronium ions in solution.
d. sodium ions in solution.

_____24. A substance that ionizes or dissociates into ions when
placed in water is always a(an)
a. conductor.   b. electrolyte.
c. strong acid.   d. strong base.

_____25. Which of the following statements helps explain why there
are millions of carbon compounds?
a. Carbon has four valence electrons.
b. Carbon atoms form bonds with other carbon atoms.
c. Carbon atoms can form single, double, and triple bonds.
d. all of the above

_____ **26.** Which of the following is NOT an example of a fossil fuel?
   a. coal   **b.** petroleum
   c. natural gas   **d.** methanol

_____ **27.** Natural polymers are produced
   a. only in plant cells.
   b. only in animal cells.
   c. in both plant and animal cells.
   d. in neither plant nor animal cells.

_____ **28.** What type of nuclear decay produces energy instead of a particle?
   a. alpha decay   **b.** beta decay
   c. gamma decay   **d.** electron decay

_____ **29.** Which of the following statements is true?
   a. Chemical reaction rates vary with the conditions of the change, but nuclear decay rates do not.
   b. Nuclear decay rates vary with the conditions of the change, but chemical reaction rates do not.
   c. Both chemical reaction rates and nuclear decay rates vary with the conditions of the change.
   d. Neither chemical reaction rates nor nuclear decay rates vary with the conditions of the change.

_____ **30.** In what state must matter exist for fusion reactions to take place?
   a. solid   **b.** liquid   **c.** gas   **d.** plasma

Completion

Complete each statement on the line provided.

1. A(An) _____ is a way of organizing data that is used to show changes that occur in related variables.

2. _____ is a process that could be used to separated dissolved particles from the liquid in a solution.

3. A(An) _____ change occurs when a material changes shape or size but the composition of the material does not change.

4. Reducing the volume of a gas _____ its pressure if the _____ of the gas and the number of particles are constant.

5. According to _____ all matter was made up of four elements: earth, air, fire, and water.

6. In Bohr's model of the atom, _____ move in fixed orbits around the nucleus.

7. In general, a(an) _____ metal will be more reactive than an alkaline earth metal in the same period.

Name _____ Class _____ Date _____

8. A(An) _____ ion is a covalently bonded group of atoms that has a positive or negative charge.

9. The statement that in chemical reactions, the total mass of the reactants equals the total mass of the products is the law of _____.

10. A food packet taken on a camping trip has a warming packet. This packet contains water and a solute that releases heat when it is dissolved. The dissolving process for this solute and solvent can be described as _____.

11. The rate that a solid solute dissolves in a liquid solvent depends on the frequency and energy of the _____ between the particles of the solute and solvent.

12. The primary products of the complete combustion of fossil fuels are _____ and _____.

13. The energy that your body needs is released by the process of _____.

14. A sample of a radioisotope had a mass of 100.0 g. After exactly 24 days, 6.25 g of the sample remained. The half-life of the isotope is _____ days.

15. In a(an) _____, neutrons released during a fission reaction cause a series of other fission reactions.

Short Answer

In complete sentences, write the answers to the questions on the lines provided.

1. What is the temperature at which water freezes, expressed in Fahrenheit, Celsius, and kelvins?

_____

2. If you looked at a glass containing a solution and a glass containing a suspension, how could you tell which glass contained the suspension?

_____
_____
_____
_____

3. What are three common clues that a chemical change has occurred?

_____
_____
_____
_____

4. Why is the volume of a liquid constant?

_____

_____

_____

5. What did Democritus believe about matter?

_____

_____

_____

6. How did the results of J.J. Thomson's experiments change how scientists thought about atoms?

_____

_____

_____

7. Sodium chloride is a compound of sodium and chlorine. Which of these elements is the alkali metal, and which is the halogen?

_____

_____

8. Potassium, an alkali metal, and bromine, a halogen, are both in Period 4 of the periodic table. Which element has a higher ionization energy? Explain your answer.

_____

_____

_____

_____

9. Explain why ice in liquid water at 0°C is an example of physical equilibrium.

_____

_____

_____

10. Which will freeze at a higher temperature—a freshwater marsh or a saltwater marsh? Explain your answer.

_____

_____

_____

_____

11. What is the difference between a saturated solution and an unsaturated solution?

_____

_____

_____

12. What elements do organic compounds always contain?

_____

_____

_____

13. Classify the compounds ethyne, heptane, and benzene.

_____

_____

_____

14. How did the physicist Becquerel first observe the effects of nuclear decay?

_____

_____

_____

_____

15. What two problems must be overcome before fusion can be used to produce energy?

_____

_____

Using Science Skills

Use the diagram to answer each question. Write the answers on a separate sheet of paper.

1. Using Tables and Graphs Use Figure 1-1 to determine the approximate total annual precipitation.

Monthly Precipitation: Port Hardy, Canada

Figure 1-1

Physical Properties of Four Materials Used to Make Sculptures			
	Malleability	Hardness	Melting Point
Wax	Soft enough to be carved and molded	Soft but keeps its shape at room temperature	Low melting point
Unbaked clay	Can be molded	Soft	Very high melting point
Baked clay	Brittle after being baked at a high temperature	Hard	Very high melting point
Metal (a mixture of copper, zinc, and lead)	Can be hammered without shattering	Hard	High melting point

Figure 1-2

2. **Comparing and Contrasting** Use Figure 1-2 to compare the physical properties of clay before and after it is baked at a high temperature.

3. **Interpreting Graphics** Identify the phase changes in Figure 1-3 that are labeled a, b, and c.

4. **Using Analogies** Read the following analogy and explain how it applies to panels 1 and 2 in Figure 1-4: The atomic model in panel 1 is to the model in panel 2 as a drawing of the outside of a house is to a blueprint of the inside.

Figure 1-3

Figure 1-4

* Atomic number = 11

Figure 1-5

5. **Classifying** Which element in Figure 1-5 is a transition metal? Which is a noble gas?

Chemical Formula	Name	Type of Bond	Description of Bond
NaCl	(1)	ionic	(2)
CO_2	carbon dioxide	(3)	Atoms share pairs of valence electrons.
W	tungsten	(4)	Metal cations are attracted to the shared electrons that surround them.

Figure 1-6

6. **Using Tables and Graphs** Write a description to place in box (2) in Figure 1-6.

7. **Interpreting Graphics** How many of each type of atom are present on each side of the equation in Figure 1-7?

Unbalanced equation:

CH_4 + O_2 ⟶ CO_2 + H_2O

Figure 1-7

pH 0 1 2 3 4 5 6 7 8 9 10 11 12 13 14

Increasing acidity   Neutral   Increasing basicity

Figure 1-8

8. **Drawing Conclusions** Oven cleaner has a pH of 14, and household ammonia has a pH of about 11.2. What generalization might you make about whether most cleaners contain acids or bases? Use Figure 1-8 to answer this question.

Light Energy

Photosynthesis

Carbon Dioxide   **Water Vapor**   **Carbohydrates**   **Oxygen**

Cellular Respiration

Energy Released

Figure 1-9

9. **Predicting** Predict how reducing the number of plants grown worldwide might affect the composition of the atmosphere. Use Figure 1-9 to answer this question.

10. **Drawing Conclusions** A beta particle does have mass, so why is zero the mass number for a beta particle? Use Figure 1-10 to answer this question.

A **Nuclear Forces Acting on a Proton of a Small Nucleus**

Strong nuclear forces

Electric force

B **Nuclear Forces Acting on a Proton of a Large Nucleus**

Strong nuclear forces

Electric forces

Figure 1-10

Chapter 11   Motion   **Chapter Test A**

Multiple Choice

Write the letter that best answers the question or completes the statement on the line provided.

_____ 1. A passenger in the rear seat of a car moving at a steady
           speed is at rest relative to
           a. the side of the road.
           b. a pedestrian on the corner ahead.
           c. the front seat of the car.
           d. the wheels of the car.

_____ 2. Which distance can be most accurately measured with
           a ruler?
           a. the length of a river
           b. the width of a book
           c. the distance between two cities
           d. the size of an object under a microscope

_____ 3. A person drives north 3 blocks, then turns east and drives
           3 blocks. The driver then turns south and drives 3 blocks.
           How could the driver have made the distance shorter while
           maintaining the same displacement?
           a. by driving east 3 blocks from the starting point
           b. by driving north 1 block and east 4 blocks
           c. by driving west 3 blocks from the starting point
           d. by driving back to the starting point by the same route

_____ 4. Displacement vectors of 1 km south, 3 km north, 6 km
           south, and 2 km north combine to a total displacement of
           a. 12 km.   **b.** 6 km.   **c.** 4 km.   **d.** 2 km.

_____ 5. Speed is the ratio of the distance an object moves to
           a. the amount of time needed to travel the distance.
           b. the direction the object moves.
           c. the displacement of the object.
           d. the motion of the object.

_____ 6. A car traveled 88 km in 1 hour, 90 km in the next 2 hours,
           and then 76 km in 1 hour before reaching its destination.
           What was the car's average speed?
           a. 254 km/h   **b.** 63.5 km/h
           c. 209 km/h   **d.** 74.5 km/h

_____ 7. A horizontal line on a distance-time graph means the
           object is
           a. moving at a constant speed.
           b. moving faster.
           c. slowing down.
           d. at rest.

_____ 8. A distance-time graph indicates that an object moves 100 m in 4 s and then remains at rest for 1 s. What is the average speed of the object?

a. 50 m/s   b. 25 m/s   c. 20 m/s   d. 100 m/s

_____ 9. Vector addition is used when motion involves

a. more than one direction.   b. more than one velocity.

c. more than one speed.   d. all of the above

_____ 10. Which example identifies a change in motion that produces acceleration?

a. a speed skater moving at a constant speed on a straight track

b. a ball moving at a constant speed around a circular track

c. a particle moving in a vacuum at constant velocity

d. a vehicle moving down the street at a steady speed

_____ 11. Which example describes constant acceleration due ONLY to a change in direction?

a. increasing speed while traveling around a curve

b. an object at rest

c. traveling around a circular track

d. an object in free fall

_____ 12. An object moving at 30 m/s takes 5 s to come to a stop. What is the object's acceleration?

a. 30 m/s²   b. –30 m/s²   c. –6 m/s²   d. 6 m/s²

_____ 13. A speed-time graph shows that a car moves at 10 m/s for 10 s. The car's speed then steadily decreases until it comes to a stop at 30 s. Which of the following describes the slope of the speed-time graph from 10 s to 30 s?

a. linear, horizontal

b. curved, upward

c. linear, sloping downward

d. linear, sloping upward

_____ 14. A train approaching a crossing changes speed from 25 m/s to 10 m/s in 240 s. How can the train's acceleration be described?

a. The train's acceleration is positive.

b. The train is not accelerating.

c. The train will come to rest in 6 minutes.

d. The train's acceleration is negative.

_____ 15. Which of the following statements is true?

a. An object that is accelerating is always changing direction.

b. An object has an instantaneous acceleration, even if the acceleration vector is zero.

c. An object at rest has an instantaneous acceleration of zero.

d. Instantaneous acceleration is always changing.

Completion

Complete each statement on the line provided.

1. Displacement and velocity are examples of _____ because they have both magnitude and direction.

2. $\overline{V} = \dfrac{d}{t}$ is the equation that defines _____.

3. A constant slope on a distance-time graph indicates _____ speed.

4. A car that increases its speed from 20 km/h to 100 km/h undergoes _____ acceleration.

5. _____ is how fast a velocity is changing at a specific instant.

Short Answer

In complete sentences, write the answers to the questions on the lines provided.

Figure 11-1

1. From which frame of reference in Figure 11-1 does the tree appear to be in motion?

   _____

   _____

   _____

2. What is the SI unit best suited for measuring the height of a building?

   _____

   _____

3. A child rolls a ball 4 m across a room. The ball hits the wall and rolls halfway back toward the child. Using vector addition, calculate the ball's displacement.

   _____

   _____

   _____

4. Which is the most suitable SI unit for expressing the speed of a race car?

_____

_____

_____

5. Bus A travels 300 m in 12 s. Bus B travels 200 m in 12 s. Both vehicles travel at constant speed. How do the distance-time graphs for these two speeds differ?

_____

_____

_____

6. What types of changes in motion cause acceleration?

_____

_____

_____

_____

Using Science Skills

Use the diagram to answer each question. Write the answers on a separate sheet of paper.

Figure 11-2

Figure 11-2B

1. **Interpreting Graphics** Figure 11-2B illustrates the displacement of an object moving in a plane. Explain what information is provided by arrows A and B.

2. **Calculating** Using vector addition, calculate the distance traveled by the object and the displacement of the object represented by Figure 11-2B.

3. **Using Models** Arrows A and B in Figure 11-3A represent velocities. Describe the motion modeled by the vectors.

4. **Predicting** Suppose vector B in Figure 11-3B had a length of 12 m (instead of 5 m). What would be the distance the object moved? What would be the magnitude of the object's displacement?

5. **Applying Concepts** Vectors A and B in Figure 11-3A represent the path walked by a student from home to school. What does the resultant vector A + B represent?

Problem

Write the answers to each question on a separate sheet of paper.

1. During a race, a runner runs at a speed of 6 m/s. Four seconds later, she is running at a speed of 10 m/s. What is the runner's acceleration? Show your work.

2. If you ride your bike at an average speed of 2 km/h and need to travel a total distance of 20 km, how long will it take you to reach your destination? Show your work.

Essay

Write the answers to each question on a separate sheet of paper.

1. Explain how velocity is different from speed.

2. Picture a ball traveling at a constant speed around the inside of a circular structure. Is the ball accelerating? Explain your answer.

3. A girl walks from her home to a friend's home 3 blocks north. She then walks east 2 blocks to the post office, 1 block north to the library, and 1 block east to the park. From the park, she walks 2 blocks west to the movie theater. After the movie, she walks 4 blocks south to the pet store. What is the girl's displacement from her starting point to the pet store? Where is the location of the pet store in relation to her home? Calculate the distance she walked in blocks.

Chapter 11   Motion   **Chapter Test B**

Multiple Choice

Write the letter that best answers the question or completes the statement on the line provided.

Figure 11-1

_____ **1.** Examine Figure 11-1. If you were standing under the tree, which object would appear to be moving?
   a. the tree   **b.** the airplane
   c. the boy   **d.** the building

_____ **2.** One kilometer equals 1000 meters. What does the prefix kilo- mean?
   a. 1   **b.** 10   **c.** 100   **d.** 1000

_____ **3.** A person walks 1 mile every day for exercise, leaving her front porch at 9:00 AM. and returning to her front porch at 9:25 AM. What is the total displacement of her daily walk?
   a. 1 mile   **b.** 0
   c. 25 minutes   **d.** none of the above

_____ **4.** A ball is rolled uphill a distance of 3 meters before it slows, stops, and begins to roll back. The ball rolls downhill 6 meters before coming to rest against a tree. What is the magnitude of the ball's displacement?
   a. 3 meters   **b.** 6 meters
   c. 9 meter   **d.** 18 meters

_____ **5.** What is the most appropriate SI unit to express the speed of a cyclist in the last leg of a 10-km race?
   a. km/s   **b.** km/h
   c. m/s   **d.** cm/h

_____ **6.** Instantaneous speed is measured
   a. at the starting point.
   b. when the object reaches its destination.
   c. at a particular instant.
   d. over the duration of the trip.

_____ **7.** The slope of a line on a distance-time graph is
   a. distance.   **b.** time.
   c. speed.   **d.** displacement.

_____ 8. What is the speed of a bobsled whose distance-time graph
indicates that it traveled 100 m in 25 s?
a. 4 m/s   b. 250 m/s
c. 0.25 mph   d. 100 m/s

_____ 9. A river current has a velocity of 5 km/h relative to the shore,
and a boat moves in the same direction as the current at
5 km/h relative to the river. How can the velocity of the
boat relative to the shore be calculated?
a. by subtracting the river current vector from the boat's
velocity vector
b. by dividing the river current vector by the boat's velocity
vector
c. by multiplying the vectors
d. by adding the vectors

_____ 10. The rate at which velocity changes is called
a. speed.   b. vectors.
c. acceleration.   d. motion.

_____ 11. Objects in free fall near the surface of the Earth experience
a. constant speed.   b. constant velocity.
c. constant acceleration.   d. constant distance.

_____ 12. Suppose you increase your walking speed from 1 m/s to
3 m/s in a period of 2 s. What is your acceleration?
a. 1 m/s^2 b. 2 m/s^2
c. 4 m/s^2 d. 6 m/s^2

_____ 13. The slope of a speed-time graph indicates
a. direction.   b. acceleration.
c. velocity.   d. speed.

_____ 14. An object that is accelerating may be
a. slowing down.   b. gaining speed.
c. changing direction   d. all of the above

_____ 15. What is instantaneous acceleration?
a. how fast a speed is changing at a specific instant
b. how fast a velocity is changing at a specific instant
c. how fast a direction is changing at a specific instant
d. all of the above

Completion

Complete each statement on the line provided.

1. The motion of an object looks different to observers in different

   _____.

2. The SI unit for measuring _____ is the meter.

3. The direction and length of a straight line from the starting point to the ending point of an object's motion is _____.

4. The sum of two or more vectors is called the_____.

5. Speed is measured in units of _____.

6. A car's speedometer measures _____.

7. The difference between speed and velocity is that velocity indicates the _____ of motion and speed does not.

8. Because its _____ is always changing, an object moving in a circular path experiences a constant change in velocity.

9. A moving object does not _____ if its velocity remains constant.

10. Freely falling objects accelerate at 9.8 m/s² because the force of _____ acts on them.

11. The acceleration of a moving object is calculated by dividing the change in _____ by the time over which the change occurs.

Short Answer

In complete sentences, write the answers to the questions on the lines provided.

1. Distance is a measure of length. What information does displacement give in addition to distance?

   _____

   _____

   _____

   _____

2. What are two types of speed that can be used to describe the motion of a car driving on the highway?

   _____

   _____

   _____

   _____

3. What is the significance of the slope in a distance-time graph?

   _____

   _____

   _____

   _____

4. What information does the slope of a speed-time graph provide?

   _____

   _____

   _____

5. The slope of the curve at a single point on a distance-time graph of accelerated motion gives what information?

   _____

   _____

   _____

   _____

Using Science Skills

Use the diagram to answer each question. Write the answers on a separate sheet of paper.

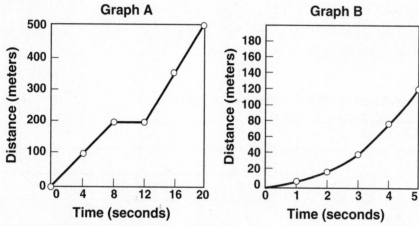

Figure 11-2

1. **Using Tables and Graphs** Which graph in Figure 11-2 shows periods of constant speed? Explain your answer.

2. **Interpreting Graphics** Look at Figure 11-2. Describe the motion of the object in Graph A.

3. **Using Models** Which graph in Figure 11-2 shows acceleration? How do you know?

4. **Calculating** Using Graph A in Figure 11-2, calculate the average speed of the object in motion from 12 s to 20 s. Explain your calculation.

5. **Comparing and Contrasting** Compare Graphs A and B in Figure 11-2. At a time of 2 seconds, which graph shows a greater velocity? How do you know?

Name _____ Class _____ Date _____

Chapter 12 Forces and Motion   **Chapter Test A**

Multiple Choice

Write the letter that best answers the question or completes the statement on the line provided.

_____ 1. Which of the following relationships is correct?
   a. 1 N = 1 kg
   b. 1 N = 1 kg•m
   c. 1 N = 1 kg•m/s
   d. 1 N = 1 kg•m/s^2

_____ 2. When a pair of balanced forces acts on an object, the net force that results is
   a. greater in size than both forces combined.
   b. greater in size than one of the forces.
   c. equal in size to one of the forces.
   d. equal to zero.

_____ 3. As you push a cereal box across a tabletop, the sliding friction acting on the cereal box
   a. acts in the direction of motion.
   b. equals the weight of the box
   c. is usually greater than static friction.
   d. acts in the direction opposite of motion.

_____ 4. An open parachute increases air resistance of a falling sky diver by
   a. decreasing the weight of the diver
   b. increasing surface area.
   c. increasing the terminal velocity.
   d. reducing fluid friction.

_____ 5. Projectile motion is caused by
   a. the downward force of gravity.
   b. an initial forward velocity.
   c. a final vertical velocity.
   d. the downward force of gravity and an initial forward velocity.

_____ 6. An orange might roll off your cafeteria tray when you stop suddenly because of
   a. the balanced forces acting on the orange.
   b. the centripetal force acting on the orange.
   c. the friction forces acting on the orange.
   d. the orange's inertia.

_____ 7. If a force of 10 N is applied to an object with a mass of 1 kg, the object will accelerate at
   a. 0.1 m/s^2.
   b. 9 m/s^2.
   c. 10 m/s^2.
   d. 11 m/s^2.

Physical Science • Chapter 12 Test A **123**

© Pearson Education, Inc. All rights reserved.

_____ 8. The acceleration due to gravity on the surface of Mars is about one-third the acceleration due to gravity on Earth's surface. The weight of a space probe on the surface of Mars is about
   a. nine times greater than its weight on Earth's surface.
   b. three times greater than its weight on Earth's surface.
   c. one-third its weight on Earth's surface.
   d. the same as its weight on Earth's surface.

_____ 9. In which of the following are action and reaction forces involved?
   a. when a tennis racket strikes a tennis ball
   b. when stepping from a curb
   c. when rowing a boat
   d. all of the above

_____ 10. What is the momentum of a 50-kilogram ice skater gliding across the ice at a speed of 2 m/s?
   a. 25 $\frac{kg}{m/s}$ b. 48 kg•m/s   c. 50 kg   d. 100 kg•m/s

_____ 11. When opposite poles of two magnets are brought together, the poles
   a. attract each other.   b. repel each other.
   c. cancel each other.   d. cause a net force of zero.

_____ 12. With which of the following is the weak nuclear force associated?
   a. lightning   b. nuclear decay
   c. ocean tides   d. static cling

_____ 13. The gravitational force between two objects increases as mass
   a. decreases or distance decreases.
   b. decreases or distance increases.
   c. increases or distance decreases.
   d. increases or distance increases.

_____ 14. The centripetal force acting on a satellite in orbit
   a acts as an unbalanced force on the satellite.
   b. changes the direction of the satellite.
   c. is a center-directed force.
   d. all of the above

Completion

Complete each statement on the line provided.

1. The type of force measured by a grocery store spring scale is

   _____.

2. If the forces acting on an object produce a net force of zero, the forces are called _____.

3. It usually takes more force to start an object sliding than it does to keep an object sliding because static friction is usually _____ than sliding friction.

4. The universal force that is most effective over the longest distances is _____.

5. The centripetal force acting on the moon continuously changes the _____ of the moon's motion.

Short Answer

In complete sentences, write the answers to the questions on the lines provided.

1. How can an arrow be used to represent the size and direction of a force?

   _____

   _____

   _____

   _____

   _____

   _____

Figure 12-1

2. Figure 12-1 shows the paths followed by three balls. Each ball started moving at the same time. Ball A was dropped and balls B and C were thrown sideways. Compare the times for each ball to reach the ground.

   _____

   _____

   _____

   _____

   _____

   _____

   _____

3. During a collision, a seat belt slows the speed of a crash-test dummy. What is the direction of the net force exerted by the seat belt compared to the direction of the dummy's motion?

_____

_____

_____

4. A billiard ball with a momentum of 20 kg•m/s strikes a second ball at rest and comes to a complete stop. What is the change in momentum of the second ball?

_____

_____

5. Compare the speed of a moving golf ball with the speed of a moving bowling ball if both balls have the same amount of momentum.

_____

_____

_____

Using Science Skills

Use the diagram to answer each question. Write the answers on a separate sheet of paper.

Time 1   Time 2

Skater A   Skater B   Skater A   Skater B

Skaters are not in motion.   Skaters are moving at identical speeds.

Figure 12-2

1. **Interpreting Graphics** In Figure 12-2, what is the momentum of each skater at Time 1?

Name _____ Class _____ Date _____

2. **Comparing and Contrasting** In Figure 12-2, compare the size and direction of the momentums of both skaters immediately after the push shown at Time 2.

3. **Interpreting Graphics** In Figure 12-2, describe the motion of Skater B after Skater A pushes her.

4. **Applying Concepts** In Figure 12-2, if Skater A is pushing Skater B, why does Skater A move?

5. **Applying Concepts** Suppose that the skaters repeat the demonstration in Figure 12-2 again. This time Skater B is holding a 10-kilogram mass. If Skater A pushes exactly as he did the first time, will Skater A's motion be different this time? Explain your answer.

Problem

Write the answers to each question on a separate sheet of paper.

1. A crane exerts a net force of 900 N upward on a 750-kilogram car as the crane starts to lift the car from the deck of a cargo ship. What is the acceleration of the car during this time? Show your work.

2. The mass of a newborn baby is 4.2 kilograms. What is the baby's weight? (The acceleration due to gravity at Earth's surface is 9.8 m/s².) Show your work.

3. A small 32-kilogram canoe broke free of its dock and is now floating downriver at a speed of 2.5 m/s. What is the canoe's momentum? Show your work.

4. A small engine causes a 0.20-kg model airplane to accelerate at a rate of 12 m/s². What is the net force on the model airplane? Show your work.

Essay

Write the answers to each question on a separate sheet of paper.

1. Why does a biker have to pedal harder to travel at a constant speed into the wind on a windy day compared to traveling on the same road at the same speed on a calm day?

Chapter 12 Forces and Motion

Multiple Choice

Write the letter that best answers the question or completes the statement on the line provided.

_____ 1. The SI unit of force is the
   a. joule.   **b.** kilogram.   **c.** meter.   **d.** newton.

_____ 2. When an unbalanced force acts on an object,
   a. the object's motion does not change.
   b. the object accelerates.
   c. the weight of the object decreases.
   d. the inertia of the object increases.

_____ 3. What kind of friction occurs as a fish swims through water?
   a. fluid   **b.** rolling   **c.** sliding   **d.** static

_____ 4. The forces acting on a falling leaf are
   a. air resistance and fluid friction.
   b. gravity and air resistance.
   c. gravity and static friction.
   d. weight and rolling friction.

Figure 12-1

_____ 5. Figure 12-1 shows the motion of three balls. The curved paths followed by balls B and C are examples of
   a. centripetal motion.   **b.** constant motion.
   c. linear motion.   **d.** projectile motion.

_____ 6. The property of matter that resists changes in motion is called
   a. friction.   **b.** gravity.   **c.** inertia.   **d.** weight.

_____ 7. According to Newton's second law of motion, the acceleration of an object equals the net force acting on the object divided by the object's
   a. mass.   **b.** momentum.
   c. velocity.   **d.** weight.

_____ 8. Your weight equals your
   a. mass.
   b. mass divided by the net force acting on you.
   c. mass times the acceleration due to gravity.
   d. mass times your speed.

_____ **9.** Newton's third law of motion describes
    a. action and reaction forces.
    b. balanced forces.
    c. centripetal forces.
    d. net force.

_____ **10.** The product of an object's mass and velocity is its
    a. centripetal force.   **b.** momentum.
    c. net force.   **d.** weight.

_____ **11.** What is conserved when two objects collide in a closed system?
    a. acceleration   **b.** momentum
    c. speed   **d.** velocity

_____ **12.** What force is responsible for the repulsion between two positively-charged particles?
    a. centripetal   **b.** electric
    c. gravitational   **d.** nuclear

_____ **13.** Which universal force acts only on the protons and neutrons in a nucleus?
    a. electric   **b.** gravitational
    c. magnetic   **d.** strong nuclear

_____ **14.** Which of the following universal forces is the most effective over long distances?
    a. electric   **b.** gravitational
    c. magnetic   **d.** strong nuclear

_____ **15.** As an astronaut travels far away from Earth, her weight
    a. decreases because gravity decreases.
    b. decreases because her mass decreases.
    c. increases because gravity increases.
    d. remains the same because her mass remains the same.

_____ **16.** The force that keeps an object moving in a circle is called
    a. centripetal force.   **b.** fluid friction.
    c. inertia.   **d.** momentum.

Completion

Complete each statement on the line provided.

1. A push or pull is an example of a(an) _____.

2. The sum of all the forces acting on an object is called the
_____.

3. The force that opposes the motion of objects that touch as they move pass each other is called _____.

4. The two forces acting on a falling object are gravity and
_____.

5. The path of motion of a thrown javelin is an example of
_____ motion.

6. The tendency of an object to resist any change in its motion is
called _____.

7. The acceleration of an object is equal to the net
_____ acting on the object divided by the object's
_____.

8. The force of gravity acting on an object is the object's
_____.

9. If a golf ball and bowling ball are rolling at the same speed, the
_____ ball has greater momentum.

10. In a closed system, the loss of momentum of one object
_____ the gain in momentum of another object.

Short Answer

*In complete sentences, write the answers to the questions on
the lines provided.*

1. What happens to the magnitude of the fluid friction acting on a
submarine as the submarine's speed increases?

_____

_____

_____

_____

_____

2. What is the direction of the net force on a falling sky diver before
she reaches terminal velocity? After she is falling at terminal
velocity?

_____

_____

_____

_____

_____

3. How can you double the acceleration of an object if you cannot
alter the object's mass?

_____

_____

_____

4. Which of the universal forces acts only on protons and neutrons in the nucleus of an atom?

_____

_____

_____

_____

5. What is the primary cause of Earth's ocean tides?

_____

_____

_____

_____

Using Science Skills

Use the diagram to answer each question. Write the answers on a separate sheet of paper.

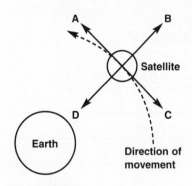

Figure 12-2

1. **Interpreting Graphics** In Figure 12-2, what is the direction of the centripetal force acting on the satellite at this location in its orbit?

2. **Predicting** What happens to the size of the centripetal force due to gravity acting on the satellite in Figure 12-2 if the satellite moves farther from Earth?

3. **Applying Concepts** The centripetal force acting on the satellite in Figure 12-2 is one of a pair of action-reaction forces. On what object is the other force in the pair acting?

4. **Interpreting Graphics** In Figure 12-2, what property of the satellite tends to keep it moving along through its orbit?

5. **Inferring** As shown in Figure 12-2, what is the direction of the fluid friction acting on the satellite as it moves through the outer layer of Earth's atmosphere?

Multiple Choice

Write the letter that best answers the question or completes the statement on the line provided.

_____ 1. If the air inside a balloon exerts a force of 1 N on an area of 0.5 m², what is the pressure inside the balloon?
- **a.** 0.5 N/m²
- **b.** 1 N/m²
- **c.** 1.5 N/m²
- **d.** 2 N/m²

_____ 2. A pressure of 10 N/m² equals
- **a.** 1 Pa.
- **b.** 10 Pa.
- **c.** 100 Pa.
- **d.** 1000 Pa.

_____ 3. Which of the following is NOT possible?
- **a.** compressing 10 liters of oxygen gas into a 1 liter volume
- **b.** compressing 2 liters of water into a 1 liter volume
- **c.** filling a balloon using helium gas from a pressurized tank
- **d.** allowing 5 liters of compressed air to expand to a volume of 100 liters

_____ 4. Two identical test tubes are filled with equal volumes of water and mercury. Which of the following statements is true?
- **a.** The weight of each liquid is the same.
- **b.** The bottom area of each test tube is the same.
- **c.** The pressure at the bottom of each test tube is the same.
- **d.** all of the above

_____ 5. The pressure of air at sea level is approximately
- **a.** 0 kPa
- **b.** 10 kPa.
- **c.** 101 kPa.
- **d.** 1000 kPa.

_____ 6. Where will the greatest increase in pressure occur if you squeeze the middle of an upright, closed soft-drink bottle?
- **a.** The greatest increase in pressure will occur at the top of the bottle.
- **b.** The greatest increase in pressure will occur in the middle of the bottle.
- **c.** The greatest increase in pressure will occur on the bottom of the bottle.
- **d.** The pressure will increase equally everywhere within the bottle.

Piston
(Surface Area of
Piston 2 = 900 cm²)

Piston
(Surface Area of
Piston 1 = 100 cm²)

Figure 13-1

_____ **7.** In Figure 13-1, Piston 1 exerts a pressure of 10 Pa on the fluid in the hydraulic lift. What is the fluid pressure on Piston 2?
a. 1 Pa   **b.** 5 Pa
c. 30 Pa   **d.** 90 Pa

_____ **8.** Which of the following states Bernoulli's principle?
a. As the speed of a fluid decreases, the pressure within the fluid decreases.
b. As the speed of a fluid increases, the pressure within the fluid decreases.
c. As the speed of a fluid changes, the pressure of the fluid remains constant.
d. none of the above

_____ **9.** Which of the following statements is true about an airplane wing during flight?
a. Air above the wing travels faster than air below the wing.
b. Air below the wing travels faster than air above the wing.
c. The wing exerts pressure equally in all directions.
d. The lift acting on the wing reduces the weight of the wing.

_____ **10.** A brick weighs 21 N. Measured underwater, it weighs 12 N. What is the size of the buoyant force exerted by the water on the brick?
a. 33 N   **b.** 21 N
c. 12 N   **d.** 9 N

_____ **11.** The strength of the buoyant force acting on an object in a fluid depends on the object's

    a. mass.   **b.** surface area.

    c. volume.   **d.** weight.

_____ **12.** The buoyant force on an object in a fluid is equal to the weight of the

    a. fluid.

    b. fluid surrounding the object.

    c. fluid displaced by the object.

    d. object.

_____ **13.** A ball is floating partially submerged in a liquid. The buoyant force acting on the ball equals the

    a. volume of the ball below the surface.

    b. volume of the ball above the surface.

    c. mass of the ball.

    d. weight of the ball.

_____ **14.** A cork is floating in salty water. As more salt is added to the water to increase its density, the cork will

    a. float at a higher level in the water.

    b. float at a lower level in the water.

    c. sink.

    d. float at the same level in the water.

_____ **15.** Two identical corks float in separate beakers. One beaker contains water. The other contains very salty water. Which of the following statements is true?

    a. The corks both float at the same level in the liquid.

    b. The cork in the very salty water floats at a lower level than the other cork.

    c. The corks will eventually sink.

    d. Both corks are subject to the same buoyant force.

Completion

Complete each statement on the line provided.

1. A pascal, the SI unit of pressure, is equal to 1 newton per

_____.

2. As a liquid is added to a beaker, the pressure exerted by the liquid on the bottom of the beaker _____.

3. The pressure exerted by a fluid at any given depth is exerted _____ in all directions.

4. As you climb a high mountain, the buoyant force exerted on you by the atmosphere_____.

5. The weight of an object that sinks in a fluid is _____ than the buoyant force acting on it.

Short Answer

In complete sentences, write the answers to the questions on the lines provided.

1. If you know the air pressure exerted on a tabletop, how can you calculate the force exerted on the tabletop?

   _____

   _____

2. Rank the following measurements in order of increasing pressure: 2 kPa, 10 N/m^2, 300 N/m^2, 0.1 Pa

   _____

   _____

3. Why aren't organisms that live on the seafloor crushed by water pressure?

   _____

   _____

   _____

   _____

4. Why does a partially inflated weather balloon expand as it rises?

   _____

   _____

   _____

   _____

5. A ball of clay sinks when placed in water. The same piece of clay floats if it is made into the shape of a boat. Compare the volume of water displaced by the ball with the volume displaced by the boat shape.

   _____

   _____

   _____

   _____

6. How are density and buoyancy related?

_____

_____

_____

_____

_____

7. If you use a spring scale to measure the weight of a submerged object that has neutral buoyancy, what will the scale read?

_____

_____

Using Science Skills

Use the diagram to answer each question. Write the answers on a separate sheet of paper.

Figure 13-2A   **Figure 13-2B**

1. **Observing** How did the position of the spoon in Figure 13-2 change after the faucet was turned on?

2. **Inferring** On which side of the spoon in Figure 13-2B is the pressure of the air greater?

3. **Applying Concepts** According to Bernoulli's principle, is the spoon shown in Figure 13-2B pulled toward the stream of water or pushed toward the stream of water? Explain your answer.

4. **Drawing Conclusion** In Figure 13-2B, what effect does the stream of water have on the motion of the air around it?

5. **Predicting** What will happen to the spoon in Figure 13-2B if the water from the faucet is allowed to flow at a faster rate?

Problem

Write the answers to each question on a separate sheet of paper.

1. The dimensions of a brick that weighs 21 N are 0.19 m × 0.090 m × 0.055 m. What pressure does the brick exert on the ground if it is resting on its largest face? Show your work.

2. Express a pressure of 2500 N/m² in kilopascals.

**Piston
(Surface Area of
Piston 2 = 900 cm²)**

**Piston
(Surface Area of
Piston 1 = 100 cm²)**

Figure 13-3

3. In Figure 13-3, a force of 1000 N is exerted on Piston 1 of the hydraulic lift shown. What force will be exerted on Piston 2? Show your work.

Essay

Write the answers to each question on a separate sheet of paper.

1. To prevent a window from exploding outward during a strong windstorm, it is left slightly open. Explain why a slightly open window might not blow out.

2. A cube of wood displaces half its volume when floating in water. When a 0.5-N washer is added to the cube, it floats just at the point where it is completely submerged in the water. What is the buoyant force acting on the cube when the washer is removed?

Name _____ Class _____ Date _____

Chapter 13   Forces in Fluids

Chapter Test B

Multiple Choice

Write the letter that best answers the question or completes the statement on the line provided.

_____ 1. In order to calculate pressure exerted on a surface, what quantity is divided by the surface area?
   a. altitude
   b. force
   c. mass
   d. volume

_____ 2. What is the SI unit of pressure?
   a. g/cm^3
   b. m/s^2
   c. a newton
   d. a pascal

_____ 3. Where is fluid pressure greatest?
   a. 30 centimeters below the surface of a swimming pool
   b. 1 meter below the surface of a swimming pool
   c. 2 meters below the surface of a swimming pool
   d. The pressure is the same in all parts of a swimming pool.

_____ 4. Which of the following materials is NOT a fluid?
   a. air
   b. cork
   c. gasoline
   d. water

_____ 5. The pressure of a fluid at a specific depth
   a. depends only on the type of fluid.
   b. is exerted only in the downward direction.
   c. varies with the total volume of the fluid.
   d. all of the above

_____ 6. Atmospheric pressure is caused by
   a. air currents.
   b. the weight of the atmosphere above a particular location.
   c. clouds.
   d. the altitude above sea level.

_____ 7. Which principle states that a change in the pressure at any point in a fluid in a closed container is transmitted equally and unchanged in all directions throughout the fluid?
   a. Archimedes' principle
   b. Bernoulli's principle
   c. Newton's principle
   d. Pascal's principle

_____ 8. The operation of a hydraulic lift system is explained by
   a. Archimedes' principle.
   b. Bernoulli's principle.
   c. Newton's principle.
   d. Pascal's principle.

_____ 9. The hydraulic system of a dump truck is designed to multiply
   a. distance.
   b. force.
   c. pressure.
   d. speed.

Physical Science • Chapter 13 Test B   **139**

_____10. The upward force acting on the wing of an airplane in flight is called
   a. drag.   b. lift.
   c. thrust.   d. weight.

_____11. The upward force acting on an object submerged in a fluid is called
   a. buoyant force.   b. drag.
   c. pressure.   d. weight.

_____12. The relationship between buoyant force and weight of a displaced fluid was first stated by
   a. Archimedes.   b. Bernoulli
   c. Newton.   d. Pascal.

_____13. Which of the following substances will float in corn syrup? (The density of corn syrup is 1.38 g/cm^3.)
   a. aluminum (2.7 g/cm^3)
   b. magnesium (1.75 g/cm^3)
   c. mercury (13.6 g/cm^3)
   d. rubber (1.23 g/cm^3)

_____14. Which of the following materials will sink in water? (The density of water 1.00 g/cm^3.)
   a. balsa wood (0.12 g/cm^3)
   b. cooking oil (0.82 g/cm^3)
   c. ethanol (0.798 g/cm^3)
   d. steel (7.18 g/cm^3)

_____15. Why does a hot-air balloon float?
   a. The shape of the balloon provides lift.
   b. The volume of the air displaced by the balloon is less than the volume of the balloon.
   c. The weight of the air displaced is less than the volume of the balloon.
   d. The weight of the balloon is less than the weight of the air displaced by the balloon.

Completion

Complete each statement on the line provided.

1. Pressure is the result of force distributed over a(an)

   _____.

2. The formula, $\dfrac{\text{Force}}{\text{Area}}$, is used to calculate _____.

3. The SI unit of pressure is the _____.

4. A substance that flows and assumes the shape of its container is a(an) _____.

5. A device that uses pressurized fluids acting on pistons of different sizes to change a force is called a(an) _____.

6. As the speed of a fluid increases, the _____ within the fluid decreases.

7. In a hydraulic lift system, the fluid pressure exerted throughout the system is _____.

8. The apparent loss of weight of an object in a fluid is called

_____.

9. The direction of the buoyant force on an object placed in a fluid is

_____.

10. A submerged submarine alters its _____ to rise or fall in the water.

Short Answer

In complete sentences, write the answers to the questions on the lines provided.

1. Which exerts greater pressure on the floor—standing flat-footed or standing on tiptoes?

_____

_____

_____

2. For a fluid that is not moving, what are the two factors that determine the pressure that the fluid exerts?

_____

_____

_____

_____

3. How do the particles of a liquid exert pressure on a container?

_____

_____

_____

_____

Name _____ Class _____ Date _____

4. How is the weight of water displaced by a floating cork related to the buoyant force?

_____

_____

_____

_____

5. Compare the weight of an object to the buoyant force acting on it if the object sinks in the fluid.

_____

_____

_____

_____

Using Science Skills

Use the diagram to answer each question. Write the answers on a separate sheet of paper.

Figure 13-1

1. **Comparing and Contrasting** How does the fluid pressure exerted on the black spheres shown in Figure 13-1 compare with the pressure exerted on the gray spheres.

2. **Inferring** In Figure 13-1, spheres of which color have the greatest density?

3. **Applying Concepts** In Figure 13-1, on how many spheres is the buoyant force less than the weight of the sphere?

4. **Applying Concepts** In Figure 13-1, on how many spheres is the buoyant force equal to the weight of the sphere?

5. **Applying Concepts** In Figure 13-1, how many spheres have neutral buoyancy?

Chapter 14   Work, Power, and Machines

Multiple Choice

Write the letter that best answers the question or completes the statement on the line provided.

_____ 1. A force acting on an object does no work if
  a. a machine is used to move the object.
  b. the force is not in the direction of the object's motion.
  c. the force is greater than the force of friction.
  d. the object accelerates.

_____ 2. If you exert a force of 10.0 N to lift a box a distance of 0.75 m, how much work do you do?
  a. 0.075 J   **b.** 7.5 J
  c. 10.75 J   **d.** 75 J

_____ 3. If you perform 30 joules of work lifting a 20-N box from the floor to a shelf, how high is the shelf?
  a. 0.5 m   **b.** 0.6 m
  c. 1.5 m   **d.** 2 m

_____ 4. If you exert a force of 500 N to walk 4 m up a flight of stairs in 4 s, how much power do you use?
  a. 31 W   **b.** 500 W
  c. 2000 W   **d.** 8000 W

_____ 5. Which of the following statements is true?
  a. To increase power, you can decrease the amount of work you do in a given amount of time, or you can do a given amount of work in less time.
  b. To increase power, you can decrease the amount of work you do in a given amount of time, or you can do a given amount of work in more time.
  c. To increase power, you can increase the amount of work you do in a given amount of time, or you can do a given amount of work in less time.
  d. To increase power, you can increase the amount of work you do in a given amount of time, or you can do a given amount of work in more time.

_____ 6. A 750-W motor might also be rated as a
  a. 0.5-horsepower motor. **b.** 1-horsepower motor.
  c. 2-horsepower motor.   **d.** 10-horsepower motor.

_____ 7. When a machine does work, it can do all of the following EXCEPT
  a. change the direction of a force.
  b. increase a force and change the distance a force moves.
  c. increase the distance a force moves and change the direction of a force.
  d. increase a force and increase the distance a force moves.

_____ **8.** How can you make the work output of a machine greater than the work input?
   a. by decreasing friction
   b. by increasing the input force
   c. by increasing the output distance
   d. none of the above

_____ **9.** If you know the input distance and output distance of a machine, which of the following can you calculate?
   a. work   **b.** actual mechanical advantage
   c. efficiency   **d.** ideal mechanical advantage

_____ **10.** A 100-m long ski lift carries skiers from a station at the foot of a slope to a second station 40 m above. What is the IMA of the lift?
   a. 0.4   **b.** 2.5
   c. 40   **d.** 140

_____ **11.** The efficiency of a machine is always less than 100 percent because
   a. a machine cannot have an IMA greater than 1.
   b. some work input is lost to friction.
   c. the work input is too small.
   d. the work output is too great.

_____ **12.** A motor with an efficiency rating of 80 percent must supply 300 J of useful work. What amount of work must be supplied to the motor?
   a. 80 J   **b.** 240 J
   c. 375 J   **d.** 540 J

_____ **13.** Which of the following is an example of a wheel and axle?
   a. a doorknob   **b.** an automobile steering wheel
   c. a jar lid   **d.** a pencil

_____ **14.** A machine is classified as a compound machine if it
   a. has moving parts.
   b. has an IMA greater than 1.
   c. is made up of two or more simple machines that operate together.
   d. is very efficient.

Completion

Complete each statement on the line provided.

1. Any part of a force that does not act in the direction of an object's motion does no _____ on an object.

2. You calculate work by multiplying the force acting in the direction of _____ by the distance the object moves.

3. The watt and the horsepower are both units of

_____.

4. As the thickness of a wedge of given length increases, its IMA

_____.

5. A watch consists of a complex systems of gears. Each gear acts as a
continuous _____.

Short Answer

*In complete sentences, write the answers to the questions on
the lines provided.*

1. If two swimmers compete in race, does the faster swimmer
develop more power?

_____

_____

_____

2. Why is the work output of a machine never equal to the work
input?

_____

_____

_____

3. If a simple machine could be frictionless, how would its IMA and
AMA compare?

_____

_____

_____

4. Compare the effects of a fixed pulley and a movable pulley on the
size and direction of the input force.

_____

_____

_____

5. In a compound machine made up of two simple machines, how is
the work output of the first simple machine related to the work
input of the second simple machine?

_____

_____

_____

Using Science Skills

Use the diagram to answer each question. Write the answers on a separate sheet of paper.

1. **Applying Concepts** Look at Figure 14-2. If Machine A moves through an input distance of 4.0 m, what is the output distance of Machine B?

2. **Classifying** What type of simple machine is Machine A in Figure 14-2?

3. **Interpreting Graphics** What is the IMA of Machine B in Figure 14-2?

4. **Interpreting Graphics** As shown in Figure 14-2, Machines A and B operate together as what type of machine?

5. **Comparing and Contrasting** In Figure 14-2, how does the work input of Machine B compare with the work output of Machine A?

Machine B

Machine A

Figure 14-2

Problem

Write the answers to each question on a separate sheet of paper.

1. A worker uses a cart to move a load of bricks weighing 680 N a distance of 10 m across a parking lot. If he pushes the cart with a constant force of 220 N, what amount of work does he do? Show your work.

2. A girl lifts a 100-N load a height of 2.0 m in a time of 0.5 s. What power does the girl produce? Show your work.

3. The input force of a pulley system must move 6.0 m to lift a 3000-N engine a distance of 0.50 m. What is the IMA of the system? Show your work.

4. A 16-N force applied to the handle of a door produces a 30-N output force. What is the AMA of the handle? Show your work.

5. A force of 12 N is applied to the handle of a screwdriver being used to pry off the lid of a paint can. As the force moves through a distance 0.3 m, the screwdriver does 32 J of work on the lid. What is the efficiency of the screwdriver? Show your work.

Chapter 14   Work, Power, and Machines

Multiple Choice

Write the letter that best answers the question or completes the statement on the line provided.

_____ 1. In which of the following is no work done?
   a. climbing stairs
   b. lifting a book
   c. pushing a shopping cart
   d. none of the above

_____ 2. What is the unit of work?
   a. joule   **b.** newton/meter
   c. watt   **d.** all of the above

_____ 3. The SI unit of power is the
   a. joule.   **b.** newton.
   c. newton-meter.   **d.** watt.

_____ 4. The power of a machine measures
   a. its rate of doing work. **b.** its strength.
   c. the force it produces.   **d.** the work it does.

_____ 5. About 746 watts equals how many horsepower?
   a. one   **b.** two
   c. four   **d.** six

_____ 6. A machine is a device that can multiply
   a. force.   **b.** power.
   c. work.   **d.** all of the above

_____ 7. How can a machine make work easier for you?
   a. by decreasing the amount of work you do
   b. by changing the direction of your force
   c. by increasing the work done by the machine
   d. none of the above

_____ 8. The actual mechanical advantage of a machine
   a. cannot be less than 1.
   b. decreases as the input distance increases.
   c. increases with greater friction.
   d. is less than the ideal mechanical advantage of the
       machine.

_____ 9. If you have to apply 30 N of force on a crowbar to lift an
       rock that weights 330 N, what is the actual mechanical
       advantage of the crowbar?
   a. 0.09   **b.** 11
   c. 300   **d.** 9900

_____10. Reducing friction in a machine
  a. decreases its actual mechanical advantage.
  b. decreases the work output.
  c. increases its efficiency.
  d. increases its ideal mechanical advantage.

_____11. A mechanical device requires 400 J of work to do 340 J of work in lifting a crate. What is the efficiency of the device?
  a. 0.9%   b. 60%
  c. 85%   d. 118%

_____12. An inclined plane reduces the effort force by
  a. increasing the distance through which the force is applied.
  b. increasing the work.
  c. reducing the effort distance.
  d. reducing the work.

_____13. An ax is an example of a(an)
  a. inclined plane.   b. lever.
  c. wedge.   d. wheel and axle.

_____14. The ideal mechanical advantage of a pulley system is equal to the
  a. distance the load has to move.
  b. length of the rope.
  c. number of rope segments supporting the load.
  d. weight of the object being lifted.

_____15. The ideal mechanical advantage of a wheel and axle is found by
  a. multiplying the circumference of the wheel by the radius of the axle.
  b. dividing the radius of the wheel by the radius of the axle.
  c. dividing the radius of the axle by the radius of the wheel.
  d. multiplying the radius of the wheel by the radius of the axle.

_____16. An example of a compound machine is a
  a. crowbar.   b. bicycle.
  c. ramp.   d. seesaw.

Completion

Complete each statement on the line provided.

1. For work to be done on an object, the object has to
  _____ .

2. The SI unit of work is the _____ .

3. The rate at which work is done is called _____ .

4. The SI unit of power is the _____ .

5. A machine is a device that changes a(an) _____ .

6. The force that is exerted on a machine is called the _____ force.

7. The _____ of a machine is the number of times that the machine increases the input force.

8. A(An) _____ can be described as an inclined plane wrapped around a cylinder.

9. The ideal mechanical advantage of a third-class lever is always _____ than 1.

10. Two or more simple machines working together make up a(an) _____ machine.

Short Answer

In complete sentences, write the answers to the questions on the lines provided.

1. How is work done when you lift a book?

   _____

   _____

   _____

   _____

2. Why don't you do work as you hold a book motionless over your head?

   _____

   _____

   _____

   _____

3. If a simple machine provides an increased output force, what happens to the output distance?

   _____

   _____

   _____

   _____

4. Which has the greater IMA—a screw with closely spaced threads or a screw with threads spaced farther apart?

   _____

   _____

5. How is a pair of scissors a compound machine? Explain your answer.

_____

_____

_____

_____

_____

_____

Using Science Skills

Use the diagram to answer each question. Write the answers on a separate sheet of paper.

Figure 14-2

1. **Calculating** What is the IMA of the ramp in Figure 14-2? Show your work.

2. **Applying Concepts** If the ramp shown in Figure 14-2 was coated with a smoother surface, how would the AMA of the ramp change?

3. **Applying Concepts** If the ramp shown in Figure 14-2 was coated with a smoother surface, how would the ramp's efficiency change? Explain your answer.

4. **Classifying** What type of simple machine is the ramp shown in Figure 14-2?

5. **Comparing and Contrasting** In a post office, a 3-m long ramp is used to move carts onto a dock that is higher than 1 m. How does the IMA of this ramp compare with the IMA of the ramp shown in Figure 14-2?

Name _____ Class _____ Date _____

Chapter 15 Energy

Chapter Test A

Multiple Choice

Write the letter that best answers the question or completes the statement on the line provided.

_____ **1.** What is transferred by a force moving an object through a distance?
  a. force
  b. mass
  c. motion
  d. energy

_____ **2.** A small 30-kilogram canoe is floating downriver at a speed of 2 m/s. What is the canoe's kinetic energy?
  a. 32 J
  b. 60 J
  c. 120 J
  d. 900 J

_____ **3.** A 12-kg sled is moving at a speed of 3.0 m/s. At which of the following speeds will the sled have twice as much kinetic energy?
  a. 1.5 m/s
  b. 4.2 m/s
  c. 6.0 m/s
  d. 9.0 m/s

_____ **4.** Why is the gravitational potential energy of an object 1 meter above the moon's surface less than its potential energy 1 meter above Earth's surface?
  a. The object's mass is less on the moon.
  b. The object's weight is more on the moon.
  c. The moon's acceleration due to gravity is less.
  d. both a and c

_____ **5.** The gravitational potential energy of an object is always measured relative to the
  a. location where the object's kinetic energy is zero.
  b. position of maximum mechanical energy.
  c. reference level from which the height is measured.
  d. surface of Earth.

_____ **6.** The total potential and kinetic energy of all the microscopic particles in an object make up its
  a. chemical energy.
  b. electric energy.
  c. nuclear energy.
  d. thermal energy.

_____ **7.** Walking converts what type of energy into mechanical energy?
  a. chemical
  b. electromagnetic
  c. nuclear
  d. thermal

_____ **8.** Solar cells convert what type of energy into electrical energy?
  a. chemical
  b. electromagnetic
  c. nuclear
  d. thermal

_____ **9.** If no friction acts on a diver during a dive, then which of the following statements is true?
   a. The total mechanical energy of the system increases.
   b. Potential energy can be converted into kinetic energy but not vice versa.
   c. $(KE+ PE)_{beginning} = (KE + PE)_{end}$
   d. all of the above

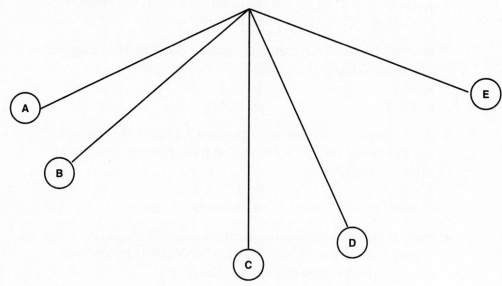

Figure 15-1

_____ **10.** The kinetic energy of the pendulum bob in Figure 15-1 increases the most between locations
   a. A and B.   **b.** A and C.
   c. B and D.   **d.** C and D.

_____ **11.** Which of the following statements is a consequence of the equation $E = mc^2$?
   a. Energy is released when matter is destroyed.
   b. Mass and energy are equivalent.
   c. The law of conservation of energy must be modified to state that mass and energy are conserved in any process.
   d. all of the above

_____ **12.** Nonrenewable energy resources include all of the following EXCEPT
   a. coal.   **b.** hydrogen fuel cells.
   c. oil.   **d.** uranium.

_____ **13.** Fossil fuels currently account for the majority of the world's energy use because they are
   a. distributed evenly throughout the world.
   b. nonpolluting.
   c. relatively inexpensive and readily available.
   d. renewable energy resources.

_____14. A benefit of a hydrogen fuel cell is that its byproduct is
       a. carbon dioxide.   **b.** oxygen.
       c. water.   **d.** uranium.

_____15. Based on your knowledge of energy conservation, which of
the following statements is true?
      a. Manufacturers can increase a light bulb's energy
efficiency by using technology that increases the amount
of electromagnetic energy the bulb converts from a given
amount of electrical energy.
      b. Energy can be conserved by turning off lights when they
are not in use.
      c. both a and b
      d. neither a nor b

Completion

Complete each statement on the line provided.

1. Energy and work are measured in the SI unit called the
      _____.

2. The kinetic energy of an object is proportional to the square of its
      _____.

3. When a pole-vaulter flexes the pole, the pole-vaulter increases the
pole's _____ potential energy.

4. Flat collector plates through which water flows are found in
_____ solar energy systems.

5. Turning off unused lights or appliances is an example of energy
      _____.

Short Answer

*In complete sentences, write the answers to the questions on
the lines provided.*

1. Show that the unit "kg•m^2/s^2," calculated from the kinetic energy
equation, is equivalent to a joule.

      _____

      _____

      _____

2. Sled A (with its riders) has twice the mass of Sled B (with its
riders). If both sleds have the same kinetic energy, which sled is
moving faster? Explain your answer.

      _____

      _____

      _____

3. In what two ways can you increase the elastic potential energy of a spring?

_____

_____

_____

_____

_____

4. Why can you model the thermal energy of an object as the "mechanical energy" of the particles that make it up?

_____

_____

_____

_____

_____

5. Describe one energy conversion that takes place in a hydroelectric power plant.

_____

_____

_____

_____

_____

6. What energy conversion takes place as an arrow is shot from a bow?

_____

_____

_____

_____

_____

7. Explain how biomass energy depends on the sun.

_____

_____

_____

_____

_____

Using Science Skills

Use the diagram to answer each question. Write the answers on a separate sheet of paper.

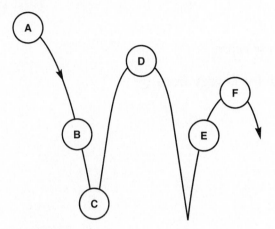

Figure 15-2

1. **Interpreting Graphics** At what location in Figure 15-2 does the ball have the least gravitational potential energy?

2. **Comparing and Contrasting** Compare the gravitational potential energy of the ball at locations B and E shown in Figure 15-2. Explain your answer.

3. **Applying Concepts** In Figure 15-2, does the total mechanical energy of the ball between locations A and F ever equal zero? Explain your answer.

4. **Inferring** In Figure 15-2, is the total mechanical energy of the ball conserved as the ball bounces? Explain your answer.

5. **Applying Concepts** Compare the kinetic energy of the ball in Figure 15-2 as it strikes the floor just before the second bounce with the first bounce (location C).

Problem

Write the answers to each question on a separate sheet of paper.

1. What is the kinetic energy of a 74.0-kg sky diver falling at a terminal velocity of 52.0 m/s? Show your work.

2. A 0.49-kg squirrel jumps from a tree branch that is 3.6 m high to the top of a bird feeder that is 1.5 m high. What is the change in gravitational potential energy of the squirrel? (The acceleration due to gravity is 9.8 m/s^2.) Show your work.

3. A small dog is trained to jump straight up a distance of 1.1 m. How much kinetic energy does the 7.7-kg dog need to jump this high? (The acceleration due to gravity is 9.8 m/s^2.) Show your work.

4. In a nuclear reaction, an amount of matter having a mass of 1.0×10^{-14} kg is converted into energy, which is released. How much energy is released? (The speed of light is 3.0×10^8 m/s.) Show your work.

Essay

Write the answer to the question on a separate sheet of paper.

1. Compare and contrast biomass energy with the energy from fossil fuels.

Chapter 15   Energy   **Chapter Test B**

Multiple Choice

Write the letter that best answers the question or completes the statement on the line provided.

_____ **1.** Work is a transfer of
      a. energy.   **b.** force.
      c. mass.   **d.** motion.

_____ **2.** The energy of motion is called
      a. kinetic energy.   **b.** potential energy.
      c. thermal energy.   **d.** work.

_____ **3.** An object's gravitational potential energy is directly related to all of the following EXCEPT
      a. its height relative to a reference level.
      b. its mass.
      c. its speed.
      d. the acceleration due to gravity.

_____ **4.** Which of the following is an example of an object with elastic potential energy?
      a. a wind-up toy that has been wound up
      b. a compressed basketball
      c. a stretched rubber band
      d. all of the above

_____ **5.** A 4-kilogram cat is resting on top of a bookshelf that is 2 meters high. What is the cat's gravitational potential energy relative to the floor if the acceleration due to gravity is 9.8 m/s²?
      a. 6 J   **b.** 8 J
      c. 20 J   **d.** 78 J

_____ **6.** Which of the following increases when an object becomes warmer?
      a. chemical energy
      b. elastic potential energy
      c. nuclear energy
      d. thermal energy

_____ **7.** The energy stored in gasoline is
      a. chemical energy.
      b. electromagnetic energy.
      c. mechanical energy.
      d. nuclear energy.

_____ **8.** Nuclear power plants are designed to convert nuclear energy into what type of energy?
      a. chemical   **b.** electrical
      c. geothermal   **d.** mechanical

_____ 9. Which of the following statements is true according to the law of conservation of energy?
   a. Energy cannot be created.
   b. Energy cannot be destroyed.
   c. Energy can be converted from one form to another.
   d. all of the above

_____ 10. The mechanical energy of an object equals its
   a. chemical energy plus its nuclear energy.
   b. kinetic energy plus its potential energy.
   c. nuclear energy.
   d. thermal energy.

_____ 11. The equation $E = mc^2$ relates energy and
   a. force.   b. gravity.
   c. mass.   d. work.

_____ 12. In which of the following does Einstein's famous equation apply?
   a. chemical reactions
   b. collisions between objects
   c. electromagnetic energy conversions
   d. nuclear fission and fusion reactions

_____ 13. What is biomass energy?
   a. the chemical energy stored in living things
   b. the electromagnetic energy stored in living things
   c. the nuclear energy stored in living things
   d. the thermal energy stored in living things

_____ 14. A drawback of solar energy is that it
   a. cannot be converted directly into electrical energy.
   b. depends on the climate.
   c. produces water pollution.
   d. is not a renewable resource.

_____ 15. Which of the following types of transportation is NOT mass transportation?
   a. bus   b. car
   c. streetcar   d. train

Completion

Complete each statement on the line provided.

1. Energy of an object increases when _____ is done on the object.

2. If the _____ of an object doubles, its kinetic energy doubles.

3. Energy that is stored due to position or shape is called _____ energy.

4. Mechanical energy does not include kinetic energy or _____ energy

5. The sum of the kinetic energy and potential energy of an object is called its _____ energy.

6. Wind turbines convert _____ energy into electrical energy.

7. The process of changing energy from one form to another is called energy _____.

8. "Energy cannot be created or destroyed" is a statement of the law of _____.

9. In the equation $E = mc^2$, c is the speed of _____.

10. Energy resources that exist in limited amounts and, once used, cannot be replaced except over the course of millions of years are called _____ energy resources.

11. Geothermal energy, in addition to being renewable, offers the benefit of being _____.

Short Answer

In complete sentences, write the answers to the questions on the lines provided.

1. What evidence is there that energy is transferred as a golf club does work on a golf ball?

   _____

   _____

   _____

   _____

2. What are the two general types of energy that can be used to classify many forms of energy?

   _____

   _____

   _____

   _____

3. What is the most familiar form of electromagnetic energy?

   _____

   _____

   _____

   _____

4. What is a characteristic of a renewable energy resource?

_____

_____

_____

_____

5. Why might a consumer buy a more energy-efficient refrigerator even though it may cost more than a conventional refrigerator?

_____

_____

_____

_____

Using Science Skills

Use the diagram to answer each question.
Write the answers on a separate sheet of paper.

1. **Applying Concepts** In Figure 15-1, the block in C has 5 J of kinetic energy. How much work did the compressed spring do on the block? Explain your answer.

2. **Classifying** What form of energy does the compressed spring have in Figure 15-1?

3. **Inferring** In Figure 15-1, what has happened to the stored energy of the spring between A and B?

4. **Applying Concepts** In Figure 15-1, how would the kinetic energy of the block in C be different if the tabletop was not frictionless? Explain your answer.

5. **Interpreting Graphics** In Figure 15-1, how has the kinetic energy of the block changed between A and B?

Figure 15-1

Chapter 16   Thermal Energy and Heat   **Chapter Test A**

Multiple Choice

Write the letter that best answers the question or completes the statement on the line provided.

_____ **1.** From his observations of cannon drilling, Count Rumford concluded that heat could NOT be a form of
   a. kinetic energy.   **b.** potential energy.
   c. matter.   **d.** radiation.

_____ **2.** Heat is the transfer of thermal energy from one object to another because of a difference in
   a. specific heat.   **b.** phase.
   c. temperature.   **d.** waste heat.

_____ **3.** As the temperature of an object rises, so does the
   a. kinetic energy of the object.
   b. mass of the object.
   c. thermal energy of the object.
   d. potential energy of the object.

_____ **4.** Thermal energy depends on an object's
   a. mass.   **b.** phase (sold, liquid, or gas).
   c. temperature.   **d.** all of the above

_____ **5.** How do you know that a sealed calorimeter is a closed system?
   a. because temperature is conserved
   b. because the masses of the sample and water are equal
   c. because thermal energy is not transferred to the environment
   d. because work is done on the test sample

_____ **6.** Matter is needed to transfer thermal energy by
   a. conduction   **b.** convection.   **c.** radiation.   **d.** both a and b

_____ **7.** The vacuum inside the thermos bottle shown in Figure 16-1 stops which type of thermal energy transfer to keep the liquid hot?
   a. convection   **b.** conduction
   c. radiation   **d.** both a and b

Rubber stopper
Outside plastic case
Outer glass layer
Vacuum
Silvered inner glass layer
Hot beverage

Figure 16-1

_____ **8.** According to the first law of thermodynamics, the amount of work done by a heat engine equals the amount of
   a. work done on the engine.
   b. waste heat it produces.
   c. thermal energy added to the engine minus the waste heat.
   d. thermal energy added to the engine plus the waste heat.

Name _____ Class _____ Date _____

_____ **9.** Disorder in the universe increases because
     a. spontaneous changes produce more order in a system.
     b. work produces disorder in a system.
     c. work produces waste heat, which leaves a system.
     d. all of the above

_____ **10.** One consequence of the third law of thermodynamics is that
     a. heat engines have efficiencies less than 100 percent.
     b. in some energy conversions, energy is not conserved.
     c. engines cannot discharge waste heat.
     d. the work a heat engine produces is less than the waste heat it produces.

_____ **11.** In most four-stroke internal combustion engines, when does the piston move downward?
     a. during the compression stroke only
     b. during the compression and exhaust strokes
     c. during the intake and exhaust strokes
     d. during the power and intake strokes

_____ **12.** In forced-air heating systems, where are warm-air vents usually located?
     a. above windows   **b.** near the floor
     c. next to cold-air ducts   **d.** under radiators

_____ **13.** Which of the following happens in a heat pump?
     a. The compressor increases the pressure and temperature of the refrigerant.
     b. The compressor blows cold refrigerant into the room.
     c. The compressor absorbs heat from the refrigerant.
     d. none of the above

_____ **14.** Which of the following describes an advantage of radiant heaters?
     a. They are portable.
     b. They can easily be turned on or off.
     c. They direct warm air to where it is needed.
     d. all of the above

Completion

Complete each statement on the line provided.

1. Heat is the transfer of thermal energy because of a _____ difference.

2. If the temperature change of an aluminum nail is negative, thermal energy is transferred _____ the nail _____ the surroundings.

3. In a calorimeter, the increase in the thermal energy of the water and the decrease in the thermal energy of the sample are _____.

4. As the fluid in a heat pump evaporates, _____ is transferred from the surroundings to the fluid.

5. Having air cleaned as it passes through _____ near the furnace is an advantage of a(n) _____ heating system.

Short Answer

In complete sentences, write the answers to the questions on the lines provided.

1. Why does a rubber band become warm when you stretch it repeatedly?

_____

_____

_____

2. What role do free electrons have in conduction in metals?

_____

_____

_____

3. Explain how energy is conserved in a heat pump.

_____

_____

_____

4. You add several drops of red food coloring to the water in a beaker without stirring. After a short time, the water has a red color throughout. Was the system of the food coloring and water more organized before or after you added the food coloring to the water? Which law of thermodynamics explains the change in order?

_____

_____

_____

5. As what type of combustion engine would you classify steam turbines used in power plants? Why?

_____

_____

_____

Using Science Skills

Use the diagram to answer each question. Write the answers on a separate sheet of paper.

1. **Interpreting Data** Compare the average kinetic energy of the water molecules in the three beakers in Figure 16-2.

2. **Applying Concepts** Compare the thermal energy of the water in the three beakers in Figure 16-2.

Figure 16-2

3. **Applying Concepts** Equal amounts of thermal energy are transferred to the water in each container shown in Figure 16-2. Explain why the water in B has the highest final temperature.

4. **Predicting** In Figure 16-2, what will be the final temperature of the water in each container after 200 g of 70°C water is added? Assume no heat is transferred to the environment.

5. **Drawing Conclusions** The water in the three containers shown in Figure 16-2 is combined with no heat transfer to the environment. Explain whether the temperature of the mixture will be closer to 50°C or 70°C.

Problem

Write the answers to each question on a separate sheet of paper.

1. How many kilojoules of heat must be transferred to a 420-g aluminum pizza pan to raise its temperature from 22°C to 232°C? The specific heat of aluminum in this temperature range is 0.96 J/g•°C. Show your work.

2. As 315 g of hot milk cools in a mug, it transfers 31,000 J of heat to the environment. What is the temperature change of the milk? The specific heat of milk is 3.9 J/g•°C. Show your work.

3. A 410-g cylinder of brass is heated to 95.0°C and placed in a calorimeter containing 335 g of water at 25.0°C. The water is stirred, and its highest temperature is recorded as 32.0°C. From the thermal energy gained by the water, determine the specific heat of brass. The specific heat of water is 4.18 J/g•°C. Show your work.

Essay

Write the answers to each question on a separate sheet of paper.

1. How do convection currents form in air?

2. How can a heat pump warm a house by causing a refrigerant to evaporate and condense?

Chapter 16   Thermal Energy and Heat   **Chapter Test B**

Multiple Choice

Write the letter that best answers the question or completes the statement on the line provided.

_____ **1.** Which of the following is a unit of temperature?
  a. Celsius degree   **b.** joule
  c. kilogram   **d.** calorie

_____ **2.** What property of an object is related to the average kinetic energy of the particles in that object?
  a. specific heat   **b.** mass
  c. conductivity   **d.** temperature

_____ **3.** Which of the following devices is based on the property of thermal expansion?
  a. balance   **b.** calorimeter
  c. convection oven   **d.** thermometer

_____ **4.** In the formula $Q = m \times c \times \Delta T$, which quantity represents the specific heat?
  a. c **b.** m **c.** Q **d.** ΔT

_____ **5.** The specific heat of copper is 0.385 J/g·°C. Which equation would you use to calculate correctly the amount of heat needed to raise the temperature of 0.75 g of copper from 10°C to 25°C?
  a. $Q = 0.385\ \mathrm{J/g}\bullet°C \times (25°C - 10°C)$
  b. $Q = 0.75\ \mathrm{g} \times 0.385\ \mathrm{J/g}\bullet°C \times 25°C$
  c. $Q = 0.75\ \mathrm{g} \times 0.385\ \mathrm{J/g}\bullet°C \times 15°C$
  d. $Q = 0.75\ \mathrm{g} \times 0.385\ \mathrm{J/g}\bullet°C \times 10°C$

_____ **6.** In the formula $Q = m \times c \times \Delta T$, which quantity is measured in units of J/g•°C?
  a. c **b.** m **c.** Q **d.** ΔT

_____ **7.** What does a calorimeter directly measure?
  a. change in temperature
  b. kinetic energy
  c. specific heat
  d. radiation

_____ **8.** Energy from the sun reaches Earth mostly by
  a. conduction.   **b.** convection.
  c. radiation.   **d.** thermal expansion.

_____ **9.** Which of the following materials conducts heat well?
  a. glass   **b.** plastic   **c.** metal   **d.** wood

_____10. To which of the following does the first law of
thermodynamics apply?
   a. heating objects
   b. transferring thermal energy
   c. doing work on a system
   d. all of the above

_____11. The second law of thermodynamics states that thermal
energy can flow from colder objects to hotter objects
   a. by convection.
   b. only if work is done on the system.
   c. spontaneously.
   d. when thermal expansion takes place.

_____12. Which of the following states that absolute zero cannot be
reached?
   a. the first law of thermodynamics
   b. the second law of thermodynamics
   c. the third law of thermodynamics
   d. the second and third laws of thermodynamics

_____13. Which of the following happens in a steam engine?
   a. Fuel is burned outside the engine
   b. Heat is converted into work
   c. Hot steam pushes a piston.
   d. all of the above

_____14. Which central heating system involves a furnace and a
blower?
   a. electric baseboard   b. forced-air
   c. hot-water   d. steam

_____15. A fluid that vaporizes and condenses inside the tubing of a
heat pump is called the
   a. compressor.   b. fuel.   c. refrigerant.   d. condenser.

_____16. Which type of central heating system is often used when
heating many buildings from a central location?
   a. electric baseboard   b. forced-air
   c. hot-water   d. steam

Completion

Complete each statement on the line provided.

1. A measure of how hot or cold an object is compared to a reference
point can be measured in units of _____ or
_____.

2. A hot dinner plate has _____ thermal energy than
a similar dinner plate at room temperature.

3. The decrease in volume of a material due to a temperature increase is called _____.

4. The transfer of thermal energy with no overall transfer of matter is called _____.

5. The transfer of energy as waves moving through space is called _____.

6. The thermos bottle in Figure 16-1 has two insulators—the glass layers and the vacuum. The _____ is the better thermal insulator.

7. A material that conducts thermal energy well is called a thermal _____.

8. The study of the conversion between heat and other forms of energy is called _____.

Rubber stopper
Outside plastic case
Outer glass layer
Vacuum
Silvered inner glass layer
Hot beverage

Figure 16-1

9. Thermal energy that is not converted into work by a heat engine is called _____.

10. In most automobile engines, the linear motion of the strokes is turned into _____ motion by the crankshaft.

11. A steam-heating system is most similar to a(an) _____ heating system.

Short Answer

In complete sentences, write the answers to the questions on the lines provided.

1. Describe the spontaneous flow of heat between objects at different temperatures.

   _____

   _____

   _____

2. In general, what is the order of increasing thermal expansion among solids, liquids, and gases when a given amount of thermal energy is added?

   _____

   _____

3. How does placing the lid of a jar under hot water help loosen it?

   _____

   _____

   _____

4. Explain what happens to the surrounding air when a refrigerant condenses and why this happens.

_____

_____

_____

_____

5. How has keeping foods refrigerated helped society?

_____

_____

_____

_____

Using Science Skills

Use the diagram to answer each question. Write the answers on a separate sheet of paper.

Figure 16-2

1. **Inferring** In Figure 16-2, is the temperature of the material within the cylinder greatest during the intake stroke, compression stroke, power stroke, or exhaust stroke?

2. **Interpreting Visuals** Sequence the four strokes of the engine shown in Figure 16-2 in the following order: intake stroke, compression stroke, power stroke, and exhaust stroke.

3. **Applying Concepts** What is the engine in Figure 16-2 designed to do?

4. **Applying Concepts** According to the second law of thermodynamics, why can't the engine in Figure 16-2 have an efficiency of 100 percent?

5. **Classifying** What type of combustion engine is shown in Figure 16-2?

Chapter 17 Mechanical Waves and Sound   **Chapter Test A**

Multiple Choice

Write the letter that best answers the question or completes the statement on the line provided.

_____ 1. A mechanical wave generally does NOT
   a. move the medium from one place to another
   b. move through a medium.
   c. move through solids.
   d. disturb the medium.

_____ 2. Transverse and longitudinal waves both
   a. have compressions and rarefactions.
   b. transfer energy through a medium.
   c. move at right angles to the vibration of the medium.
   d. are capable of moving the medium a long distance.

_____ 3. A disturbance sends ripples across water in a tub. These
      ripples are an example of a
   a. rarefaction.   b. longitudinal wave.
   c. compression.   d. surface wave.

_____ 4. In an earthquake, a P wave is a longitudinal wave. It moves
      through soil and rock as a
   a. wavy line.
   b. series of faults.
   c. series of compressions and rarefactions.
   d. series of crests and troughs.

_____ 5. A period is the length of time it takes for
   a. a disturbance to start a wave.
   b. two complete wavelengths to pass a fixed point.
   c. a wave to travel the length of a rope.
   d. one complete wavelength to pass a fixed point.

_____ 6. A wave has a wavelength of 15 mm and a frequency of
      4.0 hertz. What is its speed?
   a. 60 mm/s   b. 60 hertz/s
   c. 3.8 mm/s   d. 0.27 mm/s

_____ 7. To what is amplitude related?
   a. the amount of energy carried by the wave
   b. the maximum displacement from the rest position
   c. neither A nor B
   d. both A and B

_____ 8. How does reflection differ from refraction and diffraction?
   a. Reflection is the only property in which the wave does not continue moving forward.
   b. Reflection is the only property that involves a change in the wave.
   c. Reflection affects all types of mechanical waves, but refraction and diffraction do not.
   d. Reflection is the only property that changes the direction of a wave.

_____ 9. For refraction to occur in a wave, the wave must
   a. strike an obstacle larger than the wavelength.
   b. change direction within a medium.
   c. enter a new medium at an angle.
   d. enter a new medium head-on.

_____ 10. Which wave will probably be diffracted the most?
   a. a longitudinal wave
   b. the wave with the highest amplitude
   c. the wave with the longest wavelength
   d. the wave that strikes a solid barrier with the slowest speed

_____ 11. The formation of a standing wave requires
   a. the traveling of a wave for a long distance.
   b. constructive interference between two waves of slightly different frequencies.
   c. that refraction and diffraction occur at the same time in a wave.
   d. interference between incoming and reflected waves.

_____ 12. In which medium does sound travel the fastest?
   a. salt water   b. fresh wat
   c. air   d. cast iron

_____ 13. A piano, violin, or guitar uses the resonance of a wooden soundboard to
   a. amplify the sound.   b. dampen the sound.
   c. raise the pitch.   d. limit standing waves.

_____ 14. When a sound source approaches you, the pitch you hear is
   a. lower than when the source is stationary.
   b. higher than when the source is stationary.
   c. the same as when the source is stationary.
   d. first higher and then lower than the pitch of the source when stationary.

Name _____ Class _____ Date _____

_____15. The part of the ear that sends coded nerve signals to the
brain is
a. the outer ear.　　　b. the inner ear.
c. the middle ear.　　　d. the eardrum.

Completion

Complete each statement on the line provided.

1. The crest of a transverse wave is most similar to a(an)
_____ in a longitudinal wave.

2. Waves in a rope are transverse waves because the medium's
vibration is _____ to the direction in which the
wave travels.

3. A pebble drops straight down into a tub of water, setting off
_____ waves that travel between the water and air.

4. On a piano, striking strings with the hammers sets up
_____ between the strings and the soundboard.

5. When a train streaks by blowing its whistle, the changing pitch
you hear is due to the _____.

Short Answer

*In complete sentences, write the answers to the questions on
the lines provided.*

1. Why is a mechanical wave not always produced when a source
vibrates?

_____

_____

_____

2. Consider the properties of a wave—
wave speed, amplitude, wavelength,
period, and frequency. Which two
properties could you determine the
numerical values of by using only the
information given in Figure 17-1?

Figure 17-1

_____

_____

_____

3. How can you change the wavelength of a wave in a rope without changing the amplitude?

_____

_____

_____

_____

4. How could you compare the energy carried in two different longitudinal waves?

_____

_____

_____

_____

5. Describe how a wave must enter a new medium in order for refraction to occur.

_____

_____

_____

6. What sounds can damage hearing?

_____

_____

_____

_____

Using Science Skills

Use the diagram to answer each question. Write the answers on a separate sheet of paper.

1. **Analyzing Data** What is the difference between wave A and wave B in Figure 17-2?

2. **Inferring** In Figure 17-2, both wave A and wave B were started by the same type of force—an up-and-down motion. What conclusion can you make about the energy of these two wave-starting forces?

3. **Predicting** Suppose you add the following panel E to the diagram: a wave pattern with a frequency of four waves per second. How will wavelength in this panel compare with the wavelength in panel D? How will it compare with the wavelength in panel C? Assume all the waves travel at the same speed.

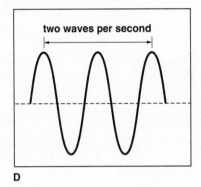

Figure 17-2

4. **Analyzing Data** What is the difference between wave C and wave D in Figure 17-2?

5. **Drawing Conclusions** Consider both frequency and wavelength in Figure 17-2. How does each variable change between wave C and wave D? What is the relationship between the change? Assume the waves travel at the same speed.

Essay

Write the answers to each question on a separate sheet of paper.

1. In a large cave, you can hear an echo a few seconds after you speak. Explain how this happens in terms of wave properties.

2. Explain the difference between reflection and refraction.

3. Sound waves have relatively long wavelengths. We can hear people around a corner before we can see them. Which wave behavior does this illustrate? Explain how wavelength relates to this behavior.

4. While practicing on the trumpet, you notice that every time you play a particular note, a window in the room rattles. How can you explain this rattling in terms of wave behaviors?

5. Compare the visible part of the ear to a satellite dish in terms of form and function.

Chapter 17   Mechanical Waves and Sound   Chapter Test B

Multiple Choice

Write the letter that best answers the question or completes the statement on the line provided.

_____ 1. A mechanical wave moves through a medium, which can be
   a. a liquid.   **b.** a solid.
   c. a gas.   **d.** all of the above

_____ 2. Which type of mechanical wave needs a source of energy to produce it?
   a. a transverse wave   **b.** a longitudinal wave
   c. a surface wave   **d.** all of the above

_____ 3. Which wave causes the medium to vibrate only in a direction parallel to the wave's motion?
   a. a transverse wave   **b.** a surface wave
   c. a longitudinal wave   **d.** none of the above

_____ 4. When a surfer rides an ocean wave on her surfboard, she is actually riding on
   a. a crest that is toppling over.
   b. a trough of the wave.
   c. the rest position of the wave.
   d. a region of rarefaction.

_____ 5. Figure 17-1 shows a wave movement during 1 second. What is the frequency of this wave?
   a. 2 hertz
   b. 2 meters/second
   c. 0.5 second
   d. 1 hertz

Figure 17-1

_____ 6. To determine the speed of a wave, you would use which of the following formulas?
   a. speed = frequency × amplitude
   b. speed = wavelength × frequency
   c. speed = wavelength × amplitude
   d. speed = wavelength × period

_____ 7. To find amplitude, measure
   a. from a trough to the rest position.
   b. from a crest to the rest position.
   c. neither A nor B
   d. either A or B

_____ 8. When a wave strikes a solid barrier, it behaves like a basketball hitting a backboard. This wave behavior is called
   a. constructive interference.
   b. diffraction.
   c. refraction.
   d. reflection.

_____ 9. In refraction, when two parts of a wave travel through different mediums, the parts move
   a. at different speeds.
   b. in step.
   c. always in the same direction.
   d. in opposite directions.

_____ 10. What is one property of a wave that determines how much it will diffract when it encounters an obstacle?
   a. frequency   b. amplitude
   c. period   d. wavelength

_____ 11. Suppose two waves collide and the temporary combined wave that results is smaller than the original waves. What term best describes this interaction?
   a. diffraction
   b. destructive interference
   c. standing wave formation
   d. constructive interference

_____ 12. A sound wave is an example of a
   a. transverse wave.   b. longitudinal wave.
   c. standing wave.   d. surface wave.

_____ 13. Sonar equipment sends sound waves into deep water and measures
   a. refraction of the transmitted wave.
   b. only the direction of the reflected wave.
   c. the time delay of the returning echoes.
   d. interference of the transmitted and reflected waves.

_____ 14. An ambulance siren sounds different as it approaches you than when it moves away from you. What scientific term would you use to explain how this happens?
   a. ultrasound   b. diffraction
   c. rarefaction   d. the Doppler effect

_____ 15. Which part of the ear amplifies the vibrations from sound waves?
   a. outer ear   b. inner ear
   c. middle ear   d. both a and b

Name _____ Class _____ Date _____

Completion

Complete each statement on the line provided.

1. You can make a wave in a rope by adding _____ at one end of the rope.

2. Instead of crests and troughs, as in an ocean wave, a longitudinal wave has compressions and _____.

3. A wave in a rope is a transverse wave, but a sound wave is a(n) _____ wave.

4. To determine the speed of a wave, you must know the wave's wavelength and _____.

5. Amplitude measures the greatest displacement of a wave from the _____.

6. Ocean waves will not bend if they approach the shore _____.

7. At the _____ of a standing wave, there is no displacement from the rest position.

8. The standard measure used to compare sound intensities is the _____.

9. When a person plucks a guitar string, the number of half wavelengths that fit into the length of the string determines the _____ of the sound produced.

10. The part of the ear that collects sound waves and focuses them inward is the _____ ear.

Short Answer

In complete sentences, write the answers to the questions on the lines provided.

1. What is a medium?

_____

_____

_____

2. What type of mechanical wave is produced by pushing sharply on the end of a spring toy?

_____

_____

3. When you shake the end of a rope to make a wave, how can you increase the amplitude of the wave?

_____

_____

4. How do the frequencies of ultrasound compare to the frequencies that people normally hear?

_____

_____

_____

5. What is the Doppler effect?

_____

_____

_____

Using Science Skills

Use the diagram to answer each question. Write the answers on a separate sheet of paper.

1. **Interpreting Illustrations** What kind of wave does A in Figure 17-2 represent? What kind of wave does B represent?

2. **Comparing and Contrasting** Figure 17-2 shows how someone starts the waves. How are these ways of starting waves alike? How are they different?

Figure 17-2

3. **Inferring** Compare the two waves in Figure 17-2. To what in wave B do the compressions of wave A correspond? To what in wave B do the rarefactions correspond?

4. **Inferring** What represents one wavelength in wave A of Figure 17-2? Define and describe the portion of the wave.

5. **Using Analogies** In Figure 17-2, wave A is produced by a spring toy, representing the concept of a sound wave in air. In sound, what is being squeezed together in the compressions, and what is being released in the rare factions?

Chapter 18   The Electromagnetic Spectrum and Light   Chapter Test A

Multiple Choice

Write the letter that best answers the question or completes the statement on the line provided.

_____ 1. Electromagnetic waves vary in
   a. the speed they travel in a vacuum.
   b. wavelength and frequency.
   c. the way they reflect.
   d. their direction.

_____ 2. An electromagnetic wave in a vacuum has a wavelength of
   0.032 m. What is its frequency?
   a. $f = 3.00 \times 10^8$ m/s   b. $f = 9.38 \times 10^9$ m/s
   c. $f = 3.00 \times 10^9$ m/s   d. $f = 9.38 \times 10^8$ m/s

_____ 3. Because light travels in a straight line and casts a shadow,
   Isaac Newton hypothesized that light is
   a. radiation.   b. a stream of particles.
   c. a wave.   d. heat.

_____ 4. Which of the following occurs as light travels farther from
   its source?
   a. Far from the source, photons spread through a small
      area.
   b. The intensity of light increases as photons move away
      from the source.
   c. The source gives off less light as photons move away
      from it.
   d. Farther from the source, photons spread over a larger
      area.

_____ 5. The full range of frequencies of electromagnetic radiation
   is called
   a. visible light.
   b. radio waves.
   c. the electromagnetic spectrum.
   d. invisible radiation.

_____ 6. The visible light spectrum ranges between
   a. radar waves and X-rays.
   b. television waves and infrared rays.
   c. infrared rays and ultraviolet rays.
   d. ultraviolet rays and gamma rays.

_____ 7. X-ray photographs show softer tissue
   a. as invisible.
   b. as dark, highly exposed areas.
   c. the same as dense bones.
   d. as bright white areas.

_____ **8.** In order of the light-transmitting capabilities of materials from none to all, which is the correct sequence?
  a. transparent → opaque → translucent
  b. opaque → transparent → translucent
  c. opaque → translucent → transparent
  d. translucent → transparent → opaque

_____ **9.** Polarized sunglasses work by
  a. blocking light waves that vibrate in one plane.
  b. gradually refracting light as it passes through the lenses
  c. bending light as it passes from air into the lenses.
  d. reflecting most of the light that strikes the sunglasses.

_____ **10.** When droplets of water in the atmosphere act like prisms, the colors in sunlight undergo
  a. interference.   **b.** absorption.
  c. polarization.   **d.** dispersion.

_____ **11.** Blue light and yellow light combine to produce white light because
  a. they absorb each other's wavelengths.
  b. blue, yellow, and white are primary colors.
  c. they are complementary colors of light.
  d. they are both primary colors of light.

_____ **12.** The primary colors of pigments
  a. are cyan, yellow, and magenta.
  b. are the same as the secondary colors of light.
  c. combine in equal amounts to produce black.
  d. all of the above

_____ **13.** Which of the following is NOT true regarding neon lights?
  a. Light is emitted as electrons move through a gas in a tube.
  b. All neon lights are colored by the color of the tubing.
  c. Neon lights may contain other gases, such as helium or krypton.
  d. Each kind of gas produces its own distinctive color.

_____ **14.** Light whose waves all have the same wavelength, direction, and coincidental peaks is called
  a. coherent light.   **b.** incandescent light.
  c. fluorescent light.   **d.** neon light.

_____ **15.** Which kind of light is used to carry information through optical fibers?
  a. incandescent   **b.** fluorescent
  c. sodium-vapor light   **d.** laser

Completion

Complete each statement on the line provided.

1. A transparent object _____ almost all of the light that strikes it.

2. An ultraviolet light wave has a wavelength of 300 nm and a frequency of 7.0×10^{14} Hz. The ultraviolet light is NOT traveling through a(an) _____.

3. In microwave cooking, the food is heated _____ in the areas near the surface of the food than in the center.

4. Light amplification by stimulated emission of radiation is known as _____ light.

5. The following electromagnetic waves are arranged in order of increasing frequency: infrared, _____, ultraviolet.

Short Answer

In complete sentences, write the answers to the questions on the lines provided.

1. What is a basic difference between electromagnetic waves and sound waves?

_____

_____

_____

_____

_____

_____

_____

2. What is the photoelectric effect?

_____

_____

_____

_____

3. Describe what happens to photons as they travel away from a light source.

_____

_____

_____

_____

4. Both gamma rays and X-rays are used to see inside the body. Which one is used to make images of bones? How are the other rays used?

_____

_____

_____

_____

5. What two factors influence the color of an object?

_____

_____

_____

_____

6. What is common to all light sources including incandescent, fluorescent, neon, halogen, laser, and sodium-vapor devices?

_____

_____

_____

Using Science Skills

Use the diagram to answer each question. Write the answers on a separate sheet of paper.

Figure 18-1

1. **Classifying** Examine Figure 18-1, which represents a pencil in a glass container of a liquid. Is the liquid transparent, translucent, or opaque to visible light? Explain.

2. **Applying Concepts** Explain why the pencil in Figure 18-1 appears to be broken.

3. **Interpreting Graphics** Figure 18-1 represents white light striking an object. Explain why the beam of white light is also labeled with colors.

4. **Drawing Conclusions** What color is the object in Figure 18-1? Explain your answer.

5. **Applying Concepts** Suppose the light striking the object in Figure 18-1 was a combination of red and green. What color would the object be when viewed in this light? Explain your answer.

Problem

Write the answer to the question on a separate sheet of paper.

1. A communications satellite transmits a radio wave at a frequency of 9.4×10^9 Hz. What is the signal's wavelength? Assume the wave travels in a vacuum. Show your work.

Essay

Write the answers to each question on a separate sheet of paper.

1. Is light a particle or a wave? Briefly explain your answer and give examples.

2. What is the electromagnetic spectrum? Give examples of each kind of wave and relate each example to its relative position in the spectrum.

3. What is polarized light? What is unpolarized light? Name at least one familiar kind of polarizing filter and explain how it works.

4. Describe the economic advantage of using sodium-vapor lights and a disadvantage of the color it produces.

Chapter 18   The Electromagnetic Spectrum and Light   **Chapter Test B**

Multiple Choice

Write the letter that best answers the question or completes the statement on the line provided.

_____ **1.** In 1926, Michelson was able to measure the speed of light using
     a. lanterns.   **b.** stars.
     c. mirrors.   **d.** sunlight.

_____ **2.** To calculate the frequency of an electromagnetic wave, you need to know the speed of the wave and its
     a. wavelength.   **b.** intensity.
     c. refraction.   **d.** amplitude.

_____ **3.** Light acts like
     a. a wave.
     b. a particle.
     c. both a wave and a particle.
     d. neither a wave nor a particle.

_____ **4.** Photons travel outward from a light source in
     a. a single straight line.   **b.** increasing intensity.
     c. a small, dense area.   **d.** all directions.

_____ **5.** Infrared rays have a shorter wavelength than
     a. ultraviolet rays.   **b.** X-rays.
     c. radar waves.   **d.** gamma rays.

_____ **6.** The waves with the longest wavelengths in the electromagnetic spectrum are
     a. infrared rays.   **b.** radio waves.
     c. gamma rays.   **d.** X-rays.

_____ **7.** Cellular telephones utilize
     a. radar waves.
     b. very high frequency waves.
     c. very low frequency waves.
     d. microwaves.

_____ **8.** A translucent material
     a. scatters some light.   **b.** transmits all light.
     c. absorbs all light.   **d.** reflects all light.

_____ **9.** Which of the following occurs as a light wave bends when it passes from one medium into another?
     a. constructive interference
     b. refraction
     c. destructive interference
     d. reflection

_____**10.** Newton's prism experiments showed that white sunlight is made up of
  a. the full electromagnetic spectrum.
  b. only blue light when separated by a prism.
  c. all the colors of the visible spectrum.
  d. only the longest wavelengths.

_____**11.** What an object is made of and the color of light that strikes it determines the
  a. color of the object.   **b.** transparency of the object.
  c. opacity of the object.   **d.** translucence of the object.

_____**12.** The primary colors of light are
  a. green, blue, and black.
  b. cyan, magenta, and yellow.
  c. red, yellow, and blue.
  d. blue, green, and red.

_____**13.** An incandescent light bulb produces light when electrons flow through the
  a. air.   **b.** glass.
  c. filament.   **d.** vacuum.

_____**14.** Many streets and parking lots are illuminated with
  a. laser lights.   **b.** tungsten-halogen lights.
  c. sodium-vapor lights.   **d.** fluorescent lights.

_____**15.** A fluorescent light bulb usually contains
  a. a vacuum.   **b.** oxygen.
  c. mercury vapor.   **d.** fluorescent powder.

Completion

Complete each statement on the line provided.

1. Electromagnetic waves are _____ waves consisting of changing electric and magnetic fields.

2. Warm objects give off more _____ radiation than cool objects give off.

3. The speed of light in a vacuum is _____ m/s.

4. The farther away you are from a light source, the _____ intense it is.

5. Objects that scatter some of the light that is transmitted through them are _____.

6. When viewed in red light, an object that reflects all the colors of light will appear _____.

7. Combining equal amounts of the three primary pigments produces _____.

8. Electromagnetic waves can travel through a(an)
   _____ .

9. Light is produced when _____ change energy
   levels in an atom.

10. Visible light waves have a shorter _____ than
    infrared waves have.

11. The electromagnetic waves with the shortest wavelengths are
    _____ rays.

12. To form white light from the combination of only two colors of
    light, the colors must be _____ .

Short Answer

*In complete sentences, write the answers to the questions on
the lines provided.*

1. In which medium does light travel faster, air or glass?

   _____

   _____

2. Which type of electromagnetic wave has the longest wavelength
   and lowest frequency?

   _____

   _____

3. Which waves have wavelengths longer than those of visible light?
   Give an example of how each kind of wave is used.

   _____

   _____

   _____

   _____

4. Magenta is a secondary color of light. What type of color is
   magenta when it is a pigment?

   _____

   _____

   _____

5. What distinguishes a laser from other common light sources?

   _____

   _____

   _____

   _____

Using Science Skills

Use the diagram to answer each question. Write the answers on a separate sheet of paper.

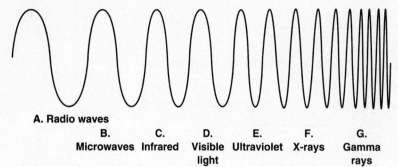

A. Radio waves
B. Microwaves
C. Infrared
D. Visible light
E. Ultraviolet
F. X-rays
G. Gamma rays

Figure 18-1

1. **Comparing and Contrasting** Which waves in Figure 18-1 carry AM and FM signals? How do the frequencies of AM and FM signals compare?

2. **Analyzing Data** How does photon energy change with increasing frequency? Use Figure 18-1 to answer this question.

3. **Interpreting Graphics** Which waves in Figure 18-1 are used to expose heat-sensitive film? Where are these waves located in the electromagnetic spectrum?

4. **Classifying** In Figure 18-1, which waves can be separated into different wavelengths of colored light?

5. **Inferring** Look at Figure 18-1. Without knowing the specific frequencies and wavelengths of the colors of the visible spectrum, at which end of the visible spectrum would you place red? At which end would you place violet? *Hint:* Use the names of the waves outside the visible spectrum to help you.

Chapter 19   Optics   **Chapter Test A**

Multiple Choice

Write the letter that best answers the question or completes the statement on the line provided.

_____ **1.** What is the angle of incidence?
   a. the angle that the reflected ray makes with a line drawn perpendicular to the reflecting surface
   b. the angle that the incident ray makes with a line drawn perpendicular to the reflecting surface
   c. the angle the reflecting surface makes with the ground
   d. the angle that is parallel to the reflection angle

_____ **2.** In a plane mirror, the light rays appear to come from
   a. in front of the mirror.
   b. an angle above the mirror.
   c. a distance behind the observer.
   d. behind the mirror.

_____ **3.** What is the point called at which the reflected rays intersect in Figure 19-1?
   a. virtual image
   b. plane image
   c. focal point
   d. illumination point

Mirror

_____ **4.** Why do plane mirrors and convex mirrors form only virtual images?
   a. because they both cause light rays to spread out
   b. because reflected rays appear to come from behind the mirror
   c. because the focal point is in front of the mirror
   d. because they both show a wide angle of view

Figure 19-1

_____ **5.** Suppose a light ray traveling in air passes sideways through a glass of water and comes out the other side. How many times will the light ray refract?
   a. one time; through the water
   b. two times; through the glass and the water
   c. three times; through glass, water, and glass again
   d. four times; through glass, water, glass, and air

_____ **6.** The speed of light in water is 2.25×10^8 m/s. What is correct about the index of refraction of water?
   a. It is 0.   **b.** It is <1.
   c. It is equal to 1.   **d.** It is >1.

_____ **7.** Which index of refraction represents the most optically dense material?
   a. 1.77   **b.** 2.42   **c.** 1.33   **d.** 1.00

_____ **8.** An object located between a convex lens and its focal point forms a(an)

    a. reduced virtual image. **b.** enlarged virtual image.

    c. reduced real image.   **d.** enlarged real image.

_____ **9.** Total internal reflection occurs when the angle of incidence

    a. is zero.

    b. is less than the critical angle.

    c. exceeds the critical angle.

    d. equals the angle of reflection.

_____ **10.** Which statement is correct regarding a refracting telescope?

    a. It produces an enlarged real image.

    b. It produces an enlarged virtual image.

    c. It produces a reduced-size image.

    d. It produces a small, upside-down image.

_____ **11.** Which statement best explains how a compound microscope produces the image you see?

    a. The objective lens produces an image that becomes the "object" for the eyepiece lens.

    b. The glass slide enlarges the object placed over the light.

    c. The objective lens magnifies an image, and the eyepiece lens is used to focus the image.

    d. The eyepiece magnifies the object on the slide.

_____ **12.** Which of the following correctly describes the path that light takes when it enters the eye?

    a. cornea, pupil, lens, retina

    b. pupil, cornea, lens, retina

    c. lens, cornea, pupil, retina

    d. retina, lens, cornea, pupil

_____ **13.** How is the iris of an eye similar to the diaphragm of a film camera?

    a. They both control the amount of light passing through.

    b. They both focus light rays.

    c. They both produce an upside-down image.

    d. They both control the movement of the lens.

_____ **14.** Farsightedness can be corrected by using eyeglass lenses that are

    a. concave in shape and cause light rays entering the eyes to converge.

    b. convex.

    c. concave in shape and cause light rays entering the eyes to diverge.

    d. convex in shape and cause light rays entering the eyes to converge.

Completion

Complete each statement on the line provided.

1. The angles of incidence and reflection are the angles that rays make relative to a line drawn _____ to the surface of a mirror.

2. The image that appears to be behind a plane mirror is a(an) _____ image.

3. The type of image that can be projected on a screen is a(an) _____ image.

4. Nerve endings in the retina that are most sensitive to low-intensity light are called _____.

5. Nerves on the retina that are sensitive to color are called _____.

Short Answer

In complete sentences, write the answers to the questions on the lines provided.

1. List two facts about the blind spot in the human eye.

   _____

   _____

2. Describe how you could focus the light from a bulb into a beam.

   _____

   _____

   _____

3. What is the principle that makes fiber optics able to transmit data in the form of light pulses over long distances with little loss in signal strength?

   _____

   _____

4. What is the purpose of the diaphragm in a film camera?

   _____

   _____

5. Why must a microscope slide be made of a transparent material like glass if the glass does not magnify the image?

   _____

   _____

   _____

Name _____ Class _____ Date _____

Using Science Skills

Use the diagram to answer each question. Write the answers on a separate sheet of paper.

1. **Predicting** Figure 19-2 shows the lens of an eye that is focused on a nearby object at point Z. If the eye refocuses on a far object, what happens to the shape of the lens? How?

2. **Applying Concepts** Locate and name the part of the eye in Figure 19-2 that first refracts light. Why does light refract there?

3. **Inferring** In Figure 19-2, a real image is formed at point X. What part of the eye is located at point X? How does the brain interpret the image formed at point X?

Figure 19-2

4. **Using Models** Examine Figure 19-2. List the structures labeled A–F, and state the function of each structure.

5. **Applying Concepts** Find the location of label Y in Figure 19-2. In an eye exam, the doctor finds that your eyes form images at point Y. What is her diagnosis, and how will she most likely treat it?

Essay

Write the answers to each question on a separate sheet of paper.

1. An incident ray of light strikes a plane mirror at an angle of 45 degrees with the surface of the mirror. What is the angle of reflection? Explain your answer. It may help to sketch a ray diagram.

2. What is refraction? Compare the refraction of light in water with light in diamond.

3. Suppose a beam of light passes straight up through water toward a water-air boundary. Then, the beam is gradually rotated so the angle of incidence becomes larger and larger. What will be observed about the reflection and refraction of the beam of light?

4. Infer why it is necessary, after focusing the image, to control the amount of light that enters a film camera when taking a photograph.

5. Explain the difference between rods and cones in the retina of the human eye. Also, explain the effectiveness of rods and cones in varying light levels.

Chapter 19   Optics

Multiple Choice

Write the letter that best answers the question or completes the statement on the line provided.

_____ **1.** For reflection off a plane mirror, the angle of incidence
   a. is greater than the angle of reflection.
   b. is less than the angle of reflection.
   c. equals the angle of reflection.
   d. changes the angle of reflection.

_____ **2.** The law of reflection states that if the angle of incidence is 45 degrees, the angle of reflection is
   a. 90 degrees.   **b.** 20.25 degrees.
   c. 45 degrees.   **d.** 180 degrees.

_____ **3.** A mirror with a flat surface is a
   a. plane mirror.   **b.** convex mirror.
   c. concave mirror.   **d.** virtual mirror.

_____ **4.** Unlike a virtual image, a real image
   a. forms at the curvature of a reflecting surface.
   b. can be viewed on a screen.
   c. cannot be viewed on a screen.
   d. is always upright.

_____ **5.** A concave mirror can form
   a. only virtual images.
   b. only real images.
   c. both virtual and real images.
   d. none of the above

_____ **6.** Light refracts when it
   a. bounces off a surface.
   b. changes speed.
   c. comes from a laser.
   d. spreads out from its source.

_____ **7.** Because air causes light to slow only slightly, air's index of refraction is
   a. low.   **b.** high.
   c. moderate.   **d.** nonexistent.

_____ **8.** A concave lens can only form a
   a. real image.   **b.** reversed image.
   c. virtual image.   **d.** magnified image.

_____ **9.** Light can be transmitted through long fiber optic strands because of total
   a. refraction.   **b.** external diffraction.
   c. internal reflection.   **d.** interference.

_____10. Which optical instrument uses a large concave mirror, a plane mirror, and a convex lens to gather light, focus, and enlarge an image?
      a. refracting telescope   **b.** microscope
      c. reflecting telescope   **d.** film camera

_____11. What must be done to a film camera to bring an object into focus on the film?
      a. The lens must be moved toward or away from the film.
      b. The diaphragm must be closed.
      c. The film must be coated with a light-sensitive chemical.
      d. The film must be developed and printed.

_____12. What is the function of a diaphragm in a film camera?
      a. It directs the image to the viewfinder.
      b. It focuses incoming light rays.
      c. It opens the shutter.
      d. It controls the amount of light passing through the film camera.

_____13. Which part of a film camera focuses incoming light rays?
      a. diaphragm   **b.** lens
      c. shutter   **d.** viewfinder

_____14. A compound microscope uses
      a. a mirror to reflect an image of a small object.
      b. two convex lenses to magnify a small object.
      c. a convex mirror and a lens to enlarge an image.
      d. a mirror that flips up to let light through the lens.

_____15. The lens of the human eye focuses light by
      a. changing its index of refraction.
      b. controlling the amount of light entering the eye.
      c. changing color.
      d. changing shape.

_____16. A vision problem that results in seeing blurry images at all distances is called
      a. nearsightedness.   **b.** farsightedness.
      c. astigmatism.   **d.** a blind spot.

Completion

Complete each statement on the lin

1. The law of reflection states that the angle of reflection is equal to the angle of _____.

2. The mirror in Figure 19-1 is a(an) _____ mirror.

3. Mirrors that curve outward and away from the center are called _____ mirrors.

4. When light exits a vacuum and enters any other medium, it _____.

5. Light rays passing through a convex lens converge at the _____ point on the other side of the lens.

Mirror

Figure 19-1

6. Light rays are generally unable to _____ through the sides of curving fiber optic strands.

7. Like a human eye, a film camera has a convex _____ that forms an upside-down image.

8. The iris controls the amount of light entering the eye by adjusting the size of the _____.

9. Nearsightedness results when light rays from distant objects focus in front of the _____.

Short Answer

In complete sentences, write the answers to the questions on the lines provided.

1. What is the usual method of graphically analyzing how light rays behave when they strike mirrors or pass through lenses?

   _____

   _____

2. If you are standing 1 meter in front of a plane mirror, how far does your image appear to be behind the mirror?

   _____

   _____

3. What determines the type of image produced in a concave mirror?

   _____

   _____

4. What controls the movement of the iris of the human eye?

   _____

   _____

   _____

   _____

   _____

5. What are two causes of farsightedness?

_____

_____

_____

_____

_____

Using Science Skills

Use the diagram to answer each question. Write the answers on a separate sheet of paper.

1. **Comparing and Contrasting** Compare A, B, and C in Figure 19-2. Which best illustrates the law of reflection? Explain your answer.

Figure 19-2

2. **Interpreting Graphics** What kind of mirror is C in Figure 19-2? What kind of image does it produce?

3. **Applying Concepts** What type of mirrors are represented by A, B, and C in Figure 19-2? How does each mirror affect parallel light rays that strike it?

4. **Interpreting Graphics** What kind of image does A in Figure 19-2 produce?

5. **Applying Concepts** In an experiment, the three mirrors shown in A, B, and C in Figure 19-2 are placed the same distance from an object so that each mirror produces the same type of image. What type of image do the three mirrors form, and how do the sizes of the images compare? (Assume that the shapes of mirror A and B are similar.)

Chapter 20 Electricity   **Chapter Test A**

Multiple Choice

Write the letter that best answers the question or completes the statement on the line provided.

_____ **1.** The strength of an electric field depends on the
   a. amount of charge that produced the field.
   b. distance from the charge.
   c. amount of charge on a test charge placed in the field.
   d. both A and B

_____ **2.** What is the SI unit of electric charge?
   a. ampere   **b.** ohm
   c. volt   **d.** coulomb

_____ **3.** If a neutral metal comb is held near an object with a
   negative charge, the comb will become charged by
   a. induction.   **b.** contact.
   c. friction.   **d.** static discharge.

_____ **4.** The type of current in your school is mostly
   a. direct current.   **b.** alternating current.
   c. series current.   **d.** produced by batteries.

_____ **5.** An electrical insulator has
   a. electrons that freely move.
   b. more protons than electrons.
   c. negatively charged ions.
   d. electrons tightly bound to its atoms.

_____ **6.** Which of the following would reduce the resistance of a
   metal wire?
   a. increasing its thickness
   b. increasing its temperature
   c. increasing its length
   d. all of the above

_____ **7.** Which of the following is maintained across the terminals of
   a battery?
   a. a potential difference   **b.** a voltage drop
   c. an electric charge   **d.** both A and B

_____ **8.** The current in a clothes iron measures 5.0 amps. The
   resistance of the iron is 24 ohms. What is the voltage?
   a. 120 V   **b.** 4.8 V   **c.** 19 V   **d.** 600 V

_____ **9.** How many paths through which charge can flow would be
   shown in a circuit diagram of a series circuit?
   a. one   **b.** two
   c. none   **d.** an unlimited number

_____10. Most of the circuits in your home are
  a. series circuits.   **b.** parallel circuits.
  c. reversible circuits. **d.** closed circuits.

_____11. If you know the power rating of an appliance and the voltage of the line it is attached to, you can calculate the current the appliance uses by
  a. multiplying the voltage by the power.
  b. subtracting the power from the voltage.
  c. dividing the voltage by the power.
  d. dividing the power by the voltage.

_____12. A ground-fault circuit interrupter shuts down a circuit if it
  a. melts.
  b. senses an overload.
  c. senses unequal currents.
  d. senses moisture.

_____13. Which of the following is made from a crystalline solid that conducts a current only under certain circumstances?
  a. vacuum tube   **b.** cathode-ray tube
  c. analog devise   **d.** semiconductor

_____14. What do transistors do in a mobile phone?
  a. store electric charge
  b. maintain proper voltage
  c. store data
  d. amplify the phone's incoming signal

_____15. What solid-state component in a mobile phone maintains proper voltage levels in the circuits?
  a. transistors   **b.** capacitors   **c.** diodes   **d.** microchips

Completion

Complete each statement on the line provided.

1. Electric force is _____ proportional to the amount of charge and _____ proportional to the square of the distance between the charges.

2. When a pathway through which charges can move forms suddenly, _____ occurs.

3. Scientists usually define the direction of current as the direction in which _____ charges would flow.

4. A p-type semiconductor is made by adding a trace amount of boron to _____.

5. Communication devices use _____ circuits known as _____ to make them more portable, reliable, and affordable.

Short Answer

In complete sentences, write the answers to the questions on the lines provided.

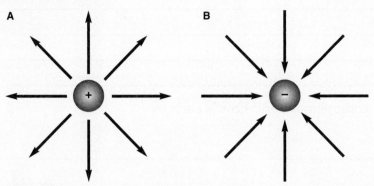

Figure 20-1

1. In Figure 20-1, where is the field of each charge the strongest?

   _____

   _____

   _____

2. What is a charge's electric field?

   _____

   _____

   _____

3. What is the law of conservation of charge?

   _____

   _____

   _____

4. Explain why metal wire coated with plastic or rubber is used in electric circuits.

   _____

   _____

   _____

5. If the voltage is 90 volts and the resistance is 30 ohms, what is the current? Explain your answer.

   _____

   _____

   _____

6. How much energy does a 50-watt light bulb use compared to a 100-watt light bulb if both are shining for the same length of time? Explain your answer.

_____

_____

_____

_____

7. What are two types of electronic signals, and how is each produced?

_____

_____

_____

_____

8. What is the difference between n-type and p-type semiconductors?

_____

_____

_____

_____

9. Name three kinds of solid-state components.

_____

_____

_____

Using Science Skills

Use the diagram to answer each question. Write the answers on a separate sheet of paper.

Circuit A   Circuit B

Circuit C

Figure 20-2

1. **Comparing and Contrasting** Compare the resistance in the three circuits shown in Figure 20-2 when the switches are closed. Explain the cause of any differences.

2. **Comparing and Contrasting** In Figure 20-2, how will the current compare in Circuits A, B, and C when the switches are closed? Explain your answer.

3. **Applying Concepts** Explain why the filaments in the light bulbs become hotter than the connecting wires in Figure 20-2.

4. **Predicting** When the switches are closed in Figure 20-2, which bulbs will be the brightest and which will be the dimmest? Assume that all of the light bulbs and batteries are identical. Explain your answer.

5. **Problem Solving** Using the same materials, how could you change the circuits in Figure 20-2 so that all the bulbs would have the same brightness? Explain your answer.

Essay

*Write the answers to each question on a separate
sheet of paper.*

1. How are friction, induction, and static discharge involved in lightning?

2. Explain why a battery causes charge to flow spontaneously when the battery is inserted in a circuit.

3. Suppose you have one light bulb in a simple circuit. If you add a second identical light bulb in series, what would happen to the brightness of the first bulb? If instead you add the second bulb in parallel, what would happen to the brightness of the first bulb? Explain your answers.

4. Why does plugging too many appliances into the same circuit cause too much current to flow through the circuit? What can happen as a result?

5. Explain the flow of electrons in p-type semiconductors and why it looks like positive charges flow.

Chapter 20   Electricity

Multiple Choice

Write the letter that best answers the question or completes the statement on the line provided.

_____ **1.** If an atom loses electrons, it becomes a
   a. negatively charged ion.
   b. positively charged ion.
   c. neutral atom.
   d. neutral ion.

_____ **2.** If the two charges represented in Figure 20-1 were brought near each other, they would
   a. attract each other.
   b. repel each other.
   c. cause static discharge.
   d. have no affect on each other.

_____ **3.** Walking across a carpet is an example of charge being transferred by
   a. contact.   **b.** induction.
   c. static electricity.   **d.** friction.

_____ **4.** What type of current is used in a battery?
   a. parallel current   **b.** alternating current
   c. direct current   **d.** potential current

_____ **5.** Which of the following materials allows charges to flow easily?
   a. glass
   b. wood
   c. an electrical conductor
   d. an electrical insulator

A

B

Figure 20-1

_____ **6.** Resistance is affected by a material's
   a. thickness.   **b.** length.
   c. temperature.   **d.** all of the above

_____ **7.** What is the difference in electrical potential energy between two places in an electric field?
   a. current   **b.** resistance
   c. potential difference   **d.** induction

_____ **8.** Which of the following represents Ohm's law?
   a. $I = V \times R$ **b.** $V = I \times R$
   c. $R = V \times I$ **d.** $V = I \times R$

_____ **9.** What is the unit of electric power?
   a. ampere   **b.** volt
   c. watt   **d.** ohm

_____ **10.** Which of the following provides electrical safety?
   a. circuit breaker
   b. fuse
   c. ground-fault circuit interrupter
   d. all of the above

_____ **11.** Information sent as patterns and codes in the controlled flow of electrons through a circuit is a(an)
   a. electronic signal.   **b.** digital signal.
   c. analog signal.   **d.** integrated signal.

_____ **12.** Electronic signals that are smoothly varying signals produced by continuously changing the voltage or current in a circuit are
   a. digital signals.   **b.** cathode rays.
   c. diode signals.   **d.** analog signals.

_____ **13.** A vacuum tube can be used to
   a. change alternating current into direct current.
   b. increase the strength of a signal.
   c. turn a current on or off.
   d. all of the above

_____ **14.** A solid-state component with three layers of semiconductors is a(an)
   a. transistor.   **b.** diode.
   c. vacuum tube.   **d.** integrated circuit.

_____ **15.** A thin slice of silicon that contains many solid-state components is a(an)
   a. transistor.   **b.** integrated circuit.
   c. diode.   **d.** cathode-ray tube.

Completion

Complete each statement on the line provided.

1. The electric field around a positive charge points _____ the charge.

2. Like charges _____ and opposite charges _____

3. The SI unit of electric current is the _____.

4. Wood, plastic, and rubber are good electrical _____, and copper is a good electrical _____.

5. The SI unit of resistance is the _____.

6. A complete path through which charge can flow is an electric _____.

7. To calculate power, multiply voltage measured in
   _____ by ____ _____
   _____ measured in amps.

8. The transfer of excess charge through a conductor to Earth is
   called _____

9. A(An) _____ signal encodes information as a
   string of 1's and 0's.

10. A cathode-ray tube is a type of _____ tube.

11. A solid-state component that combines an n-type and a p-type
    semiconductor is a(an) _____.

12. In an electronic device, a diode can be used to change alternating
    current to _____ current.

Short Answer

*In complete sentences, write the answers to the questions on
the lines provided.*

1. What are three ways that a charge can be transferred?

   _____

   _____

2. What is the difference between direct current and alternating
   current?

   _____

   _____

   _____

   _____

3. What are three common voltage sources?

   _____

   _____

4. What is a circuit breaker?

   _____

   _____

   _____

   _____

5. Electric current is used for different purposes. Compare the use of electric current by a computer and by a toaster.

_____

_____

_____

_____

Using Science Skills

Use the diagram to answer each question. Write the answers on a separate sheet of paper.

Circuit A   Circuit B

Figure 20-2

1. **Classifying** Are both circuits in Figure 20-2 series circuits? Explain your answer.

2. **Comparing and Contrasting** In which direction do the electrons move in Figure 20-2? How does this compare to the direction of the current?

3. **Interpreting Graphics** What objects and how many of each object would you need to draw if symbols were not used in Figure 20-2?

4. **Predicting** Based on the circuit diagrams in Figure 20-2, what would happen if one of the bulbs in Circuit A burned out? What would happen if one of the bulbs in Circuit B burned out? Explain your answers.

5. **Comparing and Contrasting** In Figure 20-2, what device could be added to the circuits to open the circuits? Explain how this device works. Compare this device to safety devices that stop the current in a home.

Chapter 21   Magnetism   **Chapter Test A**

Multiple Choice

Write the letter that best answers the question or completes the statement on the line provided.

A

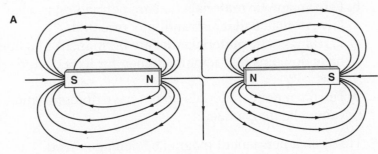

Bar Magnet

Figure 21-1

B

_____ **1.** In Figure 21-1, what magnetic poles are shown on the two bar magnets in A and B?
   a. A: north and south; B: both north
   b. A: both south; B: both north
   c. A: both north; B: both south
   d. A: north and south; B: both south

_____ **2.** Which statement describes magnetic field lines at the north pole and south pole of a bar magnet?
   a. Field lines begin near the magnet's south pole and extend toward its north pole.
   b. Field lines begin near both the magnet's north and south poles and meet in the middle.
   c. Field lines begin near the center of the magnet and extend toward the north and south poles.
   d. Field lines begin near the magnet's north pole and extend toward its south pole.

_____ **3.** Which of the following statements is true about Earth's magnetic poles?
   a. They are located at Earth's geographic poles.
   b. They are the areas where Earth's magnetic field is weakest.
   c. They are the areas where Earth's magnetic field is strongest.
   d. Earth has four magnetic poles.

_____ **4.** Which of the following statements is true about ferromagnetic materials?
  a. All ferromagnetic materials are permanent magnets.
  b. Ferromagnetic materials that are permanent magnets have domains that are randomly oriented.
  c. Ferromagnetic materials that are permanent magnets have domains that remain aligned for long periods of time.
  d. Ferromagnetic materials do not have domains and cannot be magnetized.

_____ **5.** How can a permanent magnet be demagnetized?
  a. Cut the magnet in half.
  b. Heat the magnet up.
  c. Strike the magnet with a heavy blow.
  d. both b and c

_____ **6.** If the current in a wire is directed upward, what is the direction of the magnetic field produced by the current?
  a. counterclockwise in the horizontal plane
  b. clockwise in the horizontal plane
  c. in the same direction as the current
  d. in the opposite direction to the current

_____ **7.** Which of the following statements is true about a current-carrying wire in a magnetic field?
  a. Reversing the current direction will cause the force deflecting the wire to be parallel to the magnetic field.
  b. Reversing the current direction will cause the force deflecting the wire to be perpendicular to the magnetic field but in the opposite direction.
  c. Reversing the current direction will cause the force deflecting the wire to be parallel to the velocity of the charge.
  d. Reversing the current direction will not affect the force deflecting the wire.

_____ **8.** The electromagnet in a galvanometer
  a. increases the voltage in a circuit.
  b. moves a pointer along a numbered scale in response to a current.
  c. induces an electric current.
  d. increases the current in a circuit.

_____ 9. In an electric motor, periodically changing the direction of current in the electromagnet can cause the axle to spin because
a. the electromagnet loses its magnetism.
b. mechanical energy is converted to electric energy.
c. the moving electrons push the electromagnet in the opposite direction.
d. the magnetic field reverses direction.

_____10. How can the voltage in a coil of wire be increased in the process of electromagnetic induction?
a. Move the magnet inside the coil of wire more slowly.
b. Hold the magnet stationary.
c. Move the coil of wire slowly, and keep the magnet stationary.
d. Move the magnet inside the coil of wire more rapidly.

_____11. A DC generator is similar to an AC generator except that in
a. DC generators, slip rings produce direct current.
b. DC generators, commutators produce direct current.
c. AC generators, commutators produce alternating current.
d. AC generators, no commutators or slip rings are used.

_____12. A transformer has a primary coil with 500 turns and a secondary coil with 250 turns. If the output voltage is 240 volts, what is the input voltage?
a. 96 volts   b. 120 volts   c. 480 volts   d. 500 volts

_____13. If a step-up transformer has a primary coil with 10 turns, how many turns would be required in the secondary coil in order to increase the voltage from 60 volts to 120 volts?
a. 5 turns   b. 20 turns
c. 60 turns   d. 120 turns

_____14. How are step-up transformers used in the transmission of electrical energy?
a. They increase the voltage and the current for a home.
b. They decrease the voltage before it leaves a power plant.
c. They increase the voltage for efficient long-distance transmission.
d. all of the above

_____15. How are fossil fuels used to generate electrical energy?
a. Heat from burning fuel spins magnets inside an electric motor.
b. Heat from burning fuel creates steam that spins a turbine.
c. Heat from burning fuel causes an electric motor to produce a current.
d. Heat from burning fuel creates steam that turns a transformer.

Completion

Complete each statement on the line provided.

1. The region where a magnet's force is strongest is at the
   _____ .

2. The magnetic field lines of a bar magnet begin near the magnet's
   _____ .

3. The angle between the direction a compass points and geographic north is called _____ .

4. Transformers only work with _____ current.

5. The energy source used to produce most of the electrical energy in the United States is _____ .

Short Answer

In complete sentences, write the answers to the questions on the lines provided.

1. How does magnetic declination vary?

   _____

   _____

   _____

2. Explain why Earth's magnetic North Pole would be a south pole of a bar magnet.

   _____

   _____

   _____

   _____

3. How does a vibrating electric charge produce an electromagnetic wave?

   _____

   _____

   _____

   _____

   _____

   _____

4. How does a galvanometer use a magnetic field to indicate the strength of an electric current?

_____

_____

_____

_____

_____

5. Compare generators and electric motors.

_____

_____

_____

_____

Using Science Skills

Use the diagram to answer each question. Write the answers on a separate sheet of paper.

Figure 21-2

1. **Inferring** In Figure 21-2, in what direction do magnetic field lines point in A in the area between the poles of the horseshoe magnet?

2. **Inferring** In Figure 21-2, will electrons in B be pushed in the same direction as the wire is pushed or in the opposite direction? Explain your answer.

3. **Using Models** Use Figure 21-2 to determine whether the current flows toward the negative or positive connection on a battery.

4. **Interpreting Graphics** In Figure 21-2, in what direction is the force deflecting the wire in B?

5. **Interpreting Graphics** In Figure 21-2, in what direction is the force deflecting the wire in A? How does this compare with the force deflecting the wire in B?

Essay

Write the answers to each question on a separate sheet of paper.

1. Why does a compass point to the east or west of true north in different locations?

2. What are solenoids and electromagnets, and how are they constructed?

3. Describe two household devices that use electromagnets.

4. How does a transformer decrease the voltage that is transmitted across power lines before it enters homes?

5. Explain how a step-up transformer is different from a step-down transformer.

Chapter 21 Magnetism

Multiple Choice

Write the letter that best answers the question or completes the statement on the line provided.

_____ 1. The force a magnet exerts on another magnet, on iron or a similar metal, or on moving charges is
   a. an electric force.
   b. a magnetic force.
   c. proportional to the charge of the magnet.
   d. proportional to the mass of the magnet.

_____ 2. Which of the following statements describes the interaction between magnetic poles?
   a. Like poles attract each other.
   b. Like poles repel each other, and opposite poles attract each other.
   c. Opposite poles repel each other.
   d. Like poles attract each other, and opposite poles repel each other.

_____ 3. How does the magnetic force exerted by a magnet change as the distance between two magnets increases?
   a. The magnetic force increases.
   b. The magnetic force stays the same.
   c. The magnetic force decreases.
   d. The magnetic force does not change with distance.

_____ 4. What is the name of the area surrounding Earth that is influenced by Earth's magnetic field?
   a. magnetosphere   b. atmosphere
   c. magnetic domain   d. magnetic declination

_____ 5. A region that has a large number of atoms whose magnetic fields are lined up parallel to a magnet's field is
   a. the magnetosphere.
   b. the magnetic declination.
   c. a magnetic domain.
   d. a ferromagnetic region.

_____ 6. A ferromagnetic material that has domains that remain aligned for a long period of time is called
   a. a neutral object.   b. nonmagnetic.
   c. a permanent magnet.   d. a temporary magnet.

_____ 7. What creates a magnetic field?
   a. charged particles that do not move
   b. moving electric charges
   c. gravity
   d. an isolated magnetic pole

_____ **8.** If a current-carrying wire is in a magnetic field, in what direction will a force be exerted on the wire?
   a. perpendicular to the magnetic field and parallel to the current direction
   b. parallel to both the current direction and the magnetic field
   c. perpendicular to the current direction and parallel to the magnetic field
   d. perpendicular to both the magnetic field and the current direction

_____ **9.** A coil of wire that is carrying a current and produces a magnetic field is
   a. a galvanometer.   **b.** a solenoid.
   c. a magnetic domain.   **d.** an electric motor.

_____ **10.** Which of the following is the reason "soft" iron is used for the cores of electromagnets?
   a. It is difficult to magnetize.
   b. It is easily magnetized.
   c. It has no magnetic domains.
   d. It is a permanent magnet.

_____ **11.** The device that measures current in a wire by using the deflections of an electromagnet in an external magnetic field is
   a. a galvanometer.   **b.** a solenoid.
   c. an electric motor.   **d.** a loudspeaker.

_____ **12.** The process of generating an electric current by moving an electrical conductor relative to a magnetic field is called
   a. magnetization.
   b. electromagnetic force.
   c. electromagnetic induction.
   d. alternating current.

_____ **13.** A device that changes mechanical energy to electric energy by rotating a coil of wire through a magnetic field is called a(an)
   a. transformer.   **b.** generator.
   c. electromagnet.   **d.** current meter.

_____ **14.** The strength of the output voltage and current of a transformer are determined by the
   a. number of turns in the primary and secondary coils.
   b. strength of the DC current in the primary coil.
   c. ferromagnetic material of the rings connecting the coils.
   d. direction of the current in the primary coil.

_____15. Before electric current in power lines can be safe for your
home, it must pass through a
a. turbine.   b. step-down transformer.
c. step-up transformer   d. generator.

Completion

Complete each statement on the line provided.

1. The region around a magnet that exerts magnetic force is called
a(an) _____.

2. In most materials, the magnetic fields of _____
cancel their effects.

3. The _____ are caused by charged particles from
the sun entering Earth's magnetic field.

4. In ferromagnetic materials, regions with large numbers of atoms
with aligned magnetic fields are called _____.

5. A charged particle moving in a magnetic field will be deflected in
a direction _____ to the magnetic field.

6. In a solenoid, there will be no magnetic field if there is no
_____ in the wires of the coil.

7. Moving a magnet through a wire coil can produce a(an)
_____ in the coil.

8. A(An) _____ converts mechanical energy into
electric energy.

9. Large power plants in the United States currently use
_____ generators.

10. _____ transformers decrease the current and
increase the voltage in the output circuit.

Short Answer

*In complete sentences, write the answers to the questions on
the lines provided.*

1. What are magnetic poles?

_____

_____

_____

2. In Figure 21-1, what do the lines around the bar magnets
represent?

_____

_____

_____

3. What is a generator and how does it work?

_____

_____

4. List five energy sources that are used in the United States to produce electrical energy.

_____

_____

_____

5. How is water used to produce electric energy in a hydroelectric power plant?

_____

_____

_____

Using Science Skills

Use the diagram to answer each question. Write the answers on a separate sheet of paper.

1. **Interpreting Graphics** In Figure 21-1, use the direction of the magnetic field lines to determine what type of magnetic pole is located at the magnetic South Pole.

2. **Predicting** Use Figure 21-1 to predict where Earth's magnetic field is strongest. Explain your answer.

3. **Inferring** Use Figure 21-1 to determine in what direction the north magnetic pole of the compass will point. What type of magnetic pole is the compass pointing toward?

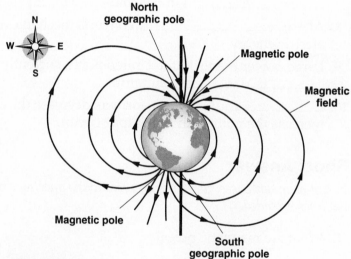

Figure 21-1

4. **Applying Skills** A scientist studying Earth's magnetic field found that at Hot Springs, Arkansas, her compass pointed 5° east of true north. In Durango, Colorado, she took another reading and found that her compass pointed 14° east of true north. Use Figure 21-1 to explain why the two readings were different.

5. **Interpreting Graphics** In Figure 21-1, where is the magnetic field the weakest?

Name _____ Class _____ Date _____

Unit 2   Physics   Unit Test A

Multiple Choice

Write the letter that best answers the question or completes the statement on the line provided.

_____ 1. Which distance can be most accurately measured with a ruler?
   a. the length of a river
   b. the width of a book
   c. the distance between two cities
   d. the size of an object under a microscope

_____ 2. A horizontal line on a distance-time graph means the object is
   a. moving at a constant speed.
   b. moving faster.
   c. slowing down.
   d. at rest.

_____ 3. A train approaching a crossing changes speed from 25 m/s to 10 m/s in 240 s. How can the train's acceleration be described?
   a. The train's acceleration is positive.
   b. The train is not accelerating.
   c. The train will come to rest in 6 minutes.
   d. The train's acceleration is negative.

_____ 4. As you push a cereal box across a tabletop, the sliding friction acting on the cereal box
   a. acts in the direction of motion.
   b. equals the weight of the box.
   c. is usually greater than static friction.
   d. acts in the direction opposite of motion.

_____ 5. The acceleration due to gravity on the surface of Mars is about one-third the acceleration due to gravity on Earth's surface. The weight of a space probe on the surface of Mars is about
   a. nine times greater than its weight on Earth's surface.
   b. three times greater than its weight on Earth's surface.
   c. one-third its weight on Earth's surface.
   d. the same as its weight on Earth's surface.

_____ 6. The centripetal force acting on a satellite in orbit
   a. acts as an unbalanced force on the satellite.
   b. changes the direction of the satellite.
   c. is a center-directed force.
   d. all of the above

© Pearson Education, Inc. All rights reserved.

Physical Science ▪ Unit 2 Test A   **217**

_____ **7.** If the air inside a balloon exerts a force of 1 N on an area of 0.5 m2, what is the pressure inside the balloon?
a. 0.5 N/m^2 **b.** 1 N/m^2 **c.** 1.5 N/m^2 **d.** 2 N/m^2

_____ **8.** Where will the greatest increase in pressure occur if you squeeze the middle of an upright, closed soft-drink bottle?
a. The greatest increase in pressure will occur at the top of the bottle.
b. The greatest increase in pressure will occur in the middle of the bottle.
c. The greatest increase in pressure will occur on the bottom of the bottle.
d. The pressure will increase equally everywhere within the bottle.

_____ **9.** The buoyant force on an object in a fluid is equal to the weight of the
a. fluid.
b. fluid surrounding the object.
c. fluid displaced by the object.
d. object.

_____ **10.** If you exert a force of 500 N to walk 4 m up a flight of stairs in 4 s, how much power do you use?
a. 31 W   **b.** 500 W   **c.** 2000 W   **d.** 8000 W

_____ **11.** Which of the following statements is true?
a. To increase power, you can decrease the amount of work you do in a given amount of time, or you can do a given amount of work in less time.
b. To increase power, you can decrease the amount of work you do in a given amount of time, or you can do a given amount of work in more time.
c. To increase power, you can increase the amount of work you do in a given amount of time, or you can do a given amount of work in less time.
d. To increase power, you can increase the amount of work you do in a given amount of time, or you can do a given amount of work in more time.

_____ **12.** Which of the following is an example of a wheel and axle?
a. a doorknob
b. an automobile steering wheel
c. a jar lid
d. a pencil

_____ **13.** A small 30-kilogram canoe is floating downriver at a speed of 2 m/s. What is the canoe's kinetic energy?
a. 32 J   **b.** 60 J   **c.** 120 J   **d.** 900 J

_____14. Walking converts what type of energy into mechanical energy?
   a. chemical   **b.** electromagnetic
   c. nuclear   **d.** thermal

_____15. The kinetic energy of the pendulum bob in Figure 15-1 increases the most between locations
   a. A and B.   **b.** A and C.
   c. B and D.   **d.** C and D.

_____16. Thermal energy depends on an object's
   a. mass.
   b. phase (sold, liquid, or gas).
   c. temperature.
   d. all of the above

_____17. According to the first law of thermodynamics, the amount of work done by a heat engine equals the amount of
   a. work done on the engine.
   b. waste heat it produces.
   c. thermal energy added to the engine minus the waste heat.
   d. thermal energy added to the engine plus the waste heat.

_____18. Which of the following happens in a heat pump?
   a. The compressor increases the pressure and temperature of the refrigerant.
   b. The compressor blows cold refrigerant into the room.
   c. The compressor absorbs heat from the refrigerant.
   d. none of the above

_____19. A mechanical wave generally does NOT
   a. move the medium from one place to another.
   b. move through a medium.
   c. move through solids.
   d. disturb the medium.

_____20. A period is the length of time it takes for
   a. a disturbance to start a wave.
   b. two complete wavelengths to pass a fixed point.
   c. a wave to travel the length of a rope.
   d. one complete wavelength to pass a fixed point.

_____21. The formation of a standing wave requires
   a. the traveling of a wave for a long distance.
   b. constructive interference between two waves of slightly different frequencies.
   c. that refraction and diffraction occur at the same time in a wave.
   d. interference between incoming and reflected waves.

_____22. Which of the following occurs as light travels farther from its source?
   a. Far from the source, photons spread through a small area.
   b. The intensity of light increases as photons move away from the source.
   c. The source gives off less light as photons move away from it.
   d. Farther from the source, photons spread over a larger area.

_____23. X-ray photographs show softer tissue
   a. as invisible.
   b. as dark, highly exposed areas.
   c. the same as dense bones.
   d. as bright white areas.

_____24. Which of the following is NOT true regarding neon lights?
   a. Light is emitted as electrons move through a gas in a tube.
   b. All neon lights are colored by the color of the tubing.
   c. Neon lights may contain other gases, such as helium or krypton.
   d. Each kind of gas produces its own distinctive color.

_____25. Why do plane mirrors and convex mirrors form only virtual images?
   a. because they both cause light rays to spread out
   b. because reflected rays appear to come from behind the mirror
   c. because the focal point is in front of the mirror
   d. because they both show a wide angle of view

_____26. Total internal reflection occurs when the angle of incidence
   a. is zero.
   b. is less than the critical angle.
   c. exceeds the critical angle.
   d. equals the angle of reflection.

_____27. Which of the following would reduce the resistance of a metal wire?
   a. increasing its thickness
   b. increasing its temperature
   c. increasing its length
   d. all of the above

_____28. A ground-fault circuit interrupter shuts down a circuit if it
   a. melts.
   b. senses an overload.
   c. senses unequal currents.
   d. senses moisture.

_____**29.** How can the voltage in a coil of wire be increased in the process of electromagnetic induction?
  a. Move the magnet inside the coil of wire more slowly.
  b. Hold the magnet stationary.
  c. Move the coil of wire slowly, and keep the magnet stationary.
  d. Move the magnet inside the coil of wire more rapidly.

_____**30.** A DC generator is similar to an AC generator except that in
  a. DC generators, slip rings produce direct current.
  b. DC generators, commutators produce direct current.
  c. AC generators, commutators produce alternating current.
  d. AC generators, no commutators or slip rings are used.

Completion

Complete each statement on the line provided.

1. A constant slope on a distance-time graph indicates _____ speed.

2. _____ is how fast a velocity is changing at a specific instant.

3. It usually takes more force to start an object sliding than it does to keep an object sliding because static friction is usually _____ than sliding friction.

4. The universal force that is most effective over the longest distances is _____

5. The pressure exerted by a fluid at any given depth is exerted _____ in all directions.

6. As you climb a high mountain, the buoyant force exerted on you by the atmosphere _____.

7. As the thickness of a wedge of given length increases, its IMA _____.

8. A watch consists of a complex systems of gears. Each gear acts as a continuous _____.

9. Flat collector plates through which water flows are found in _____. solar energy systems.

10. Turning off unused lights or appliances is an example of energy _____.

11. If the temperature change of an aluminum nail is negative, thermal energy is transferred _____ the nail _____. the surroundings.

12. In a calorimeter, the increase in the thermal energy of the water and the decrease in the thermal energy of the sample are _____.

13. The crest of a transverse wave is most similar to a(an) _____ in a longitudinal wave.

14. Waves in a rope are transverse waves because the medium's vibration is _____ to the direction in which the wave travels.

15. An ultraviolet light wave has a wavelength of 300 nm and a frequency of 7.0×10^{14} Hz. The ultraviolet light is NOT traveling through a(an) _____.

16. In microwave cooking, the food is heated _____ in the areas near the surface of the food than in the center.

17. Nerve endings in the retina that are most sensitive to low-intensity light are called _____.

18. Communication devices use _____ circuits known as _____ to make them more portable, reliable, and affordable.

19. The angle between the direction a compass points and geographic north is called _____.

20. Transformers only work with _____ current.

Short Answer

In complete sentences, write the answers to the questions on the lines provided.

1. Which is the most suitable SI unit for expressing the speed of a race car?

   _____

2. A billiard ball with a momentum of 20 kg•m/s strikes a second ball at rest and comes to a complete stop. What is the change in momentum of the second ball?

   _____

3. Why does a partially inflated weather balloon expand as it rises?

   _____

   _____

   _____

4. Compare the effects of a fixed pulley and a movable pulley on the size and direction of the input force.

   _____

   _____

   _____

   _____

5. Explain how biomass energy depends on the sun.

_____

_____

_____

_____

_____

6. What role do free electrons have in conduction in metals?

_____

_____

7. How could you compare the energy carried in two different longitudinal waves?

_____

_____

8. Why must a microscope slide be made of a transparent material like glass if the glass does not magnify the image?

_____

_____

_____

9. What is the law of conservation of charge?

_____

_____

_____

10. How does a vibrating electric charge produce an electromagnetic wave?

_____

_____

_____

_____

Using Science Skills

Use the diagram to answer each question. Write the answers on a separate sheet of paper.

Figure 2-1A

Figure 2-1B

1. **Interpreting Graphics** Figure 2-1 illustrates the displacement of an object moving in a plane. Explain what information is provided by arrows A and B.

2. **Comparing and Contrasting** In Figure 2-2, compare the size and direction of the momentums of both skaters immediately after the push shown at Time 2.

3. **Observing** How did the position of the spoon in Figure 2-3 change after the faucet was turned on?

Skaters are not in motion.   Skaters are moving at identical speeds.

Figure 2-2

Figure 2-3A   **Figure 2-3B**

4. **Applying Concepts** Look at Figure 2-4.
   If Machine A moves through an input
   distance of 4.0 m, what is the output distance
   of Machine B?

5. **Inferring** In Figure 2-5, is the total mechanical
   energy of the ball conserved
   as the ball bounces? Explain your answer.

Machine B

Machine A

Figure 2-4

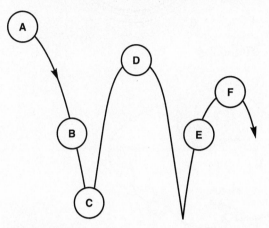

Figure 2-5

6. **Interpreting Data**
   Compare the average
   kinetic energy of the water
   molecules in the three
   beakers in Figure 2-6.

7. **Analyzing Data** What is
   the difference between
   wave A and wave B
   in Figure 2-7?

50°C   70°C   70°C

200 g   200 g   400 g

Figure 2-6

wavelength = 80 cm

amplitude
= 40 cm

A

wavelength = 80 cm

amplitude
= 20 cm

B

 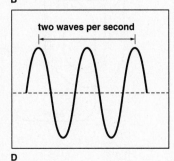

one wave per second

C

two waves per second

D

Figure 2-7

8. **Predicting** Figure 2-8 shows the lens of an eye that is focused on a nearby object at point Z. If the eye refocuses on a far object, what happens to the shape of the lens? How?

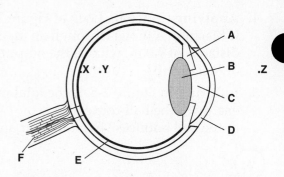

9. **Comparing and Contrasting** Compare the resistance in the three circuits shown in Figure 2-9 when the switches are closed. Explain the cause of any differences.

Figure 2-8

Circuit A

Figure 2-9

Circuit B

Circuit C

10. **Using Models** Use Figure 2-10 to determine whether the current flows toward the negative or positive connection on a battery.

Figure 2-10

A

B

Problem

Write the answers to each question on a separate sheet of paper.

1. During a race, a runner runs at a speed of 6 m/s. Four seconds later, she is running at a speed of 10 m/s. What is the runner's acceleration? Show your work.

Essay

Write the answers to each question on a separate sheet of paper.

1. Why does a biker have to pedal harder to travel at a constant speed into the wind on a windy day compared to traveling on the same road at the same speed on a calm day?

2. A cube of wood displaces half its volume when floating in water. When a 0.5-N washer is added to the cube, it floats just at the point where it is completely submerged in the water. What is the buoyant force acting on the cube when the washer is removed?

3. Sound waves have relatively long wavelengths. We can hear people around a corner before we can see them. Which wave behavior does this illustrate? Explain how wavelength relates to this behavior.

4. How does a transformer decrease the voltage that is transmitted across power lines before it enters homes?

Multiple Choice

Write the letter that best answers the question or completes the statement on the line provided.

_____ **1.** One kilometer equals 1000 meters. What does the prefix kilo- mean?

    a. 1   **b.** 10   **c.** 100   **d.** 1000

_____ **2.** What is the speed of a bobsled whose distance-time graph indicates that it traveled 100 m in 25 s?

    a. 4 m/s   **b.** 250 m/s

    c. 0.25 mph   **d.** 100 m/s

_____ **3.** According to Newton's second law of motion, the acceleration of an object equals the net force acting on the object divided by the object's

    a. mass.   **b.** momentum.   **c.** velocity.   **d.** weight.

_____ **4.** What is the SI unit of pressure?

    a. g/cm^3 **b.** m/s^2

    c. a newton   **d.** a pascal

_____ **5.** Which principle states that a change in the pressure at any point in a fluid in a closed container is transmitted equally and unchanged in all directions throughout the fluid?

    a. Archimedes' principle

    b. Bernoulli's principle

    c. Newton's principle

    d. Pascal's principle

_____ **6.** The relationship between buoyant force and weight of a displaced fluid was first stated by

    a. Archimedes.   **b.** Bernoulli.   **c.** Newton.   **d.** Pascal.

_____ **7.** What is the unit of work?

    a. joule   **b.** newton/meter

    c. watt   **d.** all of the above

_____ **8.** How can a machine make work easier for you?

    a. by decreasing the amount of work you do

    b. by changing the direction of your force

    c. by increasing the work done by the machine

    d. none of the above

_____ **9.** An inclined plane reduces the effort force by

    a. increasing the distance through which the force is applied.

    b. increasing the work.

    c. reducing the effort distance.

    d. reducing the work.

_____10. Which of the following is an example of an object with elastic potential energy?

      a. a wind-up toy that has been wound up

      b. a compressed basketball

      c. a stretched rubber band

      d. all of the above

_____11. A 4-kilogram cat is resting on top of a bookshelf that is 2 meters high. What is the cat's gravitational potential energy relative to the floor if the acceleration due to gravity is 9.8 m/s²?

      a. 6 J   **b.** 8 J   **c.** 20 J   **d.** 78 J

_____12. What is biomass energy?

      a. the chemical energy stored in living things

      b. the electromagnetic energy stored in living things

      c. the nuclear energy stored in living things

      d. the thermal energy stored in living things

_____13. Which of the following is a unit of temperature?

      a. Celsius degree   **b.** joule

      c. kilogram   **d.** calorie

_____14. What does a calorimeter directly measure?

      a. change in temperature

      b. kinetic energy

      c. specific heat

      d. radiation

_____15. Which central heating system involves a furnace and a blower?

      a. electric baseboard   **b.** forced-air

      c. hot-water   **d.** steam

_____16. When a surfer rides an ocean wave on her surfboard, she is actually riding on

      a. a crest that is toppling over.

      b. a trough of the wave.

      c. the rest position of the wave.

      d. a region of rarefaction.

_____17. To determine the speed of a wave, you would use which of the following formulas?

      a. speed = frequency × amplitude

      b. speed = wavelength × frequency

      c. speed = wavelength × amplitude

      d. speed = wavelength × period

_____18. Sonar equipment sends sound waves into deep water and measures
  a. refraction of the transmitted wave.
  b. only the direction of the reflected wave.
  c. the time delay of the returning echoes.
  d. interference of the transmitted and reflected waves.

_____19. To calculate the frequency of an electromagnetic wave, you need to know the speed of the wave and its
  a. wavelength.   b. intensity.
  c. refraction.   d. amplitude.

_____20. Light acts like
  a. a wave.
  b. a particle.
  c. both a wave and a particle.
  d. neither a wave nor a particle.

_____21. Newton's prism experiments showed that white sunlight is made up of
  a. the full electromagnetic spectrum.
  b. only blue light when separated by a prism.
  c. all the colors of the visible spectrum.
  d. only the longest wavelengths.

_____22. A concave mirror can form
  a. only virtual images.
  b. only real images.
  c. both virtual and real images.
  d. none of the above

_____23. Which optical instrument uses a large concave mirror, a plane mirror, and a convex lens to gather light, focus, and enlarge an image?
  a. refracting telescope   b. microscope
  c. reflecting telescope   d. film camera

_____24. The lens of the human eye focuses light by
  a. changing its index of refraction.
  b. controlling the amount of light entering the eye.
  c. changing color.
  d. changing shape.

_____25. Walking across a carpet is an example of charge being transferred by
  a. contact.   b. induction.
  c. static electricity.   d. friction.

_____ **26.** What is the difference in electrical potential energy between two places in an electric field?

   a. current   **b.** resistance

   c. potential difference   **d.** induction

_____ **27.** A solid-state component with three layers of semiconductors is a(an)

   a. transistor.   **b.** diode.

   c. vacuum tube.   **d.** integrated circuit.

_____ **28.** The force a magnet exerts on another magnet, on iron or a similar metal, or on moving charges is

   a. an electric force.

   b. a magnetic force.

   c. proportional to the charge of the magnet.

   d. proportional to the mass of the magnet.

_____ **29.** What creates a magnetic field?

   a. charged particles that do not move

   b. moving electric charges

   c. gravity

   d. an isolated magnetic pole

_____ **30.** The process of generating an electric current by moving an electrical conductor relative to a magnetic field is called

   a. magnetization.

   b. electromagnetic force.

   c. electromagnetic induction.

   d. alternating current.

Completion

Complete each statement on the line provided.

1. The direction and length of a straight line from the starting point to the ending point of an object's motion is _____.

2. The force that opposes the motion of objects that touch as they move pass each other is called _____.

3. The two forces acting on a falling object are gravity and _____.

4. In a hydraulic lift system, the fluid pressure exerted throughout the system is _____.

5. A machine is a device that changes a(an) _____.

6. Mechanical energy does not include kinetic energy or _____ energy.

7. "Energy cannot be created or destroyed" is a statement of the law of _____.

8. The transfer of thermal energy with no overall transfer of matter is called _____.

9. At the _____ of a standing wave, there is no displacement from the rest position.

10. Objects that scatter some of the light that is transmitted through them are _____.

11. Electromagnetic waves can travel through a(an) _____.

12. Light rays passing through a convex lens converge at the _____ point on the other side of the lens.

13. To calculate power, multiply voltage measured in _____ by _____ measured in amps.

14. In ferromagnetic materials, regions with large numbers of atoms with aligned magnetic fields are called _____.

15. A charged particle moving in a magnetic field will be deflected in a direction _____ to the magnetic field.

Short Answer

In complete sentences, write the answers to the questions on the lines provided.

1. What are two types of speed that can be used to describe the motion of a car driving on the highway?

   _____

   _____

2. How can you double the acceleration of an object if you cannot alter the object's mass?

   _____

   _____

3. Which of the universal forces acts only on protons and neutrons in the nucleus of an atom?

   _____

   _____

4. Compare the weight of an object to the buoyant force acting on it if the object sinks in the fluid.

   _____

   _____

5. Which has the greater IMA—a screw with closely spaced threads or a screw with threads spaced farther apart?

_____

_____

6. What are the two general types of energy that can be used to classify many forms of energy?

_____

_____

7. What is the most familiar form of electromagnetic energy?

_____

8. In general, what is the order of increasing thermal expansion among solids, liquids, and gases when a given amount of thermal energy is added?

_____

9. When you shake the end of a rope to make a wave, how can you increase the amplitude of the wave?

_____

_____

10. Which waves have wavelengths longer than those of visible light? Give an example of how each kind of wave is used.

_____

_____

_____

11. Magenta is a secondary color of light. What type of color is magenta when it is a pigment?

_____

_____

_____

12. What is the usual method of graphically analyzing how light rays behave when they strike mirrors or pass through lenses?

_____

13. What is a circuit breaker?

_____

_____

_____

14. What is a generator and how does it work?

_____

_____

_____

15. List five energy sources that are used in the United States to produce electrical energy.

_____

_____

_____

Using Science Skills

Use the diagram to answer each question. Write the answers on a separate sheet of paper.

1. **Interpreting Graphics** In Figure 2-1, what is the direction of the centripetal force acting on the satellite at this location in its orbit?

2. **Comparing and Contrasting** How does the fluid pressure exerted on the black spheres shown in Figure 2-2 compare with the pressure exerted on the gray spheres.

3. **Calculating** What is the IMA of the ramp in Figure 2-3? Show your work.

Figure 2-1

Figure 2-2

Figure 2-3

3.0 m

1.0 m

4. **Applying Concepts** In Figure 2-4, the block in C has 5 J of kinetic energy. How much work did the compressed spring do on the block? Explain your answer.

5. **Inferring** In Figure 2-5, is the temperature of the material within the cylinder greatest during the intake stroke, compression stroke, power stroke, or exhaust stroke?

6. **Interpreting** Illustrations What kind of wave does A in Figure 2-6 represent? What kind of wave does B represent?

Figure 2-5   **Figure 2-4**

Figure 2-6

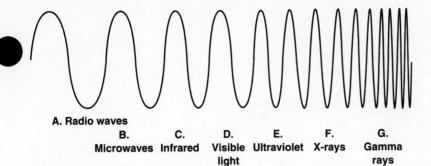

A. Radio waves

B. Microwaves   C. Infrared   D. Visible light   E. Ultraviolet   F. X-rays   G. Gamma rays

Figure 2-7

7. **Comparing and Contrasting** Which waves in Figure 2-7 carry AM and FM signals? How do the frequencies of AM and FM signals compare?

A   B   C

Figure 2-8

8. **Applying Concepts** What type of mirrors are represented by A, B, and C in Figure 2-8? How does each mirror affect parallel light rays that strike it?

Circuit A   Circuit B

Figure 2-9

9. **Classifying** Are both circuits in Figure 2-9 series circuits? Explain your answer.

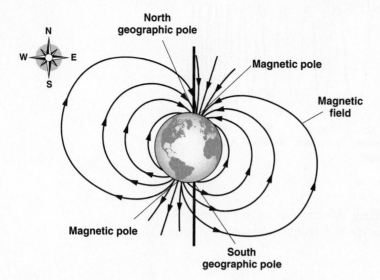

North
geographic pole

Magnetic pole

Magnetic
field

Magnetic pole

South
geographic pole

Figure 2-10

10. **Interpreting Graphics** In Figure 2-10, use the direction of the
magnetic field lines to determine what type of magnetic pole is
located at the magnetic South Pole.

Chapter 22   Earth's Interior   **Chapter Test A**

Multiple Choice

Write the letter that best answers the question or completes the statement on the line provided.

_____ 1. Forces that shape Earth's surface can be divided into
  a. constructive and physical.
  b. constructive and destructive.
  c. chemical and destructive.
  d. chemical and physical.

_____ 2. The two layers that make up the lithosphere are the
  a. upper mantle and lower mantle.
  b. oceanic crust and continental crust.
  c. inner core and outer core.
  d. crust and upper mantle.

_____ 3. What is a mineral's cleavage?
  a. the resistance of a mineral to scratching
  b. a type of fracture in which a mineral breaks along regular, well-defined planes c. the color of a mineral's powder
  d. a type of fracture in which a mineral breaks along a curved surface

_____ 4. Intense heat, intense pressure, or reactions with hot water can modify a pre-existing rock to form a(an)
  a. metamorphic rock.   b. sedimentary rock.
  c. igneous rock.   d. organic rock.

_____ 5. What changes are involved when mud from a lake bottom turns into a sedimentary rock, then into a metamorphic rock?
  a. compaction and cementation, then melting
  b. heat and pressure, then weathering
  c. compaction and cementation, then heat and pressure
  d. melting, then compaction and cementation

_____ 6. Why was Wegener's hypothesis of continental drift originally rejected by geologists?
  a. Wegener did not have any data to support his hypothesis.
  b. The continents of South America and Africa do not fit well together.
  c. Wegener could not explain how the continents could move through the ocean floor.
  d. Wegener's data was incorrect.

_____ 7. A subducting oceanic plate
  a. is less dense than the plate it moves under.
  b. is pushed up and over the continental crust.
  c. sinks into the mantle, forming a trench.
  d. moves horizontally in the opposite direction past the other plate.

_____ **8.** The heat that drives mantle convection comes from the cooling of Earth's interior and
   a. the sun.
   b. the decay of radioactive isotopes.
   c. sea-floor spreading.
   d. trenches.

_____ **9.** Stress in Earth's crust is caused by
   a. folds.   **b.** plate movements.   **c.** earthquakes.   **d.** faults.

_____ **10.** P waves
   a. cause Earth to vibrate in the direction of the wave's motion.
   b. cause Earth to vibrate at right angles to the direction the wave moves.
   c. travel along Earth's surface.
   d. move in a rolling motion similar to ocean waves.

_____ **11.** Geologists have inferred that Earth's outer core is liquid because
   a. P waves cannot pass through the outer core.
   b. S waves speed up in the outer core.
   c. S waves are bent downward as they travel through the outer core.
   d. S waves cannot pass through the outer core.

_____ **12.** What causes the magna inside a volcano to rise towards the surface?
   a. It is a thick liquid, denser than the surrounding rock.
   b. It does not contain dissolved gases.
   c. It is less dense than the surrounding rock.
   d. It is cooler than the surrounding rock.

_____ **13.** What causes the magna inside a volcano to rise towards the surface?
   a. It is a thick liquid, denser than the surrounding rock.
   b. It does not contain dissolved gases.
   c. It is less dense than the surrounding rock.
   d. It is cooler than the surrounding rock.

_____ **14.** A steep-sided volcano formed entirely of ash and cinders is a
   a. shield volcano.   **b.** composite volcano.
   c. cinder cone.   **d.** hot spot.

_____ **15.** A sequence of rock layers consists of horizontal layers of sandstone, granite, and limestone. What type of intrusive igneous feature does the granite layer represent?
   a. a sill   **b.** a dike
   c. a batholith   **d.** a volcanic neck

Completion

Complete each statement on the line provided.

1. The type of sedimentary rock that forms when fragments of pre-existing rocks are cemented together is called a(an) _____ rock.

2. Alfred Wegener proposed that a continent was formed by continental drift. This supercontinent was called _____.

3. Due to sea-floor spreading, the youngest rocks in the ocean floor are found near a(an) _____.

4. The seismic waves that compress and expand the ground are called _____ waves.

5. The mineral pyrite has a metallic _____.

Short Answer

In complete sentences, write the answers to the questions on the lines provided.

1. How is the streak of a mineral obtained?

   _____

   _____

   _____

2. Describe the physical properties of the three layers of the mantle.

   _____

   _____

   _____

3. What is the difference between how an intrusive rock and an extrusive rock forms?

   _____

   _____

   _____

4. Why did most geologists initially reject Alfred Wegener's hypothesis of continental drift?

   _____

   _____

   _____

   _____

   _____

5. Use Figure 22-1 to determine when the P waves and S waves reached a seismograph station located 40 km from the earthquake epicenter.

_____

_____

_____

Using Science Skills

Use the diagram to answer each question. Write the answers on a separate sheet of paper.

Figure 22-1

1. Interpreting Graphics In Figure 22-2, what process is occurring in the area labeled D, and what feature will result at C?

2. Interpreting Graphics In Figure 22-2, what is occurring at A?

3. Interpreting Graphics In Figure 22-2, what is occurring at the feature labeled B?

4. Using Models Use Figure 22-2 to identify where new crust is being created and where it is being destroyed. Give the letter on the diagram and the terms used to describe these areas.

Figure 22-2

5. Classifying In Figure 22-4, what type of plate boundary is illustrated at E?

Essay

Write the answers to each question on a separate sheet of paper.

1. How does the subduction of an oceanic plate result in the formation of a volcano?

2. Describe the rock cycle.

3. Use plate tectonics to explain where mountains form.

4. How can earthquakes be used to map the location of a plate boundary?

5. Your teacher provides you with two white mineral samples. One is quartz and one is calcite. Describe the tests you could use to identify the samples.

Multiple Choice

Write the letter that best answers the question or completes the statement on the line provided.

_____ 1. The study of Earth's composition, structure, and history is called
  a. seismology.   **b.** physics.
  c. chemistry.   **d.** geology.

_____ 2. The three main layers of Earth's interior are the
  a. crust, core, and lithosphere.
  b. crust, mantle, and core.
  c. mantle, inner core, and outer core.
  d. crust, mantle, and aesthenosphere.

_____ 3. A naturally occurring, inorganic solid with a crystal structure and a characteristic chemical composition is a
  a. rock.   **b.** fossil.
  c. mineral.   **d.** piece of granite.

_____ 4. Rocks are classified as
  a. sandstone, limestone, or granite.
  b. organic, intrusive, or clastic.
  c. igneous, metamorphic, or sedimentary.
  d. sedimentary, intrusive, or metamorphic.

_____ 5. A series of processes in which rocks are continuously changed from one type to another is called
  a. a volcanic eruption.   **b.** the rock cycle.
  c. geology.   **d.** melting.

_____ 6. The hypothesis that the continents move slowly over Earth's surface and once were joined into one supercontinent is called
  a. plate tectonics.   **b.** continental drift.
  c. sea-floor spreading.   **d.** subduction.

_____ 7. New ocean crust is formed along
  a. mid-ocean ridges.   **b.** subduction zones.
  c. mountain belts.   **d.** trenches.

_____ 8. Plates slide pass each other, and crust is neither created nor destroyed at a
  a. convergent boundary.   **b.** divergent boundary.
  c. mid-ocean ridge.   **d.** transform boundary.

_____ 9. What is a break in a rock mass along which movement occurs?
  a. fold   **b.** earthquake
  c. fault   **d.** epicenter

_____10. What is the name of the location within Earth where an earthquake begins?
   a. fold   **b.** focus   **c.** epicenter   **d.** core

_____11. The amount of energy released by an earthquake is measured on the
   a. Richter scale.
   b. moment magnitude scale.
   c. modified Mercalli scale.
   d. seismic scale.

_____12. The area where magma collects inside a volcano before an eruption is called
   a. the crater.   **b.** a caldera.
   c. a vent.   **d.** the magma chamber.

_____13. What determines whether a volcano erupts quietly or explosively?
   a. the size of the volcano
   b. the age of the volcano
   c. the characteristics of the magma
   d. the magnitude of nearby earthquakes

_____14. Shield volcanoes are produced by
   a. explosive eruptions of lava and ash.
   b. quiet eruptions of lava.
   c. explosive eruptions of ash and cinders.
   d. quiet eruptions that alternate with explosive eruptions.

_____15. The largest type of intrusive igneous feature is a
   a. sill.   **b.** dike.   **c.** volcanic neck.   **d.** batholith.

Completion

Complete each statement on the line provided.

1. The study of the composition, structure, and the history of Earth is called _____.

2. The crust and upper mantle together form the

   _____.

3. The color of the powder a mineral leaves on an unglazed porcelain tile is called the mineral's _____.

4. Igneous rocks that form at Earth's surface are called

   _____ rocks.

5. The process by which oceanic plates sink into the mantle through a trench is called _____.

6. The sinking of dense slabs of lithosphere and

   _____ from within Earth drive the mantle convection current.

7. In Figure 22-1, the P wave will reach a seismograph located 40 kilometers from the earthquake epicenter in _____ seconds.

8. A(an) _____ is a device that is used to detect and record seismic waves.

9. A(an) _____ is the bowl-shaped pit at the top of a volcano.

10. A(an) _____ volcano is created by alternating lava flows and explosive eruptions.

Figure 22-1

Short Answer

In complete sentences, write the answers to the questions on the lines provided.

1. By what three ways can metamorphic rocks form?

_____

_____

_____

2. What theory explains how Earth's plates form and move?

_____

_____

_____

_____

3. What three factors determine magma viscosity?

_____

_____

_____

4. How do calderas form?

_____

_____

_____

_____

_____

5. In what two types of locations do most volcanoes occur?

_____

_____

_____

_____

Using Science Skills

Use the diagram to answer each question. Write the answers on a separate sheet of paper.

Figure 22-2

1. **Classifying** What type of rock would fit into Figure 22-2 at the location shown by the letter F?

2. **Interpreting Graphics** In Figure 22-2, what processes are represented by the arrow labeled A?

3. **Interpreting Graphics** In Figure 22-2, what process is represented by the arrow labeled E?

4. **Drawing Conclusions** Use Figure 22-2 to describe how an igneous rock could turn into a sedimentary rock and then into a metamorphic rock.

5. **Using Models** Use Figure 22-2 to describe the process involved in the formation of a sedimentary rock.

Chapter 23   Earth's Surface

Multiple Choice

Write the letter that best answers the question or completes the statement on the line provided.

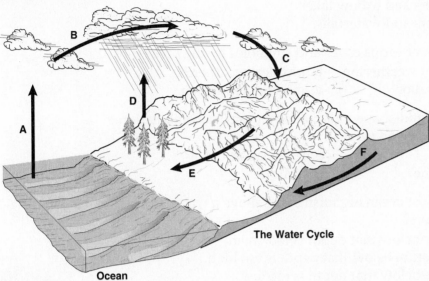

The Water Cycle

Ocean

Figure 23-1

_____ **1.** In Figure 23-1, what process does the arrow labeled A represent?
 a. transpiration   **b.** condensation
 c. evaporation   **d.** precipitation

_____ **2.** Which processes are involved in erosion?
 a. precipitation, evaporation, and condensation
 b. weathering, runoff, and transpiration
 c. weathering, evaporation, and runoff
 d. weathering, the force of gravity, and wind

_____ **3.** Which of the following rock types and conditions would result in the highest rate of chemical weathering?
 a. granite in a cold and dry area
 b. limestone in a hot and rainy area
 c. slate in a hot and rainy area
 d. granite in a hot and dry area

_____ **4.** Tilted telephone poles and fences curving in a downward direction on a hillside are evidence of
 a. a landslide. **b.** a mudflow. **c.** a slump. **d.** creep.

_____ **5.** Meanders, V-shaped valleys, and oxbow lakes are all features formed by
 a. glaciers.   **b.** water erosion.
 c. water deposition. **d.** groundwater erosion.

_____ 6. The portion of a stream that flows through gently sloping flood plains is often characterized by
     a. V-shaped valleys and waterfalls.
     b. steep valleys and rapids.
     c. meanders and oxbow lakes.
     d. meanders and waterfalls.

_____ 7. Groundwater forms caves and sinkholes by the process of
     a. chemical weathering.   **b.** physical weathering.
     c. condensation.   **d.** mineral deposition.

_____ 8. What pyramid-shaped glacial formation is a combination of several connected ridges?
     a. a horn   **b.** a U-shaped valley
     c. a moraine   **d.** a cirque

_____ 9. Why do most ocean organisms live above a water depth of 500 meters?
     a. Pressure below that depth is too great.
     b. Temperature below that depth is too high.
     c. Pressure below that depth is too low.
     d. Light below that depth is too bright.

_____ 10. What type of ocean current brings cold water from the deep ocean to the surface?
     a. a density current   **b.** upwelling
     c. a surface current   **d.** a current caused by wind

_____ 11. Which of the following is an example of a feature caused by wave erosion?
     a. a delta   **b.** an alluvial fan   **c.** a sea stack   **d.** a spit

_____ 12. Geologists could use which of the following to compare the age of sedimentary rock layers in Bryce Canyon with sedimentary rock layers in the Grand Canyon?
     a. radioactive isotopes   **b.** index fossils
     c. relative dating   **d.** all of the above

_____ 13. When did the first land plants and animals appear in the fossil record?
     a. in the Mesozoic Era
     b. in the Paleozoic Era
     c. during the Triassic period
     d. during the Carboniferous period

Completion

Complete each statement on the line provided.

1. When a stream flows out of a mountain range onto a flat area of land, it deposits sediments in a(an) _____.

2. The carbonic acid that is involved in the formation of caves is formed when rainwater combines with _____ in the air.

3. The _____ is a gently sloping plain covered with shallow water along the edges of continents.

4. In mountainous areas, valley glaciers cut _____ valleys.

5. Wave erosion is caused by abrasion and the _____ of waves.

Short Answer

In complete sentences, write the answers to the questions on the lines provided.

1. What are the processes that make up the water cycle?

   _____

   _____

   _____

   _____

   _____

2. Compare and contrast weathering and erosion.

   _____

   _____

   _____

   _____

   _____

3. How are landslides and mudflows alike?

   _____

   _____

   _____

   _____

   _____

4. Describe three ways that wind erosion moves sediment.

   _____

   _____

   _____

   _____

5. Describe how a glacier erodes the land.

_____

_____

_____

_____

Using Science Skills

Use the diagram to answer each question. Write the answers on a separate sheet of paper.

1. **Inferring** Which rock layer is the youngest layer shown in Figure 23-2?

2. **Analyzing Data** In Figure 23-2, would a fossil in layer D be younger or older than fossils found in layer B?

3. **Analyzing Data** In Figure 23-2, is the fault older or younger than the dike? Explain.

4. **Interpreting Graphics** In Figure 23-2, on either side of the fault, which rock layers were a single layer before the faulting?

5. **Drawing Conclusions** In Figure 23-2, what can be concluded about the relative ages of the rock layers below layer F? What can be concluded about the absolute ages of these layers?

Figure 23-2

Essay

Write the answers to each question on a separate sheet of paper.

1. Describe the two types of glaciers.

2. Explain how a stream transports sediment of various sizes.

3. Describe the journey of a water molecule through the water cycle.

4. Describe and discuss what causes surface currents and deep currents in the ocean.

5. In order to be useful, an index fossil must be easy to identify, have been widespread, and lived during a short, well-defined period of time. Explain why each of these three factors is important to the usefulness of index fossils in the relative dating of sedimentary rocks.

Chapter 23   Earth's Surface   **Chapter Test B**

Multiple Choice

Write the letter that best answers the question or completes the statement on the line provided.

_____ **1.** In the water cycle, the process that changes a liquid into a gas is called
   a. transpiration.   **b.** evaporation.
   c. condensation.   **d.** precipitation.

_____ **2.** Most of Earth's liquid fresh water is found in
   a. groundwater.   **b.** lakes and streams.
   c. reservoirs.   **d.** glaciers.

_____ **3.** A permeable layer of rock that is saturated with water is called a(an)
   a. water table.   **b.** lake.   **c.** watershed.   **d.** aquifer.

_____ **4.** Which of the following is an example of erosion?
   a. to wear down and carry away rock and soil through the force of gravity
   b. to wear down and carry away rock and soil through the action of wind
   c. to wear down and carry away rock and soil through the action of water
   d. all of the above

_____ **5.** Which of the following is NOT an agent of chemical weathering?
   a. rainwater   **b.** oxidation
   c. frost wedging   **d.** carbonic acid

_____ **6.** A rapid mass movement of large amounts of rock and soil down a slope is called a
   a. landslide.   **b.** slump.   **c.** creep.   **d.** mudflow.

_____ **7.** A stream's ability to erode depends mainly on
   a. its temperature.
   b. the size of the sediment in the stream.
   c. its speed.
   d. the shape of its valley.

_____ **8.** A sediment deposit formed when a stream flows into a lake or the ocean is called a(an)
   a. alluvial fan.   **b.** delta.   **c.** meander.   **d.** natural levee.

_____ **9.** Caves are formed by erosion from
   a. glaciers.   **b.** streams.   **c.** wind.   **d.** groundwater.

_____**10.** Unsorted sediment deposited by a glacier is called
   a. a cirque.   **b.** till.   **c.** a horn.   **d.** an erratic.

____11. Wind erodes the land by
  a. deflation and oxidation.
  b. abrasion and chemical weathering.
  c. deflation and plucking.
  d. deflation and abrasion.

____12. Deposits formed from windblown dust are called
  a. moraines.   b. dunes.   c. loess.   d. cirques.

____13. Which of the following describes the changing conditions in the ocean as depth increases?
  a. pressure increases, light decreases, and temperature decreases
  b. pressure decreases, light decreases, and temperature decreases
  c. pressure increases, light increases, and temperature decreases
  d. pressure increases, light increases, and temperature increases

____14. Surface currents in the ocean are caused by
  a. deep upwelling.
  b. salinity changes with depth.
  c. density differences of ocean water.
  d. wind blowing across the ocean surface.

____15. What is the process that moves sand along a shore?
  a. abrasion   b. hydraulic action
  c. a spit   d. longshore drift

____16. The absolute age of an igneous rock found on a beach can be determined by using
  a. radioactive isotopes.
  b. fossils.
  c. the law of superposition.
  d. relative dating.

____17. The Triassic, Jurassic, and Cretaceous periods are divisions of
  a. Precambrian time.   b. the Cenozoic Era.
  c. the Paleozoic Era.   d. the Mesozoic Era.

Completion

Complete each statement on the line provided.

1. A rock that allows water to flow through it is said to be
   _____.

2. Fresh water on Earth occurs in lakes, ponds, rivers, streams, in groundwater, in the atmosphere as water vapor, and in _____.

3. _____ is the process by which rocks are chemically altered or physically broken down into fragments at or near Earth's surface.

4. The main agent of chemical weathering is _____.

5. Slumping, landslides, mudflows, and _____ are all forms of mass movement.

6. _____ is the process in which particles move in a stream by bouncing along the bottom.

7. A(An) _____ glacier is a thick sheet of ice that covers large areas of land.

8. Deposits of windblown dust are called _____.

9. The process by which sand is moved along a shore is called _____.

10. Humans evolved during the _____ Era.

Short Answer

In complete sentences, write the answers to the questions on the lines provided.

1. What are three common features of fast-moving streams in mountainous areas?

   _____
   _____
   _____

2. What are two features formed by deposition that are often found in caves?

   _____
   _____

3. Describe the changes in amount of light, temperature, and pressure as depth in the ocean increases.

   _____
   _____
   _____
   _____
   _____
   _____
   _____

4. List at least four agents of erosion.

_____

_____

_____

_____

5. What are the four largest divisions of the geologic time scale?

_____

_____

_____

_____

Using Science Skills

Use the diagram to answer each question. Write the answers on a separate sheet of paper.

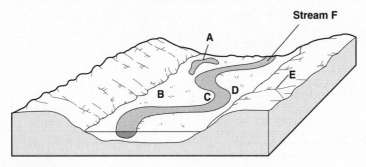

Figure 23-1

1. **Inferring** In Figure 23-1, is the stream flow moving faster at point C or at point D? Explain your answer.

2. **Interpreting Graphics** What is the feature labeled A in Figure 23-1?

3. **Inferring** In Figure 23-1, what process is occurring at C? What process is occurring at D?

4. **Interpreting Graphics** Use Figure 23-1 to describe the area that forms the floodplain for stream F.

5. **Inferring** In Figure 23-1, what are the smaller streams, which are labeled E, called?

Multiple Choice

Write the letter that best answers the question or completes the statement on the line provided.

_____ **1.** As altitude increases,
   a. air pressure decreases and density increases.
   b. air pressure increases and density decreases.
   c. air pressure and density increase.
   d. air pressure and density decrease.

_____ **2.** The ozone layer is located in the
   a. lower troposphere.   **b.** lower thermosphere.
   c. upper ionosphere.   **d.** upper stratosphere.

_____ **3.** As Earth completes one orbit around the sun, it has completed one
   a. rotation.   **b.** year.   **c.** revolution.   **d.** both b and c

_____ **4.** Which of the following lists all the zones in the correct order, starting at the North Pole and ending at the South Pole?
   a. polar, temperate, tropic, polar
   b. polar, temperate, tropic, temperate, polar
   c. polar, tropic, temperate, polar
   d. polar, tropic, temperate, tropic, polar

_____ **5.** Earth's atmosphere is heated mainly by
   a. heat that travels directly from the sun.
   b. visible light as it passes through the air.
   c. reflected sunlight.
   d. energy reradiated by Earth's surface.

_____ **6.** The daily breezes that occur in a city that is located near a large body of water are examples of
   a. local winds.   **b.** monsoons.
   c. global winds.   **d.** westerlies.

_____ **7.** Low, flat layers of clouds that often cover much of the sky and produce steady and widespread rain are
   a. cumulonimbus clouds. **b.** cirrus clouds.
   c. nimbostratus clouds.   **d.** altostratus clouds.

_____ **8.** Round, solid pieces of ice more than 5 millimeters in diameter fall as
   a. hail.   **b.** sleet.   **c.** snow.   **d.** freezing rain.

_____ **9.** Which of the following air masses forms over land north of 50° north latitude?
   a. maritime polar   **b.** temperate continental
   c. continental polar   **d.** continental tropical

_____**10.** A cold front forms when a cold air mass
    a. collides with a warm air mass and pushes the warm air up.
    b. collides with a warm air mass and slides over the warm air.
    c. collides with another cold air mass.
    d. stops moving over a particular area.

_____**11.** Which of the following is a characteristic of an anticyclone?
    a. has a center of high pressure
    b. has clockwise winds in the Northern Hemisphere
    c. is generally associated with clear weather
    d. all of the above

_____**12.** A small, intense storm formed when a vertical cylinder of rotating air develops is a
    a. thunderstorm. **b.** tornado. **c.** monsoon. **d.** hurricane.

_____**13.** Lines on a weather map that connect points that have the same air temperature are called
    a. millibars.   **b.** isobars.   **c.** isotherms.   **d.** front lines.

_____**14.** Which of the following factors affect a region's temperature?
    a. latitude and altitude
    b. distance from large bodies of water
    c. ocean currents
    d. all of the above

_____**15.** Which of the following climate changes may be affected by human activities?
    a. ice age **b.** El Niño **c.** global warming **d.** monsoon

Completion

Complete each statement on the line provided.

1. Plants need _____ from the air for photosynthesis, and many animals need _____ from the air to breathe.

2. Of the four layers of the atmosphere, the _____ has the hottest temperatures.

3. On the two days each year when the sun is directly overhead at noon at latitude 23.5° north or 23.5° south, a _____ occurs.

4. Air spirals in toward the center of a cyclone but flows away from the center of a(an) _____.

5. _____ is a short-term variation in climate that is caused by a change in the normal direction of winds, which causes ocean currents to shift direction.

Name _____ Class _____ Date _____

Short Answer

In complete sentences, write the answers to the questions on the lines provided.

1. Describe what the temperatures on Earth would be like during the day and at night if the atmosphere did not exist.

   _____

   _____

   _____

   _____

2. What is the difference between sleet and freezing rain?

   _____

   _____

   _____

   _____

3. How does a thunderstorm form?

   _____

   _____

   _____

   _____

Front A   Front B   Front C   Front D

Figure 24-1

4. What is the name of each type of front represented by the symbols in Figure 24-1?

   _____

   _____

   _____

   _____

5. What are three factors that affect a region's pattern of precipitation?

   _____

   _____

   _____

   _____

Using Science Skills

Use the diagram to answer each question. Write the answers on a separate sheet of paper.

Figure 24-2

1. **Inferring** What factors are used to classify the air masses in Figure 24-2?

2. **Classifying** Based on their locations in Figure 24-2, name the types of air masses represented by A and D and describe the characteristics of each.

3. **Comparing and Contrasting** Based on their locations in Figure 24-2, name the types of air masses represented by B and C. How are they similar, and how are they different?

4. **Predicting** Based on Figure 24-2, what would you expect weather conditions to be like in the southeastern section of the United States at the time this map was drawn? Explain your answer.

5. **Applying Concepts** What does the symbol L represent in 24-2, and what type of weather system is it the center of? What are the characteristics of this weather system?

Essay

Write the answers to each question on a separate sheet of paper.

1. Explain why temperate zones in the Northern Hemisphere and the Southern Hemisphere have the same seasons but are six months apart.

2. What are trade winds and what causes them? How are trade winds in the Northern Hemisphere different from those in the Southern Hemisphere?

3. What are humidity, relative humidity, and dew point? Explain what happens to each if the temperature of the air decreases.

4. Compare the weather that might occur in an area as a warm front passes through, after the warm front has passed through, as a cold front passes through, and after the cold front has passed through.

5. What information can meteorologists obtain from Doppler radar, automated weather stations, and weather satellites? How do high-speed computers help meteorologists?

Multiple Choice

Write the letter that best answers the question or completes the statement on the line provided.

_____ **1.** What gas makes up about 78 percent of dry air?
  a. oxygen   **b.** nitrogen
  c. hydrogen   **d.** carbon dioxide

_____ **2.** Most weather takes place in the
  a. stratosphere.   **b.** thermosphere.
  c. troposphere.   **d.** mesosphere.

_____ **3.** Day and night are caused by Earth's
  a. rotation. **b.** revolution. **c.** orbit. **d.** tilt.

_____ **4.** Which region usually has temperatures cooler than
  temperatures near the equator?
  a. tropic zone   **b.** polar zone
  c. temperate zone **d.** both b and c

_____ **5.** About how much of the solar energy that reaches Earth
  passes through the atmosphere and is absorbed by the
  surface of Earth?
  a. 20 percent   **b.** 30 percent
  c. 50 percent   **d.** 80 percent

_____ **6.** Which of the following is NOT an example of a global
  wind?
  a. westerlies   **b.** trade winds
  c. polar easterlies **d.** sea breezes

_____ **7.** A cloud is a dense, visible mass of
  a. tiny water droplets. **b.** ice crystals.
  c. water vapor.   **d.** both a and b

_____ **8.** Which of the following forms of precipitation falls as a
  liquid?
  a. rain **b.** freezing rain **c.** hail **d.** both a and b

_____ **9.** A maritime tropical air mass that affects weather in the
  Unites States might form over
  a. the Gulf of Mexico. **b.** Mexico.
  c. Canada.   **d.** the North Atlantic ocean.

_____**10.** What type of front forms when two unlike air masses form a
  boundary but neither is moving?
  a. warm **b.** cold **c.** stationary **d.** occluded

_____**11.** Which of the following is a weather system with a center of
  low pressure?
  a. cyclone **b.** anticyclone **c.** warm front **d.** cold front

_____**12.** A tropical storm with sustained winds of at least
119 kilometers per hour is called a
a. tornado. **b.** thunderstorm. **c.** monsoon. **d.** hurricane.

Front A	Front B	Front C	Front D

Figure 24-1

_____**13.** Which of the symbols in Figure 24-1 represents a warm
front?
a. Front A   **b.** Front B   **c.** Front C   **d.** Front D

_____**14.** A description of the pattern of weather over many years is a
region's
a. weather forecast.   **b.** air mass.
c. climate.   **d.** weather system.

_____**15.** An example of a long-term climate change that occurs
naturally is
a. an ice age.   **b.** an El Niño.
c. global warming.   **d.** the greenhouse effect.

Completion

Complete each statement on the line provided.

1. The _____ forms a protective boundary between
Earth and space and provides conditions that are suitable for life.

2. The seasons are caused by the _____ of Earth's
_____ as Earth moves around the sun.

3. The latitude of the equator is _____, and the
latitude of the North Pole is _____.

4. Wind is air blowing from an area of _____
pressure to an area of _____ pressure.

5. The three basic cloud forms are _____,
_____, and _____.

6. Rain, sleet, and snow are types of _____.

7. The sharply defined boundary that forms where two unlike air
masses meet is called a(an) _____.

8. A major type of storm associated with lightning, strong winds,
and heavy rain or hail is called a(an) _____.

9. _____ works by bouncing radio waves off particles
of precipitation in moving storms and then measuring the
frequency of the waves that return.

10. The two main factors that determine a region's climate are
_____ and _____.

Name _____ Class _____ Date _____

Short Answer

In complete sentences, write the answers to the questions on the lines provided.

1. List the four layers of the atmosphere, starting with the layer closest to Earth.

   _____

   _____

   _____

   _____

2. Why is Earth generally warmer near the equator and colder toward the poles?

   _____

   _____

   _____

   _____

3. What is the greenhouse effect?

   _____

   _____

   _____

   _____

   _____

4. What weather is associated with a cyclone?

   _____

   _____

   _____

   _____

   _____

5. What are some ways that people could limit the effects of global warming? Explain how these ways would help.

   _____

   _____

   _____

   _____

   _____

   _____

Using Science Skills

Use the diagram to answer each question. Write the answers on a separate sheet of paper.

Cold front   **Occluded front**   **Warm front**

Figure 24-2

1. **Inferring** What causes clouds to form in the three fronts in Figure 24-2?

2. **Interpreting Graphics** Explain what is happening to the two air masses in the cold front in Figure 24-2.

3. **Comparing and Contrasting** Based on your observations of Figure 24-2, how are a cold front and a warm front alike?

4. **Comparing and Contrasting** Based on your observations of Figure 24-2, how are a cold front and a warm front different?

5. **Interpreting Graphics** What has happened to the warm air mass in the occluded front in Figure 24-3?

Multiple Choice

Write the letter that best answers the question or completes the statement on the line provided.

_____ **1.** Which of the following is the most likely reason that ancient observers believed that Earth was the center of the universe?
   a. The Earth seemed to move on its axis.
   b. Earth's motions are only recently known because of high-powered telescopes.
   c. Objects in the sky appear to circle around Earth.
   d. Ancient observers believed the universe was stationary.

_____ **2.** Which of the following helps explain why the planets remain in motion around the sun?
   a. density   **b.** gravity   **c.** inertia   **d.** both b and c

_____ **3.** What led to the discovery of three more planets than those that the ancient observers knew about?
   a. the invention of the telescope in 1600
   b. the Hubble telescope launched in 1990
   c. space missions in the Apollo program
   d. observations by *Sputnik 1* in 1957

_____ **4.** Which of the following are currently operating the space station?
   a. Soviet cosmonauts
   b. a cooperative team of scientists from 16 countries
   c. American astronauts
   d. a cooperative team of scientists from Russia and the United States

_____ **5.** How might a nitrogen-oxygen atmosphere on the moon affect the range of temperatures on the moon?
   a. An atmosphere might hold heat in, making the moon very hot.
   b. An atmosphere might block heat radiating from the sun, making the moon very cold.
   c. An atmosphere might moderate temperatures, making them more even, such as on Earth.
   d. An atmosphere would have no effect on the range of temperatures on the moon.

_____ **6.** What is meant by the statement "The moon is geologically dead"?
   a. The moon has little erosion and no plate movement.
   b. The moon is devoid of living things.
   c. The moon has no atmosphere.
   d. The moon has no air currents or weather patterns.

_____ **7.** Soon after the collision with Earth, the materials that eventually formed the moon
  a. orbited Earth in a large, irregular clump.
  b. were bits of Earth's mantle encircling Earth.
  c. were mostly broken pieces of the object that hit Earth.
  d. none of the above

_____ **8.** Study Figure 25-1. Suppose you are an astronaut on the side of the moon facing Earth during a total lunar eclipse. Which would you see as you look toward Earth?

Figure 25-1

NOT TO SCALE

  a. Nothing; there would be total darkness.
  b. The normal view; there is always reflected light from the moon's surface.
  c. You could not see the sun because Earth blocks its light.
  d. The light from the sun behind Earth would be blinding.

_____ **9.** Which characteristic of the inner planets increases with increasing distance from the sun?
  a. equatorial diameter   **b.** period of rotation
  c. average temperature   **d.** period of revolution

_____ **10.** What evidence suggests that asteroids are like rubble heaps and not solid like rock?
  a. They are held together by weak gravity.
  b. They have not shattered on impact with other objects.
  c. They mostly have irregular shapes.
  d. They are remnants of a shattered planet.

_____ **11.** Which characteristic of the gas giants decreases with increasing distance from the sun?
  a. equatorial diameter   **b.** period of rotation
  c. number of moons   **d.** both a and c

_____ **12.** What is the difference between a meteoroid and a meteorite?
  a. A meteoroid is made of metal; a meteorite is made of rock.
  b. A meteoroid is larger than a meteorite.
  c. A meteoroid is located in space; it becomes a meteorite when it hits Earth.
  d. A meteoroid has a tail like a comet; a meteorite burns up in Earth's atmosphere.

_____**13.** In astronomical units (AU), what is the approximate distance of the outer edge of the Oort cloud from the outer edge of the Kuiper belt?
a. 100 AU
b. 20,000 AU
c. 30,000 AU
d. more than 49,000 AU

_____**14.** In the formation of our solar system, nearly all of the mass of the solar nebula became
a. the terrestrial planets.
b. the gas giants.
c. the sun.
d. the Oort cloud.

_____**15.** Which evidence provides support for the nebular theory?
a. Scientists have observed the formation of a distant solar system.
b. The nebular theory has been proven mathematically.
c. Astronomers have observed protoplanetary disks around distant newborn stars.
d. none of the above

Completion

Complete each statement on the line provided.

1. Because Earth's orbit around the sun is an ellipse, and Earth is not always the same distance from the sun, one AU is defined as the _____ distance from Earth to the sun.

2. All of the planets in our solar system have _____ with the exception of Mercury and Venus.

3. A person weighing 600 newtons (about 120 pounds) on Earth would weigh about _____ newtons on the moon.

4. The _____ belt contains perhaps tens of thousands of objects orbiting within about 100 AU of the sun.

5. The difference in the composition of the terrestrial planets and the gas giants can be explained by the different condensation _____ in the regions near and far from the sun during the formation of the solar system.

Short Answer

In complete sentences, write the answers to the questions on the lines provided.

1. What is the fundamental difference between Ptolemy's view of the universe and that of Aristarchus?

_____

2. What is the ecliptic plane?

_____

3. What is the difference between a full moon and a new moon?

_____

_____

_____

_____

4. Explain why Mars is called the most Earthlike of all the other planets.

_____

_____

_____

_____

5. Explain the odd and irregular shapes of most asteroids.

_____

_____

6. Explain why the gas giants are many times larger than Earth.

_____

_____

_____

_____

Using Science Skills

Use the diagram to answer each question. Write the answers on a separate sheet of paper.

Figure 25-2

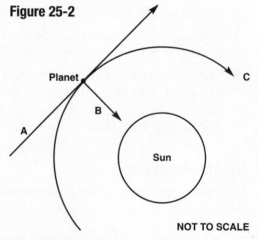

1. Applying Concepts If a planet is orbiting along path C in Figure 25-2, explain why it stays in orbit. Refer to Figure 25-2 in your explanation.

2. Inferring Based on Figure 25-2, describe the path that the planet would follow if the sun did not exist. Why would this happen?

3. Formulating Hypotheses In Figure 25-2, why would you expect B to lie in the planet's orbital plane?

4. Drawing Conclusions Saturn is the least dense of all the planets. Why does Saturn remain in orbit instead of drifting away in space or crashing into the sun?

5. Applying Concepts The period of revolution of the planet shown in Figure 25-2 is 1.88 Earth years. What planet is it? How does the period of an asteroid in the asteroid belt compare with the period of the planet shown?

Essay

Write the answers to each question on a separate sheet of paper.

1. Describe two kinds of technology in use today for the exploration of space.

2. Explain why Earth is currently in little danger of being hit by a Mars-sized object.

3. Compare the four largest moons of Jupiter.

4. Describe the tails of a comet.

5. What three criteria must any theory of the origin of the solar system satisfy? What theory satisfies all three?

Chapter 25   The Solar System   **Chapter Test B**

Multiple Choice

*Write the letter that best answers the question or completes the statement on
the line provided.*

_____ **1.** In a diagram depicting the solar system as heliocentric, what
is located at the center?
a. Earth   **b.** the sun   **c.** the moon   **d.** Mars

_____ **2.** The orbit of a planet around the sun is a(an)
a. ellipse.   **b.** straight line.   **c.** circle.   **d.** parabola.

_____ **3.** Which of the following objects does NOT orbit directly
around the sun?
a. planets   **b.** comets   **c.** moons   **d.** all of the above

_____ **4.** Who was the first American in space?
a. Yuri Gargarin   **b.** Alan Shepard
c. Chuck Yeager   **d.** Neil Armstrong

_____ **5.** Why does Earth's moon have no atmosphere?
a. The average temperature is too high.
b. There are no plants to release oxygen.
c. The moon is too far from Earth.
d. The moon's gravity is too weak to hold onto gas
molecules.

_____ **6.** On the moon, maria are
a. meteoroid craters.   **b.** low, flat plains.
c. rough mountains.   **d.** lunar seas filled with water.

_____ **7.** The moon most likely formed
a. from a collision with a Mars-sized object.
b. in another region of space and drifted toward Earth
c. from material in the solar system that came together.
d. in the same way as Earth was formed

_____ **8.** Ocean tides are the result of
a. the rotation of the Earth.
b. the sun's gravitational pull on Earth.
c. changes in Earth's orbital position around the sun.
d. differences in both the sun's and moon's gravitational
pull on Earth.

_____ **9.** The four terrestrial planets are so called because they
a. are the nearest planets to Earth.
b. were all once part of Earth.
c. are similar in structure to Earth.
d. can all be seen from Earth without a telescope.

_____ **10.** Asteroids are mainly found
    a. in the asteroid belt beyond Mars.
    b. in orbit around Jupiter.
    c. throughout the solar system.
    d. beyond the farthest known planet.

_____ **11.** Which of the gas giants has the largest diameter?
    a. Jupiter   **b.** Uranus   **c.** Saturn   **d.** Neptune

_____ **12.** Comets are made mostly of
    a. iron.   **b.** ice and rock.
    c. hydrogen and helium.   **d.** methane.

_____ **13.** Which of the following is a sparse sphere of comets that
    surrounds the sun and planets?
    a. the asteroid belt   **b.** the Kuiper belt
    c. the Oort cloud   **d.** none of the above

_____ **14.** According to the nebula theory, the solar system
    formed from
    a. accretion of protoplanets.
    b. a large, thin cloud of dust and gas.
    c. colliding planetesimals.
    d. all of the above

_____ **15.** Which of the following statements explains why the
    terrestrial planets are small and rocky instead of large and
    less dense like the gas giants?
    a. The inner planets were exposed to much higher
       temperatures.
    b. Ice-forming compounds vaporize at high temperatures.
    c. Rock-forming materials can condense at high
       temperatures.
    d. all of the above

Completion

Complete each statement on the line provided.

1. The force of gravity that the sun exerts on a planet is directed
_____ .

2. The beginning of the "space race" occurred when the
_____ launched the first artificial satellite in 1957.

3. Because there is no _____ on the moon, any liquid
water would have evaporated long ago.

4. The model of the universe in which Earth is stationary is the
_____ model.

5. The total lunar eclipse shown in Figure 25-1 is occurring during the

   _____ phase of the moon.

6. The length of a planet's day is determined by its

   _____.

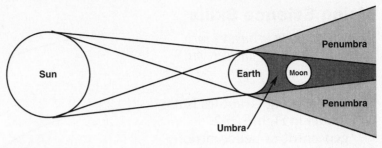

Figure 25-1

NOT TO SCALE

7. The large, irregular objects mostly located between Mars and Jupiter are

   _____.

8. Icy objects that mostly travel in long, elliptical orbits around the sun are _____.

9. The great reservoir of comets beyond the Kuiper belt is called the

   _____.

10. The material that formed our solar system originated from a solar

    _____.

Short Answer

In complete sentences, write the answers to the questions on the lines provided.

1. What are the components of our solar system?

   _____

   _____

   _____

2. Who was the first human to step onto the moon?

   _____

3. What caused most craters on the moon?

   _____

   _____

4. What is the composition of the Kuiper belt?

   _____

   _____

5. What is the theoretical source of the solar nebula from which our solar system formed?

   _____

   _____

Using Science Skills

Use the diagram to answer each question. Write the answers on a separate sheet of paper.

1. **Interpreting Graphics** Is the model in Figure 25-2 geocentric or heliocentric? Explain how you know.

2. **Classifying** In Figure 25-2, which components of the solar system are indicated by orbits 1– 9? Name each component in order from the sun, and classify each according to type.

3. **Using Models** Look at Figure 25-2. Where would you mark the position of the asteroid belt?

4. **Applying Concepts** During the time the solar system was forming, which region had sufficiently cool temperatures for ice crystals to form? Use Figure 25-2 to indicate the location.

5. **Drawing Conclusions** Given that Pluto is about 39.5 AU from the sun, where would you locate the Kuiper belt on Figure 25-2? What would be the location of the Oort cloud?

Figure 25-2

Chapter 26   Exploring the Universe   **Chapter Test A**

Multiple Choice

Write the letter that best answers the question or completes the statement on the line provided.

_____ 1. What will happen to the relative amounts of hydrogen and helium in the sun over the next few billion years?
   a. Hydrogen will increase and helium will decrease.
   b. Hydrogen will decrease and helium will increase.
   c. Both hydrogen and helium will decrease.
   d. Both hydrogen and helium will remain the same.

_____ 2. The sun remains stable over time because
   a. its supply of hydrogen is inexhaustible.
   b. the product of fusion, helium, is a stable element.
   c. the inward pull of gravity and outward push of thermal pressure are balanced.
   d. nuclear fusion is a stabilizing process.

_____ 3. The stream of electrically charged particles sent into space by the sun is called
   a. a solar flare.   **b.** a sunspot.
   c. a solar prominence.   **d.** the solar wind.

_____ 4. The parallax of a star is observed because
   a. all stars have the same apparent brightness.
   b. parallax increases with distance.
   c. stars do not move.
   d. the observer moves.

_____ 5. The apparent brightness of a star
   a. varies with the position from which it is viewed.
   b. can be calculated from its absolute brightness and mass.
   c. is greater as distance from the sun increases.
   d. is a measure of its light viewed from any position.

_____ 6. A cool, bright star would appear in which section of an H-R diagram?
   a. lower left   **b.** upper left
   c. upper right   **d.** lower right

_____ 7. Which kind of star will most likely remain on the main sequence the longest?
   a. a low-mass, red star   **b.** a yellow star like the sun
   c. a high-mass blue star   **d.** a bright white star

_____ 8. What is a pulsar?
   a. the remains of a low-mass star after it explodes
   b. a spinning neutron star emitting radio waves
   c. another name for a protostar
   d. the stage before a dying star becomes a supernova

_____ **9.** Why is studying star clusters useful?
     a. because there is such a large diversity of stars in a cluster
     b. because they are about the same age and distance from Earth
     c. because they are all about the same size and temperature
     d. because all of them are always young, bright stars

_____ **10.** Older stars are most likely found in
     a. the arms of spiral and barred-spiral galaxies.
     b. elliptical galaxies.
     c. irregular galaxies.
     d. both a and b

_____ **11.** Hubble's Law states that the speed at which a galaxy is moving away is proportional to the
     a. mass of the galaxy.
     b. number of stars in the galaxy.
     c. galaxy's distance from Earth.
     d. age of the galaxy.

_____ **12.** Which of the following provides support for the big bang theory?
     a. red shift
     b. cosmic microwave background radiation
     c. elliptical galaxies
     d. both a and b

_____ **13.** Much of the mass of the universe may be composed of
     a. electromagnetic waves.
     b. cosmic microwaves.
     c. background radiation.
     d. dark matter.

Completion

Complete each statement on the line provided.

1. Nuclear fusion within the sun takes place within the _____.

2. The apparent change in position of an object with respect to a distant background is called _____.

3. The main sequence lifetime of a star is dependent upon the star's _____.

4. A binary system in which one star passes in front of the other, blocking some light from reaching Earth is called a(an) _____ binary.

5. The observation that cosmic microwave background radiation is detected n all directions in the universe supports the hypothesis that the universe is _____.

Short Answer

*In complete sentences, write the answers to the questions on
the lines provided.*

1. In Figure 26-1, name and describe
area C and tell how it differs
from area B in the way it
transfers energy.

   _____

   _____

   _____

   _____

   _____

   _____

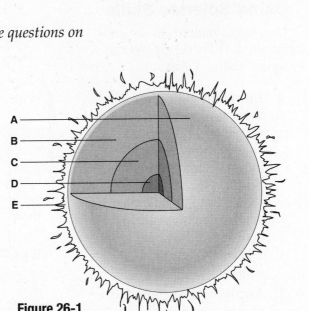

Figure 26-1

2. What characteristic of a star's spectrum do astronomers use to
determine the different elements in the star?

   _____

   _____

   _____

3. What are the very bright stars in the upper right of an H-R
diagram called?

   _____

   _____

4. What two factors cause a nebula to develop into a star?

   _____

   _____

5. How are elements other than helium produced?

   _____

   _____

   _____

   _____

6. To what do astronomers attribute the increasing rate of expansion
of the universe?

   _____

   _____

   _____

Using Science Skills

Use the diagram to answer each question. Write the answers on a separate sheet of paper.

1. **Inferring** Suppose two stars are located in region A of the H-R diagram shown in Figure 26-2. Star X appears much dimmer than Star Y as seen from Earth. Which star can be inferred to be nearer to Earth, and what other factor must be considered?

Figure 26-2

2. **Applying Concepts** How would you describe the change in the properties of stars as you move from left to right along the main sequence in the H-R diagram in Figure 26-2?

3. **Interpreting Diagrams** In which region of the H-R diagram in Figure 26-2 would you find the sun?

4. **Predicting** Use the regions of Figure 26-2 to describe the fate of the sun. Where is the sun on the diagram now? How long will it be there? What will happen to the sun when this stage ends?

5. **Classifying** Describe the classification of stars shown in Figure 26-2 that begin to fuse helium nuclei. Where are such stars located on the H-R diagram?

Essay

Write the answers to each question on a separate sheet of paper.

1. Describe the process of nuclear fusion in the sun's core.
2. What is the difference between the apparent brightness and the absolute brightness of a star?
3. The astronomer Carl Sagan once said that we are all made of "star stuff." Explain what he meant.
4. Besides shape, what is the difference between an elliptical galaxy and an irregular galaxy?
5. Discuss the hypothetical role of the amount of dark matter and dark energy in predicting the future of the universe.

Chapter 26   Exploring the Universe   **Chapter Test B**

Multiple Choice

Write the letter that best answers the question or completes the statement on the line provided.

_____ 1. The sun's energy is produced by
   a. the sun burning fuel.
   b. nuclear fission.
   c. an ordinary chemical reaction.
   d. nuclear fusion.

_____ 2. For the sun to be stable, the inward and outward forces within the sun must be
   a. in equilibrium.
   b. part of the fusion reaction.
   c. focused in the core.
   d. balanced with temperature and density.

_____ 3. Examine Figure 26-1. Which area is the convection zone?
   a. A
   b. B
   c. C
   d. D

_____ 4. The distance between stars is typically measured in
   a. light-years.
   b. kilometers.
   c. astronomical units.
   d. miles.

Figure 26-1

_____ 5. Astronomers classify stars according to their
   a. distance from Earth.
   b. color, size, and absolute brightness.
   c. age and parallax.
   d. all of the above

_____ 6. An H-R diagram
   a. is a map of the positions of the stars.
   b. graphs stars according to their size and distance.
   c. lists every known star.
   d. graphs a sample of stars according to surface temperature and absolute brightness.

_____ 7. The life cycle of a star begins with a cloud of gas and dust called a

   a. protoplanet.   **b.** constellation.   **c.** nebula.   **d.** protosun.

_____ **8.** Both high-mass and low-mass adult stars are classified as
   a. main-sequence stars.   **b.** white dwarfs.
   c. supernovas.   **d.** neutron stars.

_____ **9.** All stars remain on the main sequence
   a. until they stabilize.
   b. for about 90 percent of their lifetimes.
   c. until they become protostars.
   d. for about 10 billion years.

_____ **10.** Low-mass and medium-mass stars eventually
   a. grow into supergiants.
   b. become supernovas.
   c. become neutron stars.
   d. turn into white dwarfs.

_____ **11.** Which of the following is true about more than half of all stars?
   a. They are dying red giants.
   b. They are visible to the unaided eye.
   c. They are members of a star system.
   d. They are high-mass stars.

_____ **12.** How do open star clusters differ from associations?
   a. Associations are usually larger and have fewer stars.
   b. Open clusters are organized into constellations.
   c. Associations are usually smaller and have more stars.
   d. Open clusters typically contain loose groupings of old stars.

_____ **13.** A large group of older stars would be found in which of the following star clusters?
   a. open cluster   **b.** association
   c. globular cluster   **d.** both a and b

_____ **14.** Galaxies are classified into four groups based on their
   a. shapes.   **b.** sizes.   **c.** number of stars.   **d.** brightness.

_____ **15.** When the absorption lines of a galaxy shift toward the red end of the spectrum, it means that the galaxy is
   a. moving closer to Earth.
   b. small and young.
   c. moving away from Earth.
   d. large and old.

_____ **16.** The big bang theory explains the
   a. origin of the universe.
   b. life cycle of a star.
   c. Doppler effect.
   d. arrangement of constellations.

_____ **17.** Dark matter can be detected by its
   a. cosmic microwave background radiation.
   b. red shift.
   c. gravitational effects on visible matter.
   d. velocity.

Completion

Complete each statement on the line provided.

1. The sun's major source of fuel is _____.

2. The two forces that are balanced when a star is in equilibrium are outward pressure and _____.

3. By using a spectrograph, a star's absorption lines can identify the different _____ that a star is composed of.

4. In an H-R diagram, most stars are found in a diagonal band from the upper left to the lower right, which is called the _____.

5. A contracting cloud of dust and gas with enough mass to form a star is called a(an) _____.

6. A young star forms when the pressure from _____ supports the star against the tremendous inward pull of gravity.

7. The sun will end its life as a red giant and eventually end up as a(an) _____.

8. A group of two or more stars held together by gravity is called a(an) _____.

9. A large spherical group of older stars is called a(an) _____.

10. The theory that the universe came into being in a single moment with an enormous explosion is the _____ theory.

11. Matter that does not give off any radiation is called _____.

Short Answer

In complete sentences, write the answers to the questions on the lines provided.

1. At least how much longer is the sun expected to remain a stable main sequence star?

_____

_____

2. What is the innermost layer of the sun's atmosphere called?

_____

_____

3. Why do astronomers measure the parallax of nearby stars?

_____

_____

_____

4. How can an object's red shift tell us how fast the object is moving away from Earth?

_____

_____

_____

5. How have scientists used Hubble's Law to estimate the age of the universe?

_____

_____

_____

_____

Using Science Skills

Use the diagram to answer each question. Write the answers on a separate sheet of paper.

1. **Applying Concepts** Would you expect to find helium fusion occurring in stage F or stage G of the star shown in Figure 26-2B? Explain your answer.

2. **Using Models** Which figure—26-2A or 26-2B—models the evolution of a high-mass star? Explain how you know.

3. **Inferring** Which figure—26-2A or 26-2B—can you infer is a model of a star formed from a small nebula? Explain your answer.

4. **Interpreting Graphics** In Figure 26-2A, what is the event occurring at stage C? Explain why there are two possible outcomes (stage D and stage E).

5. **Drawing Conclusions** Relate two differences between the life cycles shown in Figure 26-2 that will allow you to conclude which star will be longer lived.

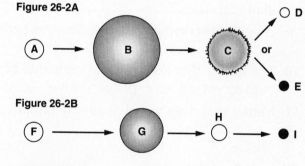

Figure 26-2A

Figure 26-2B

Figure 26-2

Unit 3   Earth and Space   **Unit Test A**

Multiple Choice

Write the letter that best answers the question or completes the statement on the line provided.

_____ **1.** Forces that shape Earth's surface can be divided into
  a. constructive and physical.
  b. constructive and destructive.
  c. chemical and destructive.
  d. chemical and physical.

_____ **2.** What is a mineral's cleavage?
  a. the resistance of a mineral to scratching
  b. a type of fracture in which a mineral breaks along regular, well-defined planes
  c. the color of a mineral's powder
  d. a type of fracture in which a mineral breaks along a curved surface

_____ **3.** Intense heat, intense pressure, or reactions with hot water can modify a pre-existing rock to form a(an)
  a. metamorphic rock.   **b.** sedimentary rock.
  c. igneous rock.   **d.** organic rock.

_____ **4.** Stress in Earth's crust is caused by
  a. folds.   **b.** plate movements.
  c. earthquakes.   **d.** faults.

_____ **5.** P waves
  a. cause Earth to vibrate in the direction of the wave's motion.
  b. cause Earth to vibrate at right angles to the direction the wave moves.
  c. travel along Earth's surface.
  d. move in a rolling motion similar to ocean waves.

_____ **6.** Geologists have inferred that Earth's outer core is liquid because
  a. P waves cannot pass through the outer core.
  b. S waves speed up in the outer core.
  c. S waves are bent downward as they travel through the outer core.
  d. S waves cannot pass through the outer core.

_____ **7.** Which of the following rock types and conditions would result in the highest rate of chemical weathering?
  a. granite in a cold and dry area
  b. limestone in a hot and rainy area
  c. slate in a hot and rainy area
  d. granite in a hot and dry area

_____ 8. Tilted telephone poles and fences curving in a downward
direction on a hillside are evidence of
a. a landslide.   b. a mudflow.
c. a slump.   d. creep.

_____ 9. Meanders, V-shaped valleys, and oxbow lakes are all
features formed by
a. glaciers.   b. water erosion.
c. water deposition.   d. groundwater erosion.

_____ 10. Which of the following is an example of a feature caused by
wave erosion?
a. a delta   b. an alluvial fan
c. a sea stack   d. a spit

_____ 11. Geologists could use which of the following to compare the
age of sedimentary rock layers in Bryce Canyon with
sedimentary rock layers in the Grand Canyon?
a. radioactive isotopes
b. index fossils c. relative dating
d. all of the above

_____ 12. When did the first land plants and animals appear in the
fossil record?
a. in the Mesozoic Era
b. in the Paleozoic Era
c. during the Triassic period
d. during the Carboniferous period

_____ 13. Which of the following lists all the zones in the correct
order, starting at the North Pole and ending at the
South Pole?
a. polar, temperate, tropic, polar
b. polar, temperate, tropic, temperate, polar
c. polar, tropic, temperate, polar
d. polar, tropic, temperate, tropic, polar

_____ 14. Earth's atmosphere is heated mainly by
a. heat that travels directly from the sun.
b. visible light as it passes through the air.
c. reflected sunlight.
d. energy reradiated by Earth's surface.

_____ 15. The daily breezes that occur in a city that is located near a
large body of water are examples of
a. local winds.   b. monsoons.
c. global winds.   d. westerlies.

_____ 16. A small, intense storm formed when a vertical cylinder of
rotating air develops is a
a. thunderstorm. b. tornado. c. monsoon. d. hurricane.

_____17. Lines on a weather map that connect points that have the same air temperature are called
   a. millibars.   **b.** isobars.   **c.** isotherms.   **d.** front lines.

_____18. Which of the following factors affect a region's temperature?
   a. latitude and altitude
   b. distance from large bodies of water
   c. ocean currents
   d. all of the above

_____19. Which of the following is the most likely reason that ancient observers believed that Earth was the center of the universe?
   a. The Earth seemed to move on its axis.
   b. Earth's motions are only recently known because of high-powered telescopes.
   c. Objects in the sky appear to circle around Earth.
   d. Ancient observers believed the universe was stationary.

_____20. Which of the following helps explain why the planets remain in motion around the sun?
   a. density   **b.** gravity
   c. inertia   **d.** both b and c

_____21. What led to the discovery of three more planets than those that the ancient observers knew about?
   a. the invention of the telescope in 1600
   b. the Hubble telescope launched in 1990
   c. space missions in the Apollo program
   d. observations by *Sputnik 1* in 1957

_____22. Which of the following are currently operating the space station?
   a. Soviet cosmonauts
   b. a cooperative team of scientists from 16 countries
   c. American astronauts
   d. a cooperative team of scientists from Russia and the United States

_____23. How might a nitrogen-oxygen atmosphere on the moon affect the range of temperatures on the moon?
   a. An atmosphere might hold heat in, making the moon very hot.
   b. An atmosphere might block heat radiating from the sun, making the moon very cold.
   c. An atmosphere might moderate temperatures, making them more even, such as on Earth.
   d. An atmosphere would have no effect on the range of temperatures on the moon.

_____ **24.** What is meant by the statement "The moon is geologically dead"?

    a. The moon has little erosion and no plate movement.

    b. The moon is devoid of living things.

    c. The moon has no atmosphere.

    d. The moon has no air currents or weather patterns.

_____ **25.** What is a pulsar?

    a. the remains of a low-mass star after it explodes

    b. a spinning neutron star emitting radio waves

    c. another name for a protostar

    d. the stage before a dying star becomes a supernova

_____ **26.** Why is studying star clusters useful?

    a. because there is such a large diversity of stars in a cluster

    b. because they are about the same age and distance from Earth

    c. because they are all about the same size and temperature

    d. because all of them are always young, bright stars

_____ **27.** Older stars are most likely found in

    a. the arms of spiral and barred-spiral galaxies.

    b. elliptical galaxies.

    c. irregular galaxies.

    d. both a and b

_____ **28.** Hubble's Law states that the speed at which a galaxy is moving away is proportional to the

    a. mass of the galaxy.

    b. number of stars in the galaxy.

    c. galaxy's distance from Earth.

    d. age of the galaxy.

_____ **29.** Which of the following provides support for the big bang theory?

    a. red shift

    b. cosmic microwave background radiation

    c. elliptical galaxies

    d. both a and b

_____ **30.** Much of the mass of the universe may be composed of

    a. electromagnetic waves.

    b. cosmic microwaves.

    c. background radiation.

    d. dark matter.

Completion

Complete each statement on the line provided.

1. The type of sedimentary rock that forms when fragments of pre-existing rocks are cemented together is called a(an) _____ rock.

2. Alfred Wegener proposed that a continent was formed by continental drift. This supercontinent was called _____.

3. Due to sea-floor spreading, the youngest rocks in the ocean floor are found near a(an) _____.

4. The seismic waves that compress and expand the ground are called _____ waves.

5. When a stream flows out of a mountain range onto a flat area of land, it deposits sediments in a(an) _____.

6. The carbonic acid that is involved in the formation of caves is formed when rainwater combines with _____ in the air.

7. The _____ is a gently sloping plain covered with shallow water along the edges of continents.

8. In mountainous areas, valley glaciers cut _____ valleys.

9. Of the four layers of the atmosphere, the _____ has the hottest temperatures.

10. On the two days each year when the sun is directly overhead at noon at latitude 23.5° north or 23.5° south, a _____ occurs.

11. Air spirals in toward the center of a cyclone but flows away from the center of a(an) _____.

12. _____ is a short-term variation in climate that is caused by a change in the normal direction of winds, which causes ocean currents to shift direction.

13. Because Earth's orbit around the sun is an ellipse, and Earth is not always the same distance from the sun, one AU is defined as the _____ distance from Earth to the sun.

14. All of the planets in our solar system have _____ with the exception of Mercury and Venus.

15. A person weighing 600 newtons (about 120 pounds) on Earth would weigh about _____ newtons on the moon.

16. The _____ belt contains perhaps tens of thousands of objects orbiting within about 100 AU of the sun.

17. Nuclear fusion within the sun takes place within the _____.

18. The apparent change in position of an object with respect to a distant background is called _____.

19. The main sequence lifetime of a star is dependent upon the star's

    _____.

20. A binary system in which one star passes in front of the other, blocking some light from reaching Earth is called a(an) _____ binary.

Short Answer

In complete sentences, write the answers to the questions on the lines provided.

1. How is the streak of a mineral obtained?

   _____

   _____

2. Describe the physical properties of the three layers of the mantle.

   _____

   _____

   _____

3. How are landslides and mudflows alike?

   _____

   _____

4. Describe three ways that wind erosion moves sediment.

   _____

   _____

   _____

   _____

5. What is the difference between sleet and freezing rain?

   _____

   _____

6. How does a thunderstorm form?

   _____

   _____

   _____

7. What is the ecliptic plane?

   _____

Name _____ Class _____ Date _____

8. What is the difference between a full moon and a new moon?

_____

_____

_____

9. What are the very bright stars in the upper right of an H-R diagram called?

_____

10. What two factors cause a nebula to develop into a star?

_____

_____

Using Science Skills

Use the diagram to answer each question. Write the answers on a separate sheet of paper.

1. **Interpreting Graphics** In Figure 3-1, what process is occurring in the area labeled D, and what feature will result at C?

2. **Interpreting Graphics** In Figure 3-1, what is occurring at A?

3. **Inferring** Which rock layer is the youngest layer shown in Figure 3-2?

4. **Analyzing Data** In Figure 3-2, would a fossil in layer D be younger or older than fossils found in layer B?

Figure 3-1

Figure 3-2

Figure 3-3

5. **Inferring** What factors are used to classify the air masses in Figure 3-3?

6. **Classifying** Based on their locations in Figure 3-3, name the types of air masses represented by A and D and describe the characteristics of each.

7. **Formulating Hypotheses** In Figure 3-4, why would you expect B to lie in the planet's orbital plane?

8. **Drawing Conclusions** Saturn is the least dense of all the planets. Why does Saturn remain in orbit instead of drifting away in space or crashing into the sun?

9. **Inferring** Suppose two stars are located in region A of the H-R diagram shown in Figure 3-5. Star X appears much dimmer than Star Y as seen from Earth. Which star can be inferred to be nearer to Earth, and what other factor must be considered?

10. **Applying Concepts** How would you describe the change in the properties of stars as you move from left to right along the main sequence in the H-R diagram in Figure 3-5?

Figure 3-4

Figure 3-5

Essay

Write the answers to each question on a separate sheet of paper.

1. How does the subduction of an oceanic plate result in the formation of a volcano?

2. Describe the journey of a water molecule through the water cycle.

3. Compare the weather that might occur in an area as a warm front passes through, after the warm front has passed through, as a cold front passes through, and after the cold front has passed through.

4. What three criteria must any theory of the origin of the solar system satisfy? What theory satisfies all three?

5. The astronomer Carl Sagan once said that we are all made of "star stuff." Explain what he meant.

Name _____ Class _____ Date _____

Unit 3   Earth and Space   **Unit Test B**

Multiple Choice

Write the letter that best answers the question or completes the statement on the line provided.

_____ 1. The study of Earth's composition, structure, and history is
called
   a. seismology.   **b.** physics.   **c.** chemistry.   **d.** geology.

_____ 2. The three main layers of Earth's interior are the
   a. crust, core, and lithosphere.
   b. crust, mantle, and core.
   c. mantle, inner core, and outer core.
   d. crust, mantle, and aesthenosphere.

_____ 3. A naturally occurring, inorganic solid with a crystal
structure and a characteristic chemical composition is a
   a. rock.   **b.** fossil.
   c. mineral.   **d.** piece of granite.

_____ 4. The area where magma collects inside a volcano before an
eruption is called
   a. the crater.   **b.** a caldera.
   c. a vent.   **d.** the magma chamber.

_____ 5. What determines whether a volcano erupts quietly
or explosively?
   a. the size of the volcano
   b. the age of the volcano
   c. the characteristics of the magma
   d. the magnitude of nearby earthquakes

_____ 6. Shield volcanoes are produced by
   a. explosive eruptions of lava and ash.
   b. quiet eruptions of lava.
   c. explosive eruptions of ash and cinders.
   d. quiet eruptions that alternate with explosive eruptions.

_____ 7. Which of the following is NOT an agent of
chemical weathering?
   a. rainwater   **b.** oxidation
   c. frost wedging   **d.** carbonic acid

_____ 8. A rapid mass movement of large amounts of rock and soil
down a slope is called a
   a. landslide.   **b.** slump.   **c.** creep.   **d.** mudflow.

_____ 9. A stream's ability to erode depends mainly on
   a. its temperature.
   b. the size of the sediment in the stream.
   c. its speed.
   d. the shape of its valley.

_____ **10.** A sediment deposit formed when a stream flows into a lake
or the ocean is called a(an)
 a. alluvial fan.   **b.** delta.
 c. meander.   **d.** natural levee.

_____ **11.** Caves are formed by erosion from
 a. glaciers.   **b.** streams.   **c.** wind.   **d.** groundwater.

_____ **12.** Unsorted sediment deposited by a glacier is called
 a. a cirque.   **b.** till.   **c.** a horn.   **d.** an erratic.

_____ **13.** Which region usually has temperatures cooler than
temperatures near the equator?
 a. tropic zone   **b.** polar zone
 c. temperate zone   **d.** both b and c

_____ **14.** About how much of the solar energy that reaches Earth
passes through the atmosphere and is absorbed by the
surface of Earth?
 a. 20 percent   **b.** 30 percent
 c. 50 percent   **d.** 80 percent

_____ **15.** Which of the following is NOT an example of a
global wind?
 a. westerlies   **b.** trade winds
 c. polar easterlies   **d.** ea breezes

_____ **16.** What type of front forms when two unlike air masses form a
boundary but neither is moving?
 a. warm   **b.** cold   **c.** stationary   **d.** occluded

_____ **17.** Which of the following is a weather system with a center of
low pressure?
 a. cyclone   **b.** anticyclone   **c.** warm front   **d.** cold front

_____ **18.** A tropical storm with sustained winds of at least 119
kilometers per hour is called a
 a. tornado.   **b.** thunderstorm.
 c. monsoon.   **d.** hurricane.

_____ **19.** Ocean tides are the result of
 a. the rotation of the Earth.
 b. the sun's gravitational pull on Earth.
 c. changes in Earth's orbital position around the sun.
 d. differences in both the sun's and moon's gravitational
   pull on Earth.

_____ **20.** The four terrestrial planets are so called because they
 a. are the nearest planets to Earth.
 b. were all once part of Earth.
 c. are similar in structure to Earth.
 d. can all be seen from Earth without a telescope.

_____21. Asteroids are mainly found
   a. in the asteroid belt beyond Mars.
   b. in orbit around Jupiter. **c.** throughout the solar system.
   d. beyond the farthest known planet.

_____22. Which of the gas giants has the largest diameter?
   a. Jupiter   **b.** Uranus   **c.** Saturn   **d.** Neptune

_____23. Comets are made mostly of
   a. iron.
   b. ice and rock.
   c. hydrogen and helium.
   d. methane.

_____24. Which of the following is a sparse sphere of comets that
surrounds the sun and planets?
   a. the asteroid belt   **b.** the Kuiper belt
   c. the Oort cloud   **d.** none of the above

_____25. Astronomers classify stars according to their
   a. distance from Earth.
   b. color, size, and absolute brightness.
   c. age and parallax.
   d. all of the above

_____26. An H-R diagram
   a. is a map of the positions of the stars.
   b. graphs stars according to their size and distance.
   c. lists every known star.
   d. graphs a sample of stars according to surface temperature
      and absolute brightness.

_____27. The life cycle of a star begins with a cloud of gas and dust
called a
   a. protoplanet.   **b.** constellation.
   c. nebula.   **d.** protosun.

_____28. Both high-mass and low-mass adult stars are classified as
   a. main-sequence stars.   **b.** white dwarfs.
   c. supernovas.   **d.** neutron stars.

_____29. All stars remain on the main sequence
   a. until they stabilize.
   b. for about 90 percent of their lifetimes.
   c. until they become protostars.
   d. for about 10 billion years.

_____30. Low-mass and medium-mass stars eventually
   a. grow into supergiants.
   b. become supernovas.
   c. become neutron stars.
   d. turn into white dwarfs.

Completion

Complete each statement on the line provided.

1. The study of the composition, structure, and the history of Earth is called _____.

2. The crust and upper mantle together form the

   _____.

3. The color of the powder a mineral leaves on an unglazed porcelain tile is called the mineral's _____.

4. A(An) _____ glacier is a thick sheet of ice that covers large areas of land.

5. Deposits of windblown dust are called _____.

6. The process by which sand is moved along a shore is called

   _____.

7. A major type of storm associated with lightning, strong winds, and heavy rain or hail is called a(an) _____.

8. _____ works by bouncing radio waves off particles of precipitation in moving storms and then measuring the frequency of the waves that return.

9. The two main factors that determine a region's climate are _____ and _____.

10. The force of gravity that the sun exerts on a planet is directed

    _____.

11. The beginning of the "space race" occurred when the _____ launched the first artificial satellite in 1957.

12. Because there is no _____ on the moon, any liquid water would have evaporated long ago.

13. In an H-R diagram, most stars are found in a diagonal band from the upper left to the lower right, which is called the

    _____.

14. A group of two or more stars held together by gravity is called a(an) _____.

15. The theory that the universe came into being in a single moment with an enormous explosion is the _____ theory.

Short Answer

In complete sentences, write the answers to the questions on the lines provided.

1. By what three ways can metamorphic rocks form?

   _____

   _____

   _____

Name _____ Class _____ Date _____

2. What theory explains how Earth's plates form and move?

_____

_____

3. What three factors determine magma viscosity?

_____

_____

4. Describe the changes in amount of light, temperature, and pressure as depth in the ocean increases.

_____

_____

_____

5. List at least four agents of erosion.

_____

_____

_____

_____

6. What are the four largest divisions of the geologic time scale?

_____

_____

_____

7. Why is Earth generally warmer near the equator and colder toward the poles?

_____

_____

_____

8. What is the greenhouse effect?

_____

_____

_____

9. What weather is associated with a cyclone?

_____

_____

10. Who was the first human to step onto the moon?

_____

_____

11. What caused most craters on the moon?

_____

_____

12. What is the composition of the Kuiper belt?

_____

_____

13. Why do astronomers measure the parallax of nearby stars?

_____

_____

14. How can an object's red shift tell us how fast the object is moving away from Earth?

_____

_____

15. How have scientists used Hubble's Law to estimate the age of the universe?

_____

_____

Using Science Skills

Use the diagram to answer each question. Write the answers on a separate sheet of paper.

1. **Classifying** What type of rock would fit into Figure 3-1 at the location shown by the letter F?

2. **Interpreting Graphics In** Figure 3-1, what processes are represented by the arrow labeled A?

Figure 3-1

Name _____ Class _____ Date _____

3. **Inferring** In Figure 3-2, is the stream flow moving faster at point C or at point D? Explain your answer.

4. **Interpreting Graphics** What is the feature labeled A in Figure 3-2?

5. **Interpreting Graphics** Explain what is happening to the two air masses in the cold front in Figure 3-3.

Figure 3-2

6. **Comparing and Contrasting** Based on your observations of Figure 3-3, how are a cold front and a warm front alike?

Figure 3-3

Figure 3-4

7. **Interpreting Graphics** Is the model in Figure 3-4 geocentric or heliocentric? Explain how you know.

8. **Classifying** In Figure 3-4, which components of the solar system are indicated by orbits 1– 9? Name each component in order from the sun, and classify each according to type.

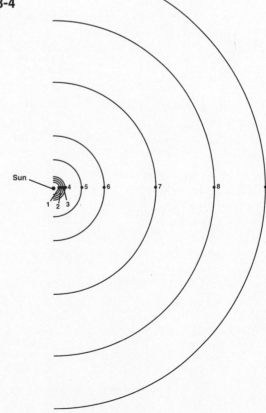

Figure 3-5A

Figure 3-5B

Figure 3-5

9. **Applying Concepts** Would you expect to find helium fusion occurring in stage F or stage G of the star shown in Figure 3-5B? Explain your answer.

10. **Using Models** Which figure—3-5A or 3-5B—models the evolution of a high-mass star? Explain how you know.

Answer Key

Chapter 1 Test A Answers

Multiple Choice

1. c	**2.** b	**3.** b	**4.** c	**5.** b	**6.** b
7. a	**8.** a	**9.** b	**10.** d	**11.** d	**12.** a
13. b	**14.** d	**15.** a			

Completion

1. unit **2.** controlled experiment **3.** chemistry
4. direct proportion **5.** significant figures

Short Answer

1. Science is a system of knowledge, while technology is the practical application of that knowledge to the solving of problems. **2.** a bar graph **3.** an inverse proportion **4.** It gets larger. **5.** The universe is very large (7.0×10^{26} meters in diameter) and very old (about 13.7 billion years old).

Using Science Skills

1. 8.8 g/cm^3 **2.** mass **3.** a direct proportion **4.** the density of the fluid **5.** g/cm^3

Essay

1. The steel ball started out slowly. Then it continued to speed up throughout the experiment.
2. A scientific law is a statement that summarizes a pattern found in nature, without attempting to explain it. A scientific theory explains the pattern.
3. Possible answers: The universe is very large and very old. A small amount of the universe is matter. Matter on Earth usually is either a solid, liquid, or gas. All matter is made of atoms. Forces cause changes in motion. Energy can be transferred from one form or object to another, but it can never be destroyed.
4. Possible answer: 1) make observations, 2) ask questions, 3) develop a hypothesis, 4) test the hypothesis, 5) analyze data, 6) draw conclusions, 7) revise hypothesis.
5. In peer reviews, scientists review and question other scientists' data. Scientists also help determine if the data is accurately reported. If the review finds errors in the data, in the conclusions, or in the experimental procedures, the hypothesis may need to be revised.

Chapter 1 Test B Answers

Multiple Choice

1. b	**2.** a	**3.** d	**4.** d	**5.** b	**6.** a
7. c	**8.** c	**9.** d	**10.** c	**11.** d	**12.** c
13. b	**14.** d	**15.** b			

Completion

1. kilogram (kg) **2.** scientific method **3.** line graph
4. technology **5.** physical science **6.** responding variable **7.** scientific law **8.** scientific model; model
9. 14 **10.** Accuracy

Short Answer

1. Always follow your teachers instructions and textbook directions exactly. **2.** to communicate with other scientists about the results of their investigations

3. a process in which scientists examine other scientists' work **4.** three **5.** 32°F, 0°C, and 273 K

Using Science Skills

1. monthly precipitation in centimeters **2.** December
3. The precipitation data might provide insight into agricultural growth trends. **4.** approximately 165 cm
5. 0.18 meters

Chapter 2 Test A Answers

Multiple Choice

1. a	**2.** d	**3.** a	**4.** d	**5.** a	**6.** c
7. d	**8.** a	**9.** c	**10.** d	**11.** b	**12.** a
13. a	**14.** b	**15.** d			

Completion

1. elements, compounds **2.** one, two **3.** compounds
4. reactive **5.** physical, chemical

Short Answer

1. Accept any of the following: by adding more of a substance in the mixture; by adding a new substance; by removing a substance from the mixture. **2.** acetic acid, and gold **3.** The viscosity of a liquid usually decreases as the liquid is heated and increases as the liquid cools. **4.** For a physical change that can be reversed, accept any of the following: freezing water, melting ice, braiding hair, wrinkling clothes. For a physical change that cannot be reversed, accept any of the following: cutting hair, slicing a tomato, peeling an orange. **5.** a chemical change

Using Science Skills

1. A heterogeneous mixture; the mixture scatters light, separates into layers, and can be separated by filtration.
2. Mixture B; it does not scatter light, does not separate into layers, and cannot be separated by filtration.
3. Mixture A; it scatters light, does not separate into layers, and cannot be separated by filtration.
4. Mixture B, Mixture A, Mixture C
5. Possible answer: Mixture B is a solution and all the particles would pass through a filter. Distillation might be used to separate the substances in Mixture B.

Essay

1. Water is a liquid at room temperature, does not burn, and can be used to put out fires. Oxygen and hydrogen are the elements that make up water. Both elements are gases at room temperature. Hydrogen can fuel a fire, and oxygen can keep a fire burning. **2.** Silver has a known density at room temperature (10.5 g/cm^3). You can measure the density of the coin and compare it to the density of silver. If the densities of the coin and silver are the same, the coin is pure silver. If the densities of the coin and silver are different, the coin contains at least one other substance in addition to silver. **3.** Filtration would be used because it is the process of separating mixtures based on the size of their particles (or pieces). A screen could be used to separate the mixture. The holes in the screen would need to be large enough to allow the soil to pass through but not the leaves, acorn, or twigs. **4.** Rust forms in the tanks because oxygen dissolved in the water reacts with iron in the steel. Nitrogen gas can be pumped into the tanks. The nitrogen displaces some of the dissolved oxygen. Because nitrogen is less reactive than oxygen, less rust forms. **5.** With no other evidence, the gas could be the result of either a physical or chemical change. A liquid could be changing to a gas, which is a physical change. A reaction that produces a gas could be occurring as the liquid is heated. Without testing the composition of the liquid before and after heating, there is no way to tell.

Chapter 2 Test B Answers

Multiple Choice

1. b	**2.** c	**3.** b	**4.** d	**5.** d	**6.** a
7. b	**8.** d	**9.** a	**10.** b	**11.** d	**12.** d
13. c	**14.** d	**15.** d			

Completion

1. pure substance; substance **2.** atom **3.** homogeneous **4.** metal **5.** melting, boiling **6.** Distillation **7.** physical **8.** Chemical **9.** precipitate **10.** a gas; carbon dioxide

Short Answer

1. They are different. **2.** The composition of a substance is fixed, while the composition of a mixture can vary. **3.** Accept any of the following: the suspension would appear cloudy, while the solution would be clear; the particles in the suspension would settle to the bottom, while the particles in the solution would not settle. **4.** a change in color, the production of a gas, and the formation of a precipitate **5.** A chemical change involves a change in the composition of matter. During a physical change, the composition of matter does not change.

Using Science Skills

1. Before clay is baked, it is soft and can be molded. After clay is baked, it is hard and brittle. **2.** wax, unbaked clay, and metal **3.** Both sculptures would be hard and would only melt at very high temperatures. The metal sculpture might be dented if it was hammered, but if the sculpture made from baked clay was hammered, it would shatter. **4.** The object would have been made from wax because wax has a low melting point. It is the only material listed that would soften enough in a sunny window to change shape. **5.** Baked clay; it is brittle and shatters.

Chapter 3 Test A Answers

Multiple Choice

1. b	**2.** c	**3.** a	**4.** b	**5.** c	**6.** a
7. a	**8.** a	**9.** c	**10.** c	**11.** d	**12.** c
13. b	**14.** a	**15.** c	**16.** b		

Completion

1. condensate **2.** collide **3.** pressure **4.** liquid, gas **5.** boiling

Short Answer

1. Plasma exists at extremely high temperatures, and a Bose-Einstein condensate can exist at extremely low temperatures. **2.** Substance A; its particles are packed close together and arranged in a regular pattern. **3.** The new pressure would be 60 kPa. **4.** At the melting point of water, some molecules gain enough energy to move from their fixed positions. **5.** Take temperature measurements of the surroundings during the phase change. If the temperature decreases, the phase change is endothermic; a system absorbs energy from its surroundings during an endothermic phase change.

Using Science Skills

1. the kilopascal; 200 kPa; 100 kPa **2.** Volume is the manipulated variable. Pressure is the responding variable. **3.** The pressure would increase, so the graph would be a straight line. **4.** The number of collisions will increase when the volume is reduced from 2.0 L to 1.0 L because particles occupy a smaller space and will collide more often with the walls of the container. **5.** V_1 is 0.5 L, and V_2 is 2.0 L.

Essay

1. Like a particle in a gas, a billiard ball moves in a straight line until it collides with another object. During a collision, kinetic energy can be transferred between billiard balls or particles in a gas. Students in a crowded hallway are closely packed like the particles in a liquid. The motion of the students is restricted by interactions with other students. The motion of particles in a liquid is limited by forces of attraction. The fixed positions of the audience in a movie theater are like the fixed locations of particles in solids. However, both the audience and the particles can move within or around their locations. **2.** The volume of the chest cavity increases as the diaphragm contracts and the rib cage is lifted. This increase in volume allows the particles in air to spread out, which lowers the air pressure in the lungs. Air rushes into the lungs because the air pressure outside the body is greater than the air pressure in the lungs. As the diaphragm relaxes and the rib cage moves down and in, the volume of the chest cavity decreases. This decrease in volume increases the air pressure, and air is forced out of the lungs. **3.** Temperature and air pressure affect the volume of a weather balloon. As the balloon rises, the temperature decreases, which should cause the volume of the balloon to decrease. However, pressure in the atmosphere also decreases, which should cause the volume of the balloon to increase. **4.** Water boils when its vapor pressure equals atmospheric pressure. Atmospheric pressure is lower at higher elevations. Therefore, the vapor pressure of water will equal atmospheric pressure at temperatures below 100°C. Pasta takes longer to cook at lower temperatures. **5.** Water can evaporate at temperatures lower than its boiling point. Evaporation can take place at the surface of water because some water molecules are moving fast enough to escape the liquid and vaporize. The higher the temperature is, the faster the water molecules move, on average, and the faster evaporation takes place.

Chapter 3 Test B Answers

Multiple Choice

1. c **2.** a **3.** c **4.** c **5.** d **6.** a
7. d **8.** c **9.** d **10.** c **11.** b **12.** d
13. b **14.** b

Completion

1. solid **2.** volumes **3.** solid **4.** kinetic **5.** Collisions
6. increases, temperature **7.** volume, temperature
8. kelvins **9.** atmospheric **10.** exothermic

Short Answer

1. Solids have a definite shape and definite volume, liquids have a definite volume but not a definite shape, and gases do not have a definite volume or a definite shape. **2.** The volume of a liquid is constant because forces of attraction keep the particles close together. **3.** The constant motion of the tires on the road causes the tires and the air in the tires to warm up. The increase in temperature increases the average kinetic energy of the air in the tires. The frequency and force of collisions between particles increases, which increases the air pressure. **4.** As water freezes, it releases energy to its surroundings, and the average kinetic energy of the water molecules decreases. **5.** At room temperature, dry ice changes from solid carbon dioxide to carbon dioxide gas, which is an example of sublimation.

Using Science Skills

1. a. vaporization; b. melting; c. freezing **2.** Each pair represents the opposing endothermic and exothermic changes that occur between the same two states of matter. **3.** Water vapor is a gas. The phase change from water to liquid dew is called condensation. The phase change from water vapor to solid frost is called deposition. **4.** Vaporization is the phase change in which a liquid changes to a gas. Freezing is the phase change in which a liquid changes to a solid. **5.** melting, vaporization, and sublimation

Chapter 4 Test A Answers

Multiple Choice

1. b **2.** a **3.** c **4.** b **5.** d **6.** d
7. d **8.** c **9.** d **10.** c **11.** d **12.** b
13. a **14.** a **15.** c

Completion

1. atoms **2.** compound **3.** nuclei **4.** orbital **5.** excited

Short Answer

1. atom; Democritus **2.** 15 **3.** 38 **4.** Bohr's model focused on electrons. **5.** It provides a visual model of

the most likely locations of electrons in an atom.

Using Science Skills

1. The particles are protons and neutrons. This atom has an atomic number of 8 and a mass number of 17. **2.** Dalton probably would not have recognized this model because he thought of the atom as a solid indivisible ball and had no knowledge of subatomic particles. **3.** Yes; Rutherford demonstrated the existence of a nucleus, named subatomic particles with a positive charge protons, and predicted the existence of neutrons. **4.** The proton has a positive charge, but the neutron has no charge. It was easier to detect the existence of a charged particle because its path could be deflected by a charged plate. **5.** Students may answer yes because the model shows the composition of the nucleus of an atom. Students may answer no because the model does not include any electrons or show the position of the nucleus in the atom.

Essay

1. Thomson's model no longer explained all the available evidence. In Thomson's model, for example, positive charge was spread evenly throughout the atom. Rutherford had concluded that the positive charge of an atom was concentrated in the center of the atom. **2.** All the atoms of an element have the same atomic number because the atomic number equals the number of protons in an atom. If one of the atoms had a different number of protons, the atom would not be a calcium atom. The mass number can vary because it is the sum of the protons and neutrons and because isotopes of an element can have different numbers of neutrons. **3.** Bohr's atomic model represents electrons as moving in fixed orbits around the nucleus like planets moving in orbits around a sun. **4.** An orbital is a region of space around the nucleus where an electron is likely to be found. The electron cloud is a visual model that represents all the orbitals in an atom. **5.** When fireworks explode, the heat produced by the explosions causes some electrons in atoms to move to higher energy levels. When the electrons return to lower energy levels, some of the energy is released as visible light. The colors vary because each element has a different set of energy levels.

Chapter 4 Test B Answers

Multiple Choice

1. b **2.** a **3.** c **4.** d **5.** d **6.** a
7. a **8.** d **9.** c **10.** b **11.** b **12.** c
13. a **14.** d **15.** c

Completion

1. Aristotle **2.** element **3.** negative **4.** alpha particles
5. neutrons **6.** number **7.** neutrons **8.** electrons
9. cloud **10.** ground

Short Answer

1. Democritus believed all matter consisted of tiny particles that could not be divided into smaller particles.

2. Scientists realized that atoms contained smaller subatomic particles. **3.** Rutherford concluded that positive charge was concentrated in the nucleus of an atom. **4.** two **5.** The atoms return from an excited state to the ground state.

Using Science Skills

1. Panel 1 depicts an atom as a solid sphere without any subatomic particles. Panel 2 shows an atom that has a subatomic structure. **2.** The main difference is the way in which electron motion is depicted. In panel 2, the movement of electrons is represented by fixed circular orbits. In panel 3, the probable locations of the moving electrons are represented by a cloud. **3.** Yes; they go from the simplest (the solid sphere in 1) to the most complex (the electron cloud model in panel 3). Students may specifically cite John Dalton in connection with panel 1 and Niels Bohr in connection with panel 2 to support their answers. **4.** The solid ball in panel 1 is like the drawing of the exterior of a house. It provides no details about the internal structure of an atom. The model in panel 2 shows the locations of different parts of the atom within the atom and their relative sizes. It is like a blueprint that shows the size and location of rooms in a house. **5.** It is helpful because it shows the general locations of the subatomic particles in an atom. It is not helpful because it implies that electrons travel in fixed paths around the nucleus.

Chapter 5 Test A Answers

Multiple Choice

1. d	**2.** c	**3.** b	**4.** d	**5.** d	**6.** d
7. c	**8.** c	**9.** a	**10.** b	**11.** c	**12.** b
13. b	**14.** d	**15.** a			

Completion

1. column **2.** low **3.** periodic law **4.** nitrogen **5.** water

Short Answer

1. He wanted to organize information about the elements for a textbook he was writing. **2.** atomic number, number of protons in each element **3.** Properties will vary the most in segment A, which is a period. **4.** Selenium is a nonmetal. Rubidium is a metal. **5.** chlorine **6.** Sulfur is not a highly reactive element under ordinary conditions.

Using Science Skills

1. These elements are all metals. The elements in Groups 1A and 2A are the alkali metals and alkaline earth metals, respectively. The elements in Groups 3B and 4B are transition metals. **2.** Rb is the most reactive element shown. Group 1A alkali metals are the most reactive metals, and the reactivity of elements in Group 1A increases from top to bottom. **3.** When elements are arranged in a periodic table in order of increasing atomic number, the properties of elements repeat from period to period so that elements in the same group have similar properties. **4.** The numbers shown are atomic numbers. An atomic number is the number of

protons and the number of electrons in an atom. The periodic table is organized in order by increasing atomic number. No two elements have the same atomic number. **5.** The elements in Group 1A, the alkali metals, are soft and extremely reactive. Atoms of these elements have a single valence electron. Atoms of elements in Group 2A have two valence electrons. The alkaline earth metals are harder, less reactive, and have higher melting points than the alkali metals in the same period.

Essay

1. You could store the compound in a jar filled with a noble gas such as argon. Students may also recall that reactive elements are stored under oil. **2.** You could see which piece conducts an electric current or which piece is a better conductor of heat. **3.** Answers should include a discussion of properties that repeat at regular intervals. **4.** Lithium is an alkali metal in Group 1A. Alkali metals are the most reactive metals. Neon is a noble gas in Group 8A. Noble gases are highly unreactive nonmetals.

Chapter 5 Test B Answers

Multiple Choice

1. d	**2.** c	**3.** b	**4.** d	**5.** c	**6.** b
7. d	**8.** a	**9.** a	**10.** b	**11.** c	**12.** a
13. c	**14.** b	**15.** d			

Completion

1. mass **2.** elements **3.** 15 **4.** carbon **5.** metalloids **6.** metallic, nonmetallic **7.** three **8.** alkali **9.** neon **10.** compounds

Short Answer

1. across a period because the atomic number is increasing by one each time **2.** the number of valence electrons **3.** The integer, 36, is the atomic number, or number of protons in an atom of krypton. The decimal number, 83.80, is the atomic mass, which is the weighted average of the atomic masses of krypton isotopes found in nature. **4.** Sodium is the alkali metal, and chlorine is the halogen. **5.** The heated filament will react with the oxygen in air but not with argon, which is a noble gas and hardly ever reacts.

Using Science Skills

1. Be, C, N, and F **2.** V is a transition metal, and He is a noble gas. **3.** F and I have the same number of valence electrons because they are in the same group in the periodic table. **4.** Beryllium is a reactive metal with two valence electrons. Iodine is a highly reactive nonmetal with seven valence electrons. **5.** The element has an atomic number of 12 and has two valence electrons. It will most resemble beryllium.

Essay

1. Mendeleev predicted the properties of these undiscovered elements from data in his periodic table. When the elements were discovered, their actual properties were found to be a close match to those

Mendeleev had predicted. Their discovery provided evidence of the usefulness of Mendeleev's periodic table.

Chapter 6 Test A Answers

Multiple Choice

1. d **2.** c **3.** a **4.** b **5.** d **6.** c
7. a **8.** d **9.** d **10.** b **11.** b **12.** c
13. d **14.** a **15.** a

Completion

1. potassium **2.** one-to-one **3.** highest **4.** iron
5. chromium

Short Answer

1. lithium, Li, and fluorine, F; an ionic compound
2. iodine, I **3.** substance AB **4.** bromine, Br **5.** Metals contain a shared pool of electrons that are free to move.

Using Science Skills

1. Potassium is a highly reactive metal with one valence electron. Iodine is a highly reactive nonmetal with seven valence electrons. When electrons are transferred from potassium atoms to iodine atoms, there is an attraction between the oppositely charged ions that form. Thus, opposites do attract in an ionic bond. **2.** Covalent bonds form between the nonmetals carbon and oxygen. In a covalent bond, atoms share electrons. When potassium and iodine react, electrons are transferred from potassium atoms to iodine atoms. Ionic bonds form between potassium cations and iodide anions. There is no sharing of electrons in an ionic bond. **3.** The compounds in rows A and C are both ionic compounds. However, KI is a binary ionic compound, which forms between a metal and a nonmetal. The compound in row C contains a polyatomic hydroxide ion (OH^-). The atoms in a polyatomic ion are joined by covalent bonds. **4.** The charge on the aluminum ion is 3+. The formula $Al(OH)_3$ indicates that there are three hydroxide ions for each aluminum ion in aluminum hydroxide. Since each hydroxide ion has a 1– charge, each aluminum ion must have a charge of 3+ for the overall charge on the compound to be zero. **5.** K_2S; because sulfur has six valence electrons, its atoms gain two electrons when they form ionic compounds. Potassium atoms donate one valence electron when they form ionic compounds. It takes two potassium atoms to donate two electrons to one sulfur atom.

Essay

1. The electron configuration of an element determines its reactivity. Fluorine, with seven valence electrons, tends to gain one electron to fill its highest occupied energy level. Neon, with eight valence electrons, has a stable electron configuration. Neon's highest occupied energy level holds the maximum possible number of electrons. **2.** An electron dot diagram shows the number of valence electrons. The chemical properties of an element depend on the number of valence

electrons in its atoms. **3.** Because water molecules are polar, there are strong attractions between water molecules. The molecules on the surface of water droplets are pulled toward the center by their attractions to water molecules below the surface. **4.** In both lattices, positively charged cations are attracted to negatively charged particles. In an ionic lattice, the negative particles are anions. In a metal lattice, the negative particles are electrons. Because the electrons are mobile, electrons still separate cations when the shape of the metal changes. When an ionic lattice is struck, ions with similar charges are pushed near one another. Repulsions between these ions cause the crystal to shatter. **5.** Possible answer: Metal wires are used to carry electric current. The cables on suspension bridges are made from thin strands of steel.

Chapter 6 Test B Answers

Multiple Choice

1. c **2.** d **3.** d **4.** d **5.** c **6.** b
7. b **8.** c **9.** d **10.** a **11.** b **12.** b
13. d **14.** c **15.** d

Completion

1. valence electron **2.** anions **3.** chloride, calcium
4. crystal **5.** electrons; valence electrons **6.** polyatomic
7. zero **8.** alkali **9.** cations **10.** copper

Short Answer

1. Group 7A, the halogens **2.** rubidium **3.** Bromine; it gains electrons rather than losing them. **4.** sodium chloride **5.** an alloy

Using Science Skills

1. The atoms of a metal lose one or more valence electrons and form cations. The atoms of a nonmetal gain one or more electrons and form anions. There is an attraction between the oppositely charged ions. **2.** sodium chloride **3.** covalent **4.** metallic **5.** In both metallic and ionic bonds, there are attractions between particles with positive and negative charges—cations and electrons in a metallic bond, and cations and anions in an ionic bond. Ionic bonds are found in compounds. Metallic bonds are found in a single metal or in alloys.

Chapter 7 Test A Answers

Multiple Choice

1. d **2.** b **3.** d **4.** d **5.** d **6.** d
7. c **8.** a **9.** a **10.** b **11.** d **12.** c
13. a **14.** c **15.** d

Completion

1. 160 g **2.** 2.3 **3.** synthesis **4.** speeds up
5. concentration

Short Answer

1. The equation was not balanced correctly because it was balanced by changing a subscript instead of changing coefficients. The correctly balanced equation is $2Mg + O_2 \rightarrow 2MgO$. **2.** 2.67 mol **3.** The reactant must be a compound because it is being broken down;

an element cannot be broken down in a chemical reaction. The products can be either compounds or elements, and substances include both compounds and elements. **4.** Some other substances, such as hydrogen, also burn. When the fuel does not contain carbon, carbon dioxide does not form.

5. Lowering the temperature lowers the rate of reaction, so the reactants in the film and batteries are less likely to react before they are used.

Using Science Skills

1. the reactants **2.** The cooked egg white has more chemical energy in its chemical bonds because energy was absorbed during the reaction. **3.** 46 kJ would be absorbed during the reaction. **4.** the amount of energy required to break the chemical bonds of the reactants **5.** The diagram on the left; rusting is an exothermic reaction because it releases energy. This diagram represents the energy changes in an exothermic reaction.

Problem

1. $Cu + 4HNO_3 \rightarrow Cu(NO_3)_2 + 2NO_2 + 2H_2O$
2. $4Fe + 3O_2 \rightarrow 2Fe_2O_3$; 9 mol O_2
3. $2Na + Cl_2 \rightarrow 2NaCl$; 149 g Cl_2

Essay

1. Single-replacement reactions are redox reactions because one element in the compound is reduced, and the free element is oxidized. Combustion is a redox reaction because oxygen is always reduced, and another element is oxidized. **2.** In a physical equilibrium, there is a difference in the form of the substance, but its chemical composition remains the same. In a chemical equilibrium, chemical changes occur, and the reactants are different substances than the products.

Chapter 7 Test B Answers

Multiple Choice

1. a	**2.** c	**3.** d	**4.** c	**5.** b	**6.** a
7. b	**8.** c	**9.** c	**10.** b	**11.** c	**12.** a
13. b	**14.** b	**15.** a			

Completion

1. conservation of mass **2.** coefficient **3.** 35.5 g/mol **4.** 24 **5.** oxygen **6.** two **7.** reduction **8.** endothermic **9.** rate **10.** LeChâtelier's principle

Short Answer

1. In addition to the ash, gases are formed. The total mass of the paper and oxygen equals the total mass of the ash and the gases formed. **2.** A balanced chemical equation shows that mass is conserved. The number of each type of atom in the reactants must equal the number of each type of atom in the products. **3.** The molar mass of Mn is 55 g/mol, so 4.0 mol of Mn have a mass of 220 g. **4.** Equilibrium exists because liquid water is freezing and ice is melting at the same rate. The equilibrium is physical because no new

substances form. **5.** There are more gas molecules on the reactant side. Increased pressure will thus cause the system to shift in the direction that decreases the pressure of the system (that is, produces fewer gas molecules) and the reaction will shift to form more product.

Using Science Skills

1. On the left side, there are 1 carbon atom, 4 hydrogen atoms, and 2 oxygen atoms. On the right side, there are 1 carbon atom, 3 oxygen atoms, and 2 hydrogen atoms. **2.** No; the total number of atoms can be the same without the number of each type of atoms on both sides being the same. **3.** 4 hydrogen atoms **4.** Place a coefficient of 2 in front of water on the right side. There will then be 4 hydrogen atoms on both sides of the equation. **5.** $CH_4 + 2O_2 \rightarrow CO_2 + H_2O$

Chapter 8 Test A Answers

Multiple Choice

1. d	**2.** d	**3.** a	**4.** d	**5.** c	**6.** a
7. b	**8.** d	**9.** c	**10.** b	**11.** d	**12.** a
13. d	**14.** c	**15.** c	**16.** c	**17.** b	

Completion

1. dispersion **2.** raises, lowers; increases, decreases **3.** away from **4.** weak **5.** eletrolyte

Short Answer

1. Dissociation is a physical change involving solutes that are ionic compounds. Ionization is a chemical change involving molecular compounds. **2.** In an exothermic chemical reaction, chemical changes occur, and the reactants and the products are not the same substances. In an exothermic solution formation by dissociation, the solute undergoes a physical change and does not change identity. Energy is released in both processes. **3.** No; stirring favors an increased rate, and cooling favors a slower rate. **4.** No; both a neutral and an acidic solution would result in the litmus paper remaining red. **5.** Water can accept a proton to become a hydronium ion or donate a proton to become a hydroxide ion. Examples: $HCl + H_2O \rightarrow Cl^- + H_3O^+$; $NH_3 + H_2O \rightarrow NH_4^+ + OH^-$

Using Science Skills

1. saturated **2.** 13.7 g KCl **3.** 147 g sucrose **4.** 775 g of water **5.** She could measure a mass that is between the two solubilities, such as 5 g. If all of the compound dissolves in 100 g of water at 20°C, it is barium nitrate. If the compound forms a saturated solution with some undissolved solute, the compound is barium hydroxide.

Problem

1. 1.50 M **2.** 0.35 L
3. $HCO_3^- + H^+ \rightarrow H_2CO_3$; $H_2CO_3 + OH^- \rightarrow HCO_3^- + H_2O$

Essay

1. Both are affected by temperature. Rate of solution is also affected by surface area and stirring because both of these factors affect the number of collisions between solute and solvent particles. Solubility is also affected by polarity of the solute and solvent and, if a gas is involved, pressure. The number of collisions does not affect solubility unless a gas is involved. **2.** One liter of the solution would contain 1.20 mol KCl, so 2.00 L would contain 2.40 mol KCl. The molar mass of KCl is 74.55 g/mol, so you would use 179 g of KCl. Add the KCl to enough distilled water to dissolve it, then add additional water to make 2.00 L of solution.

Chapter 8 Test B Answers
Multiple Choice
1. a **2.** a **3.** a **4.** a **5.** a **6.** c
7. b **8.** d **9.** a **10.** c **11.** b **12.** c
13. b

Completion
1. solvent, solute **2.** dissociation **3.** conductivity
4. exothermic **5.** collisions **6.** less **7.** unsaturated
8. hydronium ions **9.** acid **10.** ionize; form ions

Short Answer
1. A gas; the state of the solvent determines the state of the solution. **2.** A freshwater marsh; in a saltwater marsh, the dissolved salt lowers the freezing point of the water. **3.** A saturated solution contains all the solute it can hold at that temperature. More solute will dissolve at that temperature in an unsaturated solution. **4.** a solution that resists change in its pH when small amounts of acid or base are added to it **5.** a weak electrolyte

Using Science Skills
1. basic **2.** Most cleaners contain bases. **3.** Slightly acidic; other acids also form in rain when oxides of nitrogen and sulfur dissolve in water. **4.** The antacid solution must be basic, so its pH is greater than 7. **5.** Yes; since sea water has a pH greater than 7, it is a base. Red litmus paper turns blue when it comes into contact with a base.

Chapter 9 Test A Answers
Multiple Choice
1. c **2.** a **3.** c **4.** a **5.** b **6.** c
7. a **8.** b **9.** c **10.** b **11.** b **12.** a
13. b **14.** c **15.** b **16.** b

Completion
1. four **2.** gases **3.** hydrogen **4.** light, chemical
5. co-enzyme, vitamin

Short Answer
1. Each carbon atom in graphite forms strong covalent bonds to three other atoms within a layer. However, the bonds between the graphite layers are weak, allowing the layers to slide easily past one another. **2.** The compounds are isomers. Butane is a straight-chain alkane. Isobutane is a branched-chain alkane.
3. Alkenes are hydrocarbons that contain at least one carbon-carbon double bond. Alkynes are hydrocarbons that contain at least one carbon-carbon triple bond.

4. an alcohol and a salt **5.** adenine
Using Science Skills
1. E **2.** D; the amino group, $-NH_2$ **3.** B; the hydroxyl group, $-OH$ **4.** A; the functional group is a halogen.
5. C; the carboxyl group, $-COOH$

Problem
1. Complete combustion: $CH_4 + 2O_2 \rightarrow CO_2 + 2H_2O$
Incomplete combustion: $2CH_4 + 3O_2 \rightarrow 2CO + 4H_2O$
2. $CO_2 + H_2O \rightarrow H_2CO_3$

Essay
1. Diamond is a network solid in which all the atoms are linked by covalent bonds. The structure is rigid, compact, and strong. In graphite, carbon atoms are arranged in widely spaced layers. Because the attractions between layers are weak, the layers can slide easily past one another. Therefore, graphite is soft and slippery. **2.** Carbon monoxide is produced during incomplete combustion of a fossil fuel. The amount of oxygen available for combustion needs to be increased.
3. A nucleotide in DNA contains a phosphate group, a sugar (deoxyribose), and one of four organic bases. When the strands line up, pairs of bases (adenine and thymine, cytosine and guanine) are arranged like rungs on a ladder. Strong intermolecular attractions hold the strands together as they twist around one another.

Chapter 9 Test B Answers
Multiple Choice
1. d **2.** d **3.** d **4.** a **5.** c **6.** d
7. c **8.** b **9.** a **10.** a **11.** a **12.** d
13. c **14.** b

Completion
1. network solid **2.** isomers **3.** single **4.** carbon dioxide, water **5.** acidity **6.** ozone **7.** starch, cellulose
8. intermolecular attractions; attractions **9.** cellular respiration **10.** water

Short Answer
1. carbon and hydrogen **2.** Ethyne is an alkyne, heptane is an alkane, and benzene is an aromatic hydrocarbon. **3.** coal **4.** People need the energy stored in plants and the oxygen produced during photosynthesis. **5.** Vitamins that are soluble in fat can build up in body tissues over time.

Using Science Skills
1. cellular respiration; photosynthesis **2.** photosynthesis; cellular respiration **3.** Light energy is absorbed during photosynthesis. This energy is stored as chemical energy in the covalent bonds of molecules. During cellular respiration, this energy stored in the products of photosynthesis is released as heat. **4.** The amount of carbon dioxide removed from the atmosphere and the amount of oxygen released into the atmosphere would be reduced. **5.** carbon, hydrogen, and oxygen

Chapter 10 Test A Answers

Multiple Choice

1. b	**2.** a	**3.** b	**4.** a	**5.** c	**6.** a
7. a	**8.** b	**9.** b	**10.** b	**11.** b	**12.** a
13. c	**14.** d	**15.** d			

Completion

1. radioisotope **2.** gamma **3.** 0, +1 **4.** control rods, neutrons **5.** beryllium-8

Short Answer

1. Both particles are identical in mass and charge. **2.** Focusing the beam from many different directions keeps healthy tissue from being exposed to too much radiation. The only tissue that receives a large amount of radiation is the tumor. **3.** neutrons **4.** Both the nucleus and the alpha particle are positively charged. The alpha particles must be accelerated enough to overcome the repulsion of two positively charged particles. **5.** The amount of energy produced equals the amount of mass times the speed of light squared. Because the speed of light is such a large number, a very small amount of mass multiplied by this large number produces a large amount of energy.

Using Science Skills

1. polonium-218 **2.** xenon-131; 12.5 g **3.** 175 g **4.** 3240 years old **5.** protactinium-234; 42 g

Problem

1. 0.075 g **2.** 400 g **3.** 3 min

Essay

1. Possible answer: During fission, a larger nucleus is broken down into two smaller nuclei. During fusion, a larger nucleus is formed from smaller nuclei. Fission produces potentially harmful products, but fusion does not. Fission is currently used as a power source, but fusion requires too much energy and is too difficult to contain. **2.** Carbon-14 is produced in the atmosphere when neutrons produced by cosmic rays collide with nitrogen-14 atoms. Carbon-14 reacts with oxygen in the atmosphere, forming carbon dioxide. Plants take in the carbon dioxide during photosynthesis. When humans eat plants, the carbon-14 atoms in the plants are incorporated into compounds in the human body.

Chapter 10 Test B Answers

Multiple Choice

1. a	**2.** c	**3.** a	**4.** d	**5.** b	**6.** a
7. a	**8.** b	**9.** a	**10.** c	**11.** d	**12.** c
13. a	**14.** a	**15.** d			

Completion

1. helium **2.** mass number, atomic number **3.** penetrating **4.** 6 **5.** atmosphere **6.** transmutation **7.** quark **8.** atomic **9.** mass **10.** chain reaction

Short Answer

1. Uranium salts wrapped in paper left a pattern on unexposed photographic film. He concluded that the salts emitted rays that exposed the film. **2.** a beta particle **3.** Accept any of the following: collisions between cosmic rays and particles in the atmosphere; radioisotopes in air, water, rocks, plants, and animals. **4.** uranium-235 **5.** containment of the plasma and attainment of extremely high temperatures

Using Science Skills

1. The mass of the beta particle is so small ($\frac{1}{1836}$ amu) that it is not significant compared to the mass of a proton or neutron (1 amu). **2.** an alpha particle **3.** a beta particle **4.** Gamma radiation is not a particle. It is a ray of energy that has neither charge nor mass. **5.** The atomic number tells the number of protons. The mass number tells the total number of protons and neutrons. The mass number (4) minus the atomic number (2) tells you that there are 2 neutrons in an alpha particle.

Unit 1 Test A Answers

Multiple Choice

1. c	**2.** b	**3.** a	**4.** a	**5.** a	**6.** a
7. a	**8.** c	**9.** a	**10.** c	**11.** d	**12.** b
13. d	**14.** a	**15.** a	**16.** d	**17.** c	**18.** b
19. d	**20.** b	**21.** c	**22.** c	**23.** c	**24.** b
25. c	**26.** b	**27.** b	**28.** b	**29.** a	**30.** c

Completion

1. controlled experiment **2.** 3.0×10^7 **3.** heterogeneous **4.** reactive **5.** dividing **6.** liquid, gas **7.** neutron **8.** excited **9.** periodic law **10.** nitrogen **11.** fluoride **12.** trioxide **13.** released **14.** 2.3 **15.** raises, lowers; increases, decreases **16.** 1×10^{-11} M **17.** hydrogen **18.** high-density polyethylene; HDPE **19.** 0, +1 **20.** beryllium-8

Short Answer

1. life science and Earth and space science **2.** The viscosity of a liquid usually decreases as the liquid is heated and increases as the liquid cools. Motor oil does not get too thin in hot weather or too thick in cold weather. **3.** Take the temperature measurements of the surroundings during the phase change. If the temperature decreases, the phase change is endothermic; a system absorbs energy from its surroundings during an endothermic phase change. **4.** It provides a visual model of the most likely locations of electrons in an atom. **5.** chlorine **6.** bromine, Br **7.** The equation was not balanced correctly because it was balanced by changing a subscript instead of changing coefficients. The correctly balanced equation is $2Mg + O_2 \rightarrow 2MgO$. **8.** In an exothermic chemical reaction, chemical changes occur, and the reactants and the products are not the same substances. In an exothermic solution formation by dissociation, the solute undergoes a physical change and does not change identity. Energy is released in both processes. **9.** an alcohol and a salt **10.** Both the nucleus and the alpha particle are positively charged. The alpha particles must be accelerated enough to overcome the repulsion of two positively charged particles.

Using Science Skills

1. the density of the fluid 2. Mixture A; it scatters light, does not separate into layers, and cannot be separated by filtration. 3. the kilopascal; 200 kPa; 100 kPa 4. Students may answer yes because the model shows the composition of the nucleus of an atom. Students may answer no because the model does not include any electrons or show the position of the nucleus in the atom. 5. Rubidium is the most reactive element shown. Group 1A alkali metals are the most reactive metals, and the reactivity of elements in Group 1A increases from top to bottom. 6. The compounds in rows A and C are both ionic compounds. However, KI is a binary ionic compound, which forms between a metal and a nonmetal. The compound in row C contains a polyatomic hydroxide ion (OH^-). The atoms in a polyatomic ion are joined by covalent bonds.
7. the amount of energy required to break the chemical bonds of the reactants 8. 147 g sucrose 9. D
10. protactinium-234; 42 g

Problem

1. $4Fe + 3O_2 \rightarrow 2Fe_2O_3$; 9 mol O_2
2. $CO_2 + H_2O \rightarrow H_2CO_3$

Essay

1. In peer reviews, scientists review and question other scientists' data. Scientists also help determine if the data is accurately reported. If the review finds errors in the data, in the conclusions, or in the experimental procedures, the hypothesis may need to be revised.
2. Filtration would be used because it is the process of separating mixtures based on the size of their particles (or pieces). A screen could be used to separate the mixture. The holes in the screen would need to be large enough to allow the soil to pass through but not the leaves, acorn, or twigs. 3. The volume of the chest cavity increases as the diaphragm contracts and the rib cage is lifted. This increase in volume allows the particles in air to spread out, which lowers the air pressure in the lungs. Air rushes into the lungs because the air pressure outside the body is greater than the air pressure in the lungs. As the diaphragm relaxes and the rib cage moves down and in, the volume of the chest cavity decreases. This decrease in volume increases the air pressure, and air is forced out of the lungs.

Unit 1 Test B Answers

Multiple Choice

1. d	2. c	3. d	4. c	5. b	6. d
7. c	8. a	9. d	10. c	11. a	12. a
13. d	14. a	15. a	16. c	17. b	18. c
19. d	20. c	21. b	22. a	23. a	24. b
25. d	26. d	27. c	28. c	29. a	30. d

Completion

1. line graph 2. Distillation 3. physical 4. increases, temperature 5. Aristotle 6. electrons 7. alkali
8. polyatomic 9. conservation of mass 10. exothermic

11. collisions 12. carbon dioxide, water 13. cellular respiration 14. 6 15. chain reaction

Short Answer

1. 32°F, 0°C, and 273 K 2. Accept any of the following: the suspension would appear cloudy, while the solution would be clear; the particles in the suspension would settle to the bottom, while the particles in the solution would not settle. 3. a change in color, the production of a gas, and the formation of a precipitate 4. The volume of a liquid is constant because forces of attraction keep the particles close together. 5. Democritus believed all matter consisted of tiny particles that could not be divided into smaller particles. 6. Scientists realized that atoms contained smaller subatomic particles.
7. Sodium is the alkali metal, and chlorine is the halogen. 8. Bromine; it gains electrons rather than losing them. 9. Equilibrium exists because liquid water is freezing and ice is melting at the same rate. The equilibrium is physical because no new substances form. 10. A freshwater marsh; in a saltwater marsh, the dissolved salt lowers the freezing point of the water.
11. A saturated solution contains all the solute it can hold at that temperature. More solute will dissolve at that temperature in an unsaturated solution. 12. carbon and hydrogen 13. Ethyne is an alkyne, heptane is an alkane, and benzene is an aromatic hydrocarbon.
14. Uranium salts wrapped in paper left a pattern on unexposed photographic film. He concluded that the salts emitted rays that exposed the film. 15. The atomic number tells the number of protons. The mass number tells the total number of protons and neutrons. The mass number (4) minus the atomic number (2) tells you that there are 2 neutrons in an alpha particle.

Using Science Skills

1. approximately 165 cm 2. Before clay is baked, it is soft and can be molded. After clay is baked, it is hard and brittle. 3. a. vaporization; b. melting; c. freezing
4. The solid ball in panel 1 is like the drawing of the exterior of a house. It provides no details about the internal structure of an atom. The model in panel 2 shows the locations of different parts of the atom within the atom and their relative sizes. It is like a blueprint that shows the size and location of rooms in a house. 5. V is a transition metal, and He is a noble gas. 6. The atoms of a metal lose one or more valence electrons and form cations. The atoms of a nonmetal gain one or more electrons and form anions. There is an attraction between the oppositely charged ions. 7. On the left side, there are 1 carbon atom, 4 hydrogen atoms, and 2 oxygen atoms. On the right side, there are 1 carbon atom, 3 oxygen atoms, and 2 hydrogen atoms. 8. Most cleaners contain bases. 9. People need the energy stored in plants and the oxygen produced during photosynthesis. 10. 1. The mass of the beta particle is so small ($\frac{1}{1836}$ amu) that it is not significant

Chapter 11 Test A Answers

Multiple Choice

1. c **2.** b **3.** a **4.** d **5.** a **6.** b
7. d **8.** c **9.** d **10.** b **11.** c **12.** c
13. c **14.** d **15.** c

Completion

1. vectors **2.** average speed **3.** constant **4.** positive
5. Instantaneous acceleration

Short Answer

1. the airplane **2.** the meter **3.** 4 m + (–2 m) = 2 m
4. km/h **5.** The slope of the line representing Bus A is steeper than the slope of the line representing Bus B.
6. changes in speed, direction, or both

Using Science Skills

1. Arrows A and B are vectors with magnitude (distance) and direction. **2.** The object moved a total distance of 11 m + 5 m = 16 m. The object's displacement is 11 m – 5 m = 6 m to the right. **3.** Figure 11-3A models an object subject to two relative velocities. Vector A + B represents velocity of the object. **4.** The distance would be 11 m + 12 m = 23 m. The displacement magnitude would be 11 m + (–12 m) = –1 m, or 1 m to the left. **5.** the displacement

Problem

1. $a = \dfrac{V_f - V_i}{t}$ $\dfrac{10 m/s - 6 m/s}{4s} = \dfrac{4 m/s}{4s} = 1 m/s^2$

2. $\bar{V} = \dfrac{d}{t}$ $t\bar{v} = d$ $t = d/\bar{v}$ $t = 20\ km/2\ km/h = 10$

Essay

1. Speed is equal to the distance traveled divided by the time required to cover the distance. Velocity describes both speed and the direction of motion. **2.** Acceleration can be described as changes in speed, direction, or both. The ball is moving at a constant speed, but its direction is changing constantly. Because its direction is changing, the ball is experiencing constant acceleration. **3.** The girl's displacement from home is 1 block east. The pet store is located 1 block east of her home. The girl walked a total distance of 13 blocks.

Chapter 11 Test B Answers

Multiple Choice

1. b **2.** d **3.** b **4.** a **5.** b **6.** c
7. c **8.** a **9.** d **10.** c **11.** c **12.** a
13. b **14.** d **15.** b

Completion

1. frames of reference **2.** distance; length **3.** displacement **4.** resultant vector **5.** meters per second
6. instantaneous speed **7.** direction **8.** direction
9. accelerate **10.** gravity **11.** speed; velocity

Short Answer

1. direction **2.** average speed and instantaneous speed
3. The slope is the change in distance divided by the change in time, which gives speed. **4.** acceleration
5. instantaneous acceleration

Using Science Skills

1. Graph A shows periods of constant speed (0–8 s, 8–12 s, 12–20 s). **2.** The object moves at constant speed for 8 seconds, is at rest for the next 4 seconds, and then moves at constant speed for the next 8 seconds. **3.** Graph B shows acceleration. The upward slope of the line indicates that an increasing distance is covered each second. **4.** The object moved a distance of 300 m in 8 s. The object's average speed is 37.5 m/s. $\bar{v} = 300\ m/8\ s = 37.5\ m/s$
5. Graph A; the slope is steeper.

Chapter 12 Test A Answers

Multiple Choice

1. d **2.** d **3.** d **4.** b **5.** d **6.** d
7. c **8.** c **9.** d **10.** d **11.** a **12.** b
13. c **14.** d

Completion

1. weight **2.** balanced forces; balanced **3.** greater; larger **4.** gravity **5.** direction

Short Answer

1. The length of the arrow represents the size of the force, and the direction of the arrow represents the direction of the force. **2.** Each ball will reach the ground in the same amount of time. **3.** The direction of the net force is opposite the direction of the dummy's motion.
4. 20 kg•m/s **5.** The speed of the golf ball is much greater than the speed of the bowling ball.

Using Science Skills

1. 0 kg•m/s **2.** The momentums of both skaters are equal in size but opposite in direction. **3.** The push on Skater B by Skater A accelerates Skater B forward. **4.** According to Newton's third law of motion, as Skater A pushes on Skater B, an equal and opposite force pushes back on Skater A. The unbalanced force causes Skater B to accelerate backward. **5.** No; Skater A is exerting the same force on Skater B as before and so Skater B is exerting the same force on Skater A as before. The result is that Skater's A motion will be the same.

Problem

1. Acceleration = $\dfrac{\text{Net force}}{\text{Mass}}$, $a = \dfrac{F}{m}$

$a = \dfrac{900\ N}{750\ kg} = \dfrac{1.2\ N}{kg} = \dfrac{1.2\ \frac{kg•m}{s^2}}{kg} = 1.2\ m/s^2$

$a = 1/2\ m/s^2$, upward

2. Weight = Mass × Acceleration due to gravity
$W = mg$; $W = 4.2\ kg \times 9.8\ m/s^2$; $W = 41\ kg•m/s^2 = 41 N$
3. Momentum = Mass × Velocity
Momentum = 32 kg × 2.5 m/s = 80 kg•m/s, downriver
4. $a = \dfrac{F}{m}$ $F = ma = 0.20\ kg \times 12\ m/s^2 = 2.4\ kg•m/s^2 = 2.4\ N$

Essay

1. On both the calm and windy days, the net force on the biker is zero because the biker is traveling at constant speed. On a calm day, the biker must pedal so that the forward-directed force applied to the bike balances the forces of friction opposing the forward motion. The friction forces primarily take the form rolling friction and fluid friction. On a windy day, the fluid friction force is much greater, so the rider must pedal harder to maintain the same constant speed.

Chapter 12 Test B Answers
Multiple Choice
1. d **2.** b **3.** a **4.** b **5.** d **6.** c
7. a **8.** c **9.** a **10.** b **11.** b **12.** b
13. d **14.** b **15.** a **16.** a

Completion
1. force **2.** net force **3.** friction **4.** air resistance; drag **5.** projectile **6.** inertia **7.** force, mass **8.** weight **9.** bowling **10.** equals

Short Answer
1. It increases. **2.** Down; there is no net force on the sky diver. **3.** Double the net force acting on the object.
4. strong nuclear force **5.** the gravitational pull of the moon

Using Science Skills
1. D **2.** The centripetal force will become less. **3.** Earth
4. inertia **5.** c

Chapter 13 Test A Answers
Multiple Choice
1. d **2.** b **3.** b **4.** b **5.** c **6.** d
7. c **8.** b **9.** a **10.** d **11.** c **12.** c
13. d **14.** a **15.** d

Completion
1. square meter; m^2 **2.** increases **3.** equally **4.** decreases; becomes smaller **5.** greater; more

Short Answer
1. Multiply the air pressure by the area of the tabletop.
2. 0.1 Pa, 10 N/m^2, 300 N/m^2, 2 kPa **3.** The pressure within the organisms' bodies balances water pressure. As a result, the net force on their bodies is zero. **4.** Air pressure that is pushing in on the balloon decreases as the balloon rises. **5.** The boat shape displaced a greater volume of water. **6.** When an object is less dense than the fluid it is in, the object will float in the fluid. When an object is more dense than the fluid it is in, the object will sink in the fluid. **7.** 0 N or zero

Using Science Skills
1. The spoon moved toward the stream of running water. **2.** on the side opposite the stream of water
3. The spoon is pushed toward the stream of water; the pressure of the air on the side of the spoon opposite the stream of water is greater than the pressure of the air on the side of the spoon next to the stream of water.
4. The stream of water causes the nearby air to move.
5. The spoon would move closer to the stream of water.

Problem
1. Pressure = $\dfrac{\text{Force}}{\text{Area}}$ = $\dfrac{\text{Force}}{\text{Length} \times \text{Width}}$ = $\dfrac{21N}{0.19\,m \times 0.090\,m}$

Pressure = $\dfrac{21N}{0.017\,m^2}$ = 1200 N/m^2

2. 2500N/m^2 = 2500Pa $\times \dfrac{1kPa}{1000Pa}$ = 2.5kPa

3. A hydraulic lift multiples force by a factor equal to the area of the large piston divided by the small piston.

$\dfrac{\text{Surface area of Piston 2}}{\text{Surface are of Piston 1}} = \dfrac{900\ cm^2}{100\ cm^2} = 9$

The hydraulic lift will multiply the force by a factor of 9.
100N $\times$ 9 = 900N
The force exerted on Piston 2 is 900 N.

Essay
1. A window may explode outward during a windstorm because the outside pressure is much less than the pressure inside the house. By opening the window, the difference in pressures is reduced. **2.** 0.5 N; because the 0.5-N washer and the cube floating on its own both displace the same volume, the 0.5-N force equals the buoyant force acting on the cube.

Chapter 13 Test B Answers
Multiple Choice
1. b **2.** d **3.** c **4.** b **5.** a **6.** b
7. d **8.** d **9.** b **10.** b **11.** a **12.** a
13. d **14.** d **15.** d

Completion
1. area **2.** pressure **3.** pascal **4.** fluid **5.** hydraulic system **6.** pressure **7.** constant **8.** buoyancy
9. upward **10.** density

Short Answer
1. standing on tiptoes **2.** depth and type of fluid **3.** by coming into contact with the container **4.** They are equal. **5.** The buoyant force is less than the weight.

Using Science Skills
1. The fluid pressure exerted on the black spheres is greater (about twice as great). **2.** black **3.** four spheres
4. five spheres **5.** three spheres

Chapter 14 Test A Answers
Multiple Choice
1. b **2.** b **3.** c **4.** b **5.** c **6.** b
7. d **8.** d **9.** d **10.** b **11.** b **12.** c
13. b **14.** c

Completion
1. work **2.** motion **3.** power **4.** decreases **5.** lever

Short Answer
1. The swimmer that swims faster develops more power only if both swimmers do the same amount of work. **2.** Some of work input is used to overcome friction. **3.** They would be equal. **4.** A fixed pulley changes only the direction of the input force. A movable pulley changes both the direction of the input force and its size. **5.** The work output of the first simple machine is the work input of the second simple machine.

Using Science Skills
1. 1.0 m **2.** wheel and axle **3.** 4 **4.** a compound machine **5.** The work out of Machine B equals the work

output of Machine A.

Problem

1. Work = Force × Distance = 220N × 10m = 220N•m = 2200J; Work = 2200J

2. Power = $\dfrac{\text{Work}}{\text{Time}}$ = $\dfrac{\text{Force} \times \text{Distance}}{\text{Time}}$ = $\dfrac{100N \times 2.0m}{1s}$ =

200 $\dfrac{J}{s}$ = 200W; Power = 200W

3. IMA = $\dfrac{\text{Input distance}}{\text{Output distance}}$ = $\dfrac{6.0m}{0.50m}$ = 12; IMA = 12

4. AMA = $\dfrac{\text{Output force}}{\text{Input force}}$ = $\dfrac{30N}{16N}$ = 1.9; AMA = 1.9

5. Efficiency = $\dfrac{\text{Work output}}{\text{Work input}}$ × 100% =

$\dfrac{\text{Work output}}{\text{Input force} \times \text{Input distance}}$ × 100%

Efficiency = $\dfrac{32J}{12N \times 0.3m}$ × 100% = $\dfrac{32J}{36N•m}$ × 100% =

$\dfrac{32J}{36J}$ × 100% = 89%; Efficiency = 89%

Chapter 14 Test B Answers
Multiple Choice

1. d	**2.** a	**3.** a	**4.** a	**5.** a	**6.** a
7. b	**8.** d	**9.** b	**10.** c	**11.** c	**12.** a
13. c	**14.** c	**15.** b	**16.** b		

Completion

1. move **2.** joule **3.** power **4.** watt **5.** force **6.** input **7.** mechanical advantage **8.** screw **9.** less **10.** compound

Short Answer

1. Work is done because a force is applied in the direction in which the book moves. **2.** There is no movement, so no work is done. **3.** The simple machine reduces the output distance. **4.** the screw with closely spaced threads **5.** A pair of scissors contains two simple machines working together. Each arm is a first-class lever with a wedge, which is the blade, at one end.

Using Science Skills

1. Ideal mechanical advantage = $\dfrac{\text{Input distance}}{\text{Output distance}}$ = $\dfrac{3m}{1m}$
= 3 **2.** The ramp's AMA would increase. **3.** Its efficiency would increase; friction would decrease. **4.** an inclined plane **5.** It is less.

Chapter 15 Test A Answers
Multiple Choice

1. d	**2.** b	**3.** b	**4.** c	**5.** c	**6.** d
7. a	**8.** b	**9.** c	**10.** c	**11.** d	**12.** b
13. c	**14.** c	**15.** c			

Completion

1. joule **2.** speed **3.** elastic **4.** active **5.** conservation

Short Answer

1. kg•m^2/s^2 = (kgm/s^2)•m = N•m = J **2.** Sled B; it has less mass. **3.** Stretch it or compress it. **4.** because the thermal energy of an object is the kinetic and potential

energy of its particles **5.** Accept either of the following: The potential energy of stored water is converted into kinetic energy as the water falls; as the falling water does work on the turbine, it moves the turbine's blades (KE). The KE of the rotating blades is converted into electrical energy by the generator. **6.** The elastic potential energy of the bent bow and string is converted into kinetic energy of the arrow. **7.** Biomass energy is the chemical energy stored in living things. The chemical energy is produced as plants convert sunlight in the form of electromagnetic energy into chemical energy.

Using Science Skills

1. C **2.** The gravitational potential energy of the ball is the same at both locations; the height is the same. **3.** No; since the ball is always moving to the right between locations A and F, at every point between A and F, the ball has kinetic energy. Because the ball has kinetic energy at each point, it has some mechanical energy at each point. **4.** No; because the ball does not reach the same height each time it bounces, its maximum gravitational potential energy is decreasing from one bounce to the next. Because its gravitational potential energy decreases and its maximum kinetic energy does not increase, the total mechanical energy must be decreasing. **5.** The kinetic energy is less before the second bounce. Since its gravitational potential energy is zero each time it strikes the floor, its kinetic energy equals its total mechanical energy. Because the total mechanical energy has decreased with the first bounce, its kinetic energy has decreased as it strikes the floor just before the second bounce.

Problem

1. KE = $\dfrac{1}{2}mv^2$ = $\dfrac{1}{2}$(74.0kg)(52.0m/s)^2

= $\dfrac{1}{2}$(74kg) (2704m^2/s^2) = 1,000,000J

2. PE = mgh = (0.49kg)(9.8m/s^2)(3.6m – 1.5m) = 10J decreased by 10J

3. (KE)$_{beginning}$ = (PE)$_{end}$
KE = mgh = (7.7kg)(9.8m/s^2)(1.1m) = 83J
4. E = mc^2 = (1.0 × 10^{-14}kg)(3.0 × 10^{8}m/s)^2 = 9.0 × 10^{2}J

Essay

1. Biomass energy is energy that is available immediately from the chemical energy stored in living organisms. Biomass is classified as a renewable energy resource. Fossil fuels also contain chemical energy but were formed over a long period of time from once-living organisms. Fossil fuels are classified as nonrenewable energy resources.

Chapter 15 Test B Answers
Multiple Choice

1. a	**2.** a	**3.** c	**4.** d	**5.** d	**6.** d
7. a	**8.** b	**9.** d	**10.** b	**11.** c	**12.** d
13. a	**14.** b	**15.** b			

Completion

1. work **2.** mass **3.** potential **4.** chemical
5. mechanical **6.** kinetic; mechanical **7.** conversion
8. conservation of energy **9.** light **10.** nonrenewable
11. nonpolluting

Short Answer

1. The kinetic energy of the golf ball suddenly increases as the club strikes it. **2.** kinetic energy and potential energy **3.** visible light **4.** Accept either of the following: The resource can be replaced in a relatively short period of time. The resource originates either directly or indirectly from the sun. **5.** The refrigerator uses less energy due to its efficiency, so over time, the total cost may be lower.

Using Science Skills

1. 5 J; because the block gained 5 joules of energy, the spring had to do 5 joules of work on the block.
2. elastic potential energy **3.** The elastic potential energy of the spring has decreased. **4.** The block's kinetic energy would be less. Some of the elastic potential energy of the compressed spring would be converted into thermal energy due to friction. As a result, less of the spring's elastic potential energy would be converted into kinetic energy of the block. **5.** The block's kinetic energy has increased.

Chapter 16 Test A Answers

Multiple Choice

1. c   **2.** c   **3.** c   **4.** d   **5.** c   **6.** d
7. d   **8.** c   **9.** c   **10.** a   **11.** d   **12.** b
13. a   **14.** d

Completion

1. temperature **2.** from, to **3.** equal; the same
4. thermal energy **5.** filters, forced-air

Short Answer

1. Some of the work you do in stretching the rubber band increases the average kinetic energy of the particles in the rubber band, causing its temperature to rise. **2.** Free electrons collide with each other and with atoms or ions to transfer thermal energy. **3.** Energy is conserved in a heat pump because the amount of work done on the pump and the amount of thermal energy it transfers from the cold environment equals the amount of thermal energy it releases to the hotter environment. **4.** more organized before; the second law of thermodynamics **5.** external combustion engine; because the steam, which runs the turbine, is produced by fuel, which is burned outside the engine

Using Science Skills

1. The average kinetic energy of the water molecules in B equals the average kinetic energy of the molecules in C but is greater than the average kinetic energy of the molecules in A. **2.** The thermal energy of the water in C is greater than the thermal energy of the water in B, which is greater than the thermal energy of the water in A. **3.** B's water has less mass than C's water has, so B's water has a greater temperature change, making B's final water temperature higher. Even though the temperature change for A and B is the same since they have the same mass, B's final water temperature is higher because B's water had a higher beginning temperature. **4.** Temperature$_A$ = 60°C (The thermal energy transferred from the hotter water equals the thermal energy transferred to the warm water.) Because equal masses of water combine, the temperature drop of the hotter water equals the temperature rise of the warm water. The result is that the final temperature of each lies halfway between 50°C and 70°C, which is 60°C. Temperature$_B$ = Temperature$_C$ = 70° (There is no transfer of heat between materials at the same temperature.) **5.** Heat transferred from the hotter water equals heat transferred to the warm water. Since there are 600 g of hotter water and 200 g of warm water, the temperature change (drop) of the hotter water will be less than the temperature change (rise) of the warm water. As a result, the final temperature of the mixture will be closer to 70°C than to 50°C.

Problem

1. $Q = m \times c \times \Delta T = 420g \times 0.96 J/g \bullet °C \times (232°C - 22°C)$
$Q = 420g \times 0.96 J/g \bullet °C \times 210°C = 85,000J = 85kJ$
2. $Q = m \times c \times \Delta T$
$\Delta T = \dfrac{Q}{m \times c} = \dfrac{31,000J}{315g \times 3.9 J/g \bullet °C} = 25°C$
3. $Q_{water} = m_{water} \times c_{water} \times \Delta T_{water} = 335g \times 4.18 J \bullet g/°C$
$\times (32.0°C - 25.0°C)$ $Q_{water} = 335g \times 4.18 J/g \bullet °C \times 7.0°C$
$= 7000J$ The heat transferred *from* the brass equals the heat transferred *to* the water.
$Q_{brass} = Q_{water} = m_{brass} \times c_{brass} \times DT_{brass} = Q_{water}$
$c_{brass} = \dfrac{Q_{water}}{m_{brass} \times \Delta T_{brass}} = \dfrac{9800J}{410g \times (95.0°C - 32.0°C)}$

$c_{brass} = \dfrac{9800J}{410g \times 63.0°C} = 0.38 J/g \bullet °C$

Essay

1. When the air near a heat source is heated, it expands, causing its density to decrease. This less dense, warmer air is buoyed up by the colder air that pushes around and under it. As the warm air is pushed upward, it cools, becomes more dense, and then sinks. It now moves in beneath the air that is being warmed by the heat source and pushes it upward. As parts of the fluid alternately heat and cool, loops of moving fluid form within the fluid itself. These loops are called convection currents. **2.** If the pump causes a refrigerant to condense inside the house, the process will release thermal energy to the inside air and warm the air. If the pump releases the cooled refrigerant outside the house, the refrigerant will absorb thermal energy from the warmer surrounding air as the refrigerant evaporates. The absorbed thermal energy can then be used to warm the air inside the house.

Chapter 16 Test B Answers
Multiple Choice
1. a **2.** d **3.** d **4.** a **5.** c **6.** a
7. a **8.** c **9.** c **10.** d **11.** b **12.** c
13. d **14.** b **15.** c **16.** d

Completion
1. kelvins, degrees Celsius **2.** greater **3.** thermal contraction **4.** conduction **5.** radiation **6.** vacuum
7. conductor **8.** thermodynamics **9.** waste heat
10. rotary **11.** hot-water

Short Answer
1. Heat flows spontaneously from hot objects to cold objects. **2.** solids, liquids, gases **3.** When heated, the metal lid expands at a greater rate than the glass jar. The expanded lid is easier to loosen. **4.** The surrounding air is warmed. The refrigerant cools and loses thermal energy as it turns from a gas to a liquid.
5. Keeping foods refrigerated keeps them from spoiling quickly. Since there is less spoilage, there is less chance of diseases from eating spoiled foods.

Using Science Skills
1. power stroke **2.** D, C, A, B **3.** convert heat into work
4. The efficiency of a heat engine would be 100 percent if the engine could exhaust waste heat (thermal energy) to an outside environment that had a temperature of absolute zero (0 K). However, according the third law of thermodynamics, a temperature of absolute zero cannot be reached. **5.** internal combustion engine

Chapter 17 Test A Answers
Multiple Choice
1. a **2.** b **3.** d **4.** c **5.** d **6.** a
7. d **8.** a **9.** c **10.** c **11.** d **12.** d
13. a **14.** b **15.** b

Completion
1. compression **2.** at right angles; perpendicular **3.** surface **4.** standing waves; resonance **5.** Doppler effect
Short Answer
1. The vibration has to carry energy through a medium.
2. period and frequency **3.** Shake the rope faster or slower while using the same force as before. **4.** The wave with greater compressions has more energy.
5. The wave must enter the new medium at an angle.
6. sounds greater than 90 decibels, such as a jet plane or rock concert

Using Science Skills
1. Wave B has an amplitude that is one-half the amplitude of wave A. **2.** The force that caused wave A added more energy to the wave than the force that caused wave B. **3.** The wavelength in E will be one-half that of the wavelength in D; it will be one-fourth that of the wavelength in C. **4.** Wave D has a frequency twice that of wave C. Also, the wavelength in wave D is about one-half that of wave C. **5.** Between wave C and wave D, frequency doubles, but wavelength is halved. Wavelength is inversely proportional to frequency.

Essay
1. Sound waves, like other kinds of waves, reflect, or bounce back, when they strike a solid barrier. It takes time for the echo to return, traveling at the speed of sound, so there is a delay. **2.** In reflection, a wave hits a solid barrier that it cannot penetrate, so it reflects, or bounces back, in roughly the same direction from which it came. In refraction, a wave hits a change in the medium, but instead of reflecting (bouncing back), it continues on into the new medium, bending as its speed changes. **3.** Diffraction; a wave diffracts more if its wavelength is large compared to the size of the obstacle (the corner people are walking around). Because sound waves have relatively long wavelengths, we hear sound around the corner as the waves diffract, or spread out. **4.** The window must have the same natural frequency as that particular note played on the trumpet. When the note is played, resonance causes the window to rattle in much the same way as a soundboard on a musical instrument vibrates as the instrument is played. **5.** Both structures are shaped like a funnel to collect waves and focus them into an opening where they can be channeled to a specific location for processing. In the case of the ear, waves are funneled into the middle and inner ear, and then on to the brain. In the case of a satellite dish, waves are funneled into digital circuitry where they can be processed into cable television programs.

Chapter 17 Test B Answers
Multiple Choice
1. d **2.** d **3.** c **4.** a **5.** a **6.** b
7. d **8.** d **9.** a **10.** d **11.** b **12.** b
13. c **14.** d **15.** c

Completion
1. energy **2.** rarefactions **3.** longitudinal **4.** frequency
5. rest position **6.** head-on **7.** node; nodes **8.** decibel
9. frequency; pitch **10.** outer
Short Answer
1. A medium is the material through which a mechanical wave travels. **2.** a longitudinal wave **3.** Shake the rope with more force. **4.** Ultrasound frequencies are higher than the sounds that people normally hear. **5.** As the source of a sound approaches, you hear a higher frequency, and as the source moves away from you, you hear a lower frequency.

Using Science Skills
1. a longitudinal wave; a transverse wave **2.** Both waves are started by application of a force. However, wave A, the longitudinal wave, is started by a back-and-forth, or push-and-pull, movement in the same direction as the resulting wave movement, while wave B, the transverse wave, is started by an up-and down movement that is at right angles to the resulting direction in which the wave travels. **3.** Compressions in wave A correspond to crests in wave B. Rare factions in wave A

correspond to troughs in wave B. Each of these conditions represents an extreme in which the coil is being displaced from its rest position. **4.** In wave A, one wavelength equals the distance between center of a compression in the spring toy and the corresponding location in the next compression. Wavelength is the distance between a point on one wave and the same point on the next cycle of waves. **5.** In a sound wave in air, the compressions consist of regions of bunched-up air, while the rare factions consist of regions in which the molecules are more spread out.

Chapter 18 Test A Answers

Multiple Choice

1. b	**2.** b	**3.** b	**4.** d	**5.** c	**6.** c
7. b	**8.** c	**9.** a	**10.** d	**11.** c	**12.** d
13. b	**14.** a	**15.** d			

Completion

1. transmits **2.** vacuum **3.** more **4.** laser **5.** visible light

Short Answer

1. Electromagnetic waves can travel through a vacuum; sound waves cannot. Also, electromagnetic waves are transverse waves, whereas sound waves are longitudinal waves. **2.** the emission of electrons from metal caused by light striking the metal **3.** Light intensity decreases as distance from the source increases. **4.** X-rays are used to make images of bones. Gamma rays are used to make images of the brain and to kill cancer cells. **5.** what the object is made of and the color of light striking the object **6.** excited atoms emitting electrons

Using Science Skills

1. The liquid is transparent because the submerged portion of the pencil can be seen clearly regardless of the apparent break caused by refraction. **2.** Because the light bends as it moves from one medium into another, the image you see appears bent as well. **3.** White light is made up of all the frequencies that produce colored light. **4.** The object is blue. All colors are absorbed except blue. **5.** The object would appear black because there is no blue incident light to reflect.

Problem

1. wavelength = $\dfrac{\text{speed}}{\text{frequency}} = \dfrac{3.00 \times 10^8 \text{m/s}}{9.4 \times 10^9 \text{Hz}} = 0.032\text{m}$

Essay

1. According to modern theory, light is both a particle and a wave. In 1801, Thomas Young proved that light behaves like a wave by showing that light produces interference patterns like a wave. A century later, Albert Einstein proposed that light consists of discrete particles called photons and demonstrated the effects of light striking metal—the photoelectric effect. **2.** The full range of wave frequencies of electromagnetic radiation is called the electromagnetic spectrum. In order of increasing frequency, the electromagnetic spectrum includes radio waves (radio, television, microwave ovens, radar), infrared rays (heat lamps),

visible light (communication), ultraviolet rays (kill microorganisms), X-rays (medical imaging), and gamma rays (kill cancer cells). Visible light is the only part of the spectrum that we can see, and it is a very small part. **3.** Polarized light is light with waves that vibrate in only one plane. Unpolarized light vibrates in all directions. A vertical polarizing filter, such as polarized sunglasses, do not transmit light waves that vibrate in a horizontal plane, thus blocking some glaring light. **4.** Sodium-vapor lights are efficient. Where many lights are needed, such as in streets and parking lots, they can be economical to use. They give off a very bright, yellow light. The yellow light can alter the color of the objects it illuminates, which can be a disadvantage.

Chapter 18 Test B Answers

Multiple Choice

1. c	**2.** a	**3.** c	**4.** d	**5.** c	**6.** b
7. d	**8.** a	**9.** b	**10.** c	**11.** a	**12.** d
13. c	**14.** c	**15.** c			

Completion

1. transverse **2.** infrared **3.** 3.00×10^8, 300,000,000 **4.** less **5.** translucent **6.** red **7.** black **8.** vacuum **9.** electrons **10.** wavelength **11.** gamma **12.** complementary

Short Answer

1. air **2.** radio waves **3.** radio waves (radio and tele-vision signals); microwaves and radar waves (micro-wave ovens); infrared rays (heat lamps) **4.** Magenta is one of the primary colors of pigments. **5.** A laser emits a straight, narrow, intense beam of coherent light; other light sources produce light that spreads out in all directions as it moves away from the source.

Using Science Skills

1. Radio waves; FM signals usually have higher frequencies than AM signals have. **2.** High frequency waves such as X-rays and gamma rays have higher energy photons than lower frequency waves such as radio waves and infrared rays. **3.** Infrared rays are located between visible light and microwaves. **4.** visible light **5.** Red would be at the end of the visible spectrum with the lowest frequency and longest wavelength of all the colors, just above the infrared range. *Infra* means "under," so *infrared* means "under red." In the same way, *ultra* means "beyond," so *ultraviolet* means "beyond violet." Violet would be at the end of the visible spectrum with the shortest wavelength and the highest frequency.

Chapter 19 Test A Answers

Multiple Choice

1. b	**2.** d	**3.** c	**4.** b	**5.** d	**6.** d
7. b	**8.** a	**9.** c	**10.** b	**11.** a	**12.** a
13. a	**14.** d				

Completion

1. perpendicular; at right angles **2.** virtual **3.** real **4.** rods **5.** cones

Short Answer

1. Student answers may include the following: located on the retina, has no rods or cones, cannot sense light, location where the nerve endings come together to form the optic nerve. **2.** When the bulb is placed at the focal point of a concave mirror, the reflected light rays will be parallel. **3.** total internal reflection of light rays **4.** The diaphragm controls the amount of light passing into the film camera. **5.** to allow light to pass from the source below the slide up through the lenses of the microscope

Using Science Skills

1. The lens becomes longer and thinner. The muscles that control the shape of the lens relax. **2.** Light first enters the eye at D, the cornea, and refracts because the index of refraction in the cornea is different from the index of refraction in air. **3.** Point X is the retina. The brain interprets the image right-side-up. **4.** A, iris; controls the amount of light entering the eye; B, lens; focuses incoming light; C, pupil; opening that allows light rays to enter the eye D, cornea; outer coating of the eye that helps focus light; E, retina; back of the eye, which has light-sensitive cells that send image messages to the optic nerve; F, optic nerve; carries image messages to the brain **5.** nearsightedness; eyeglasses with diverging lenses to reposition the image on the retina

Essay

1. The angle of incidence is 45 degrees because the angle is measured between the incident ray and a line perpendicular to the mirror (not the ray and the mirror). The angle of reflection is equal to the angle of incidence of 45 degrees. **2.** Refraction is the bending of the light rays as they enter a new medium at an angle. Because it has a greater index of refraction, a light ray would bend more entering diamond than it would entering air. **3.** As the beam rotates and the angle of incidence increases, the amount of light reflected increases and the amount of light refracted decreases. Eventually, the angle of incidence reaches the critical angle, and the light undergoes total internal reflection. **4.** The focused light reacts with a light-sensitive chemical coating on the film. In dim light, more light needs to strike the film to record the image. In very bright light, less light is required to keep from overexposing the film. The diaphragm is the part of the film camera that controls light exposure. **5.** Rods are nerve endings that are sensitive to low light levels and are more effective at sensing objects at night. They help distinguish black, white, and shades of gray. Cones are sensitive to color, but are not as sensitive as rods in low light. In low light, it is more difficult to distinguish colors.

Chapter 19 Test B Answers

Multiple Choice

1. c   **2.** a   **3.** c   **4.** b   **5.** c   **6.** b

7. a   **8.** c   **9.** c   **10.** c   **11.** a   **12.** d
13. b   **14.** b   **15.** d   **16.** c

Completion

1. incidence **2.** concave **3.** concave **4.** slows down **5.** focal **6.** exit **7.** lens **8.** pupil **9.** retina

Short Answer

1. ray diagrams **2.** 1 meter **3.** the location of the object relative to the focal point **4.** The brain, by responding to the sensed light level in the eye, controls the amount of light in the eye by expanding and contracting the iris. **5.** a cornea that is not curved enough and an eyeball that is too short

Using Science Skills

1. C; the ray diagram shows that the angle of incidence is equal to the angle of reflection. **2.** a plane mirror; a virtual image **3.** Possible answers: A: convex mirror; a convex mirror causes light rays that are parallel to its optical axis to spread out after reflection.; B: concave mirror; a concave mirror causes light rays that are parallel to its optical axis to come together after reflection.; C: plane mirror; a plane mirror causes parallel light to remain parallel after reflection. **4.** a virtual image **5.** Each image is a virtual image. The image formed by A is reduced, the image formed by B is enlarged, and the image formed by C is the same size as the object.

Chapter 20 Test A Answers

Multiple Choice

1. d   **2.** d   **3.** a   **4.** b   **5.** d   **6.** a
7. d   **8.** a   **9.** a   **10.** b   **11.** d   **12.** c
13. d   **14.** d   **15.** c

Completion

1. directly, inversely **2.** static discharge; electric discharge **3.** positive **4.** silicon; germanium **5.** integrated, microchips

Short Answer

1. Both fields are strongest nearest the charge, where the lines representing the field are closest together. **2.** the effect an electric charge has on other charges in the space around it **3.** It is a law that states that the total charge in an isolated system is constant. **4.** The wire is a conductor and carries the charges. The plastic or rubber is an insulator and does not carry the charges. The coating helps control the current and keep it where it is needed. **5.** 3 amps, or amperes; because current is equal to voltage (90 volts) divided by resistance (30 ohms) **6.** A 50-watt light bulb uses half the energy that a 100-watt light bulb uses. Energy equals power (watts) multiplied by time. The time is the same, and the power of a 50-watt bulb is half as much, so the energy used by the 50-watt bulb is half as much. **7.** Analog signals are produced by continuously varying the voltage or current, and digital signals are produced by turning the current on and off. **8.** In n-type semiconductors, electrons flow, and in p-type semiconductors, positively charged "holes" flow. **9.** diodes, transistors, and integrated circuits

Using Science Skills

1. The light bulbs are sources of resistance, so Circuit A has the least resistance because the electrons pass through only one light bulb. Circuit B has more resistance than A has because Circuit B has two light bulbs. Circuit C has three light bulbs and the most resistance. Although other parts of the circuits, such as the wire, are sources of resistance, they are the same in all three circuits. **2.** Circuit A will have more current flowing through it than Circuit B will, and Circuit C will have the least current flowing through it. More current can flow when there is less resistance, and, since light bulbs are a source of resistance, Circuit A has the least resistance and the most current. **3.** In the filament, which is a thin wire, the resistance is high. The electrons collide more often in the filament, so the filaments become hotter than the connecting wires. **4.** The bulb in Circuit A will be the brightest. The bulbs in Circuit C will be the dimmest. Each bulb is a source of resistance, and as resistance increases, current decreases. Bulbs shine less brightly as the current decreases. **5.** All the bulbs would have the same brightness if Circuits B and C were rewired as parallel circuits. Some wires would need to be cut in half to do this. Then, the current would have a separate path through each bulb and would not be affected by the resistance of another bulb.

Essay

1. Charges can build up in a storm cloud from friction between moving air masses. Negative charge in the lower part of the cloud induces a positive charge in the ground below the cloud. As the amount of charge in the cloud increases, the force of attraction between the charges in the cloud and charges in the ground increases. Eventually, the air becomes charged, forming a pathway for electrons to travel from the cloud to the ground. The sudden discharge that follows is lightning. **2.** The battery is a source of electrical energy. A voltage drop, or potential difference, is maintained across the negative and positive terminals of a battery. Charge flows spontaneously from a higher electrical potential energy to a lower electrical potential energy. **3.** The brightness of the first bulb decreases if a second bulb is added in series but does not change if a second bulb is added in parallel. By adding a second bulb in series, the overall current is reduced because the resistance of the circuit increases. With less current, the brightness of the first bulb decreases because $P = IV$, and I decreases, while V is unchanged. By adding a second bulb in parallel, the total current increases, but the current through the first bulb is unchanged, so its brightness is unchanged. **4.** The amount of current in a circuit can increase if the devices are connected in parallel. Each device that is turned on increases the current. If the

current exceeds safety limits, the wire many overheat and start a fire unless a fuse melts or the circuit breaker switches off. **5.** A p-type semiconductor is made by adding trace amounts of boron to silicon. A space, called a hole, occurs at each boron atom. The holes are positively charged. When charge flows, electrons are attracted toward the positively charged holes in the p-semiconductor. As electrons jump from hole to hole, it looks like a flow of positive charge because the locations of the holes change.

Chapter 20 Test B Answers

Multiple Choice

1. b	**2.** a	**3.** d	**4.** c	**5.** c	**6.** d
7. c	**8.** b	**9.** c	**10.** d	**11.** a	**12.** d
13. d	**14.** a	**15.** b			

Completion

1. away from **2.** repel, attract **3.** ampere; amp **4.** insulators, conductor **5.** ohm **6.** circuit **7.** volts, current **8.** grounding **9.** digital **10.** vacuum **11.** diode **12.** direct

Short Answer

1. by friction, contact, and induction **2.** In direct current, the charge flows only in one direction. In alternating current, the charge regularly reverses its direction. **3.** batteries, solar cells, and generators **4.** 9 volts; because voltage is equal to the current multiplied by the resistance **5.** A computer uses electric current to process or transmit information, while a toaster uses electric current to change electrical energy into thermal energy.

Using Science Skills

1. No; only Circuit A is a series circuit. In Circuit A, the current can follow only one path through all three bulbs. Circuit B is a parallel circuit because the current can follow a separate path through each of the three bulbs. **2.** The electrons move from the negative terminal of the battery to the positive terminal of the battery. This is opposite the direction in which the current moves. **3.** For each circuit, three bulbs and a battery would need to be drawn. **4.** If a bulb in Circuit A burned out, the path for a charge is broken, and the other two light bulbs will go out. If a bulb in Circuit B burned out, the charge can still flow through the paths with the other two bulbs, and the other bulbs stay lit. **5.** A switch could be added. When the switch is open, the circuit is not a complete loop, and the current immediately stops. A person must manually open and close the switch. In a home, fuses and circuit breakers are safety devices that automatically stop the current if too much current flows through the circuit.

Chapter 21 Test A Answers

Multiple Choice

1. a	**2.** d	**3.** c	**4.** c	**5.** a	**6.** a
7. b	**8.** b	**9.** d	**10.** d	**11.** b	**12.** c
13. b	**14.** c	**15.** b			

Completion

1. magnetic poles; poles **2.** north pole **3.** magnetic declination **4.** alternating **5.** coal

Short Answer

1. Magnetic declination varies with your location on Earth. **2.** Opposite poles of magnets will attract each other, so the magnetic North Pole must be a south pole because it attracts the north pole of a compass needle. **3.** A vibrating electric charge induces a changing magnet field, which induces a changing electric field. The changing electric and magnetic fields regenerate each other, producing an electromagnetic wave. **4.** An electromagnet on a spring is placed between the poles of a permanent magnet. When there is current in the coil, the resulting magnetic field lines up with the field of the permanent magnet and indicates the strength of the current by deflecting a needle on a dial. **5.** Generators convert mechanical energy into electrical energy, while electric motors convert electrical energy into mechanical energy.

Using Science Skills

1. The magnetic field lines point from the north pole to the south pole. **2.** The same direction; the direction of current associated with the electron flow is the same as the direction of the current in the wire. **3.** The current always flows from the positive connection toward the negative connection on a battery. **4.** The force is perpendicular to the direction of the current, in an upward direction. **5.** The force is perpendicular to the direction of the current, in a downward direction. The force is in the opposite direction as it would be on the wire in B.

Essay

1. The magnetic poles of Earth are not at the same position as the geographic poles. A compass will point along field lines towards the magnetic poles, not the geographic poles. Therefore, the compass direction will vary depending on where you are. The angle between the direction to geographic north and the direction a compass points is called the magnetic declination.
2. A solenoid is a coil of current-carrying wire that produces a magnetic field. A solenoid can be constructed by coiling a length of wire, then connecting either end to a battery. An electromagnet is a solenoid with a core of ferromagnetic material, such as an iron bar. To build an electromagnet, wrap wire around a nail and connect the ends of the wire to a battery or other source of electric current.
3. With an electromagnet, the magnetic field can be turned on and off, which can control a diaphragm to make sounds in a loudspeaker (for example, in a telephone). The strength and direction of the magnetic field can be controlled by modifying the current. This can be used to control the speed with which a motor operates in a device such as a fan.

4. A step-down transformer is used, which has a primary coil with a large number of turns and a secondary coil with fewer turns, so the ratio of the number of secondary coil turns to the primary coil turns is the same as the ratio of the output voltage to the input voltage. This will decrease the voltage.
5. A step-up transformer increases voltage and decreases current. A step-up transformer has a primary coil with fewer turns than in the secondary coil. A step-down transformer increases current and decreases voltage. A step-down transformer has a primary coil with more turns than the secondary coil has.

Chapter 21 Test B Answers

Multiple Choice

1. b	**2.** b	**3.** c	**4.** a	**5.** c	**6.** c
7. b	**8.** d	**9.** b	**10.** b	**11.** a	**12.** c
13. b	**14.** a	**15.** b			

Completion

1. magnetic field **2.** electrons; unpaired electrons **3.** aurora **4.** magnetic domains; domains **5.** perpendicular; at right angles **6.** current **7.** electric current; current; voltage **8.** generator **9.** AC; alternating current **10.** Step-up

Short Answer

1. areas of a magnet where the magnetic force is strongest **2.** The force will be very weak. **3.** a generator is a device that induces an electric current by rotating a coil of wire in a magnetic field. **4.** Accept any five of the following: coal, oil, natural gas, hydroelectric, nuclear, wind, solar. **5.** Falling water pushes the blades of a turbine, which turns the axle of a generator or spins magnets around coils of wire.

Using Science Skills

1. The magnetic pole near the magnetic South Pole is a north magnetic pole. **2.** Earth's magnetic field is strongest at the magnetic North Pole and at the magnetic South Pole. The field lines are closest together in these regions. **3.** The north pole of a compass will point along Earth's magnetic field lines in the general direction of the magnetic pole near the geographic North Pole. This pole is a south magnetic pole. **4.** The difference in the angle between the direction toward true north and the direction toward the magnetic pole is called magnetic declination. It varied because the two readings were taken in different locations. **5.** midway between the poles, and far from Earth's surface

Unit 2 Test A Answers

Multiple Choice

1. b	**2.** d	**3.** d	**4.** d	**5.** c	**6.** d
7. d	**8.** d	**9.** c	**10.** b	**11.** c	**12.** b
13. b	**14.** a	**15.** c	**16.** d	**17.** c	**18.** a
19. a	**20.** d	**21.** d	**22.** d	**23.** b	**24.** b
25. b	**26.** c	**27.** a	**28.** c	**29.** d	**30.** b

Completion

1. constant **2.** Instantaneous acceleration **3.** greater; larger **4.** gravity **5.** equally **6.** decreases; becomes smaller **7.** decreases **8.** lever **9.** active **10.** conservation **11.** from, to **12.** equal; the same **13.** compression **14.** at right angles; perpendicular **15.** vacuum **16.** more **17.** rods **18.** integrated, microchips **19.** magnetic declination **20.** alternating

Short Answer

1. km/h **2.** 20 kgm/s **3.** Air pressure that is pushing in on the balloon decreases as the balloon rises. **4.** A fixed pulley changes only the direction of the input force. A movable pulley changes both the direction of the input force and its size. **5.** Biomass energy is the chemical energy stored in living things. The chemical energy is produced as plants convert sunlight in the form of electromagnetic energy into chemical energy. **6.** Free electrons collide with each other and with atoms or ions to transfer thermal energy. **7.** The wave with greater compressions has more energy. **8.** to allow light to pass from the source below the slide up through the lenses of the microscope **9.** It is a law that states that the total charge in an isolated system is constant. **10.** A vibrating electric charge induces a changing magnet field, which induces a changing electric field. The changing electric and magnetic fields regenerate each other, producing an electromagnetic wave.

Using Science Skills

1. Arrows A and B are vectors with magnitude (distance) and direction. **2.** The momentums of both skaters are equal in size but opposite in direction. **3.** The spoon moved toward the stream of running water. **4.** 1.0 m **5.** No; because the ball does not reach the same height each time it bounces, its maximum gravitational potential energy is decreasing from one bounce to the next. Because its gravitational potential energy decreases and its maximum kinetic energy does not increase, the total mechanical energy must be decreasing. **6.** The average kinetic energy of the water molecules in B equals the average kinetic energy of the molecules in C but is greater than the average kinetic energy of the molecules in A. **7.** Wave B has an amplitude that is one-half the amplitude of wave A. **8.** to allow light to pass from the source below the slide up through the lenses of the microscope **9.** The light bulbs are sources of resistance, so Circuit A has the least resistance because the electrons pass through only one light bulb. Circuit B has more resistance than A has because Circuit B has two light bulbs. Circuit C has three light bulbs and the most resistance. Although other parts of the circuits, such as the wire, are sources of resistance, they are the same in all three circuits. **10.** The current always flows from the positive connection toward the negative connection on a battery.

Problem

1. $a = \dfrac{V_f - V_i}{t} = \dfrac{10m/s - 6m/s}{4s} = \dfrac{4m/s}{4s} = 1m/s^2$

Essay

1. On both the calm and windy days, the net force on the biker is zero because the biker is traveling at constant speed. On a calm day, the biker must pedal so that the forward-directed force applied to the bike balances the forces of friction opposing the forward motion. The friction forces primarily take the form rolling friction and fluid friction. On a windy day, the fluid friction force is much greater, so the rider must pedal harder to maintain the same constant speed. **2.** 0.5 N; because the 0.5-N washer and the cube floating on its own both displace the same volume, the 0.5-N force equals the buoyant force acting on the cube. **3.** Diffraction; a wave diffracts more if its wavelength is large compared to the size of the obstacle (the corner people are walking around). Because sound waves have relatively long wavelengths, we hear sound around the corner as the waves diffract, or spread out. **4.** A step-down transformer is used, which has a primary coil with a large number of turns and a secondary coil with fewer turns, so the ratio of the number of secondary coil turns to the primary coil turns is the same as the ratio of the output voltage to the input voltage. This will decrease the voltage.

Unit 2 Test B Answers

Multiple Choice

1. d	**2.** a	**3.** a	**4.** d	**5.** d	**6.** a
7. a	**8.** b	**9.** a	**10.** d	**11.** d	**12.** a
13. a	**14.** a	**15.** b	**16.** a	**17.** b	**18.** c
19. a	**20.** c	**21.** c	**22.** c	**23.** c	**24.** d
25. d	**26.** c	**27.** a	**28.** b	**29.** b	**30.** c

Completion

1. displacement **2.** friction **3.** air resistance; drag **4.** constant **5.** force **6.** chemical **7.** conservation of energy **8.** conduction **9.** node; nodes **10.** translucent **11.** vacuum **12.** focal **13.** volts, current **14.** magnetic domains; domains **15.** perpendicular; at right angles

Short Answer

1. average speed and instantaneous speed **2.** Double the net force acting on the object. **3.** strong nuclear force **4.** The buoyant force is less than the weight. **5.** the screw with closely spaced threads **6.** kinetic energy and potential energy **7.** visible light **8.** solids, liquids, gases **9.** Shake the rope with more force. **10.** radio waves (radio and television signals); microwaves and radar waves (microwave ovens); infrared rays (heat lamps) **11.** Magenta is one of the primary colors of pigments. **12.** ray diagrams **13.** 9 volts; because voltage is equal to the current multiplied by the resistance **14.** A generator is a device that induces an electric current by rotating a coil of wire in a magnetic field. **15.** Accept any five of the following: coal, oil, natural gas, hydroelectric, nuclear, wind, solar.

Using Science Skills

1. D **2.** The fluid pressure exerted on the black spheres is greater (about twice as great). **3.** Ideal mechanical advantage = $\dfrac{\text{Input distance}}{\text{Output distance}} = \dfrac{3m}{1m} = 3$ **4.** 5 J; because the block gained 5 joules of energy, the spring had to do 5 joules of work on the block. **5.** power stroke **6.** a longitudinal wave; a transverse wave **7.** Radio waves; FM signals usually have higher frequencies than AM signals have. **8.** Possible answers: A: convex mirror; a convex mirror causes light rays that are parallel to its optical axis to spread out after reflection.; B: concave mirror; a concave mirror causes light rays that are parallel to its optical axis to come together after reflection.; C: plane mirror; a plane mirror causes parallel light to remain parallel after reflection. **9.** No; only Circuit A is a series circuit. In Circuit A, the current can follow only one path through all three bulbs. Circuit B is a parallel circuit because the current can follow a separate path through each of the three bulbs. **10.** The magnetic pole near the magnetic South Pole is a north magnetic pole.

Chapter 22 Test A Answers

Multiple Choice

1. d	**2.** d	**3.** b	**4.** a	**5.** c	**6.** c
7. c	**8.** b	**9.** b	**10.** a	**11.** d	**12.** c
13. c	**14.** c	**15.** a			

Completion

1. clastic **2.** Pangaea **3.** mid-ocean ridge **4.** P **5.** luster

Short Answer

1. by scraping the mineral on a piece of unglazed porcelain called a streak plate **2.** The lithosphere is cool and rigid; the aesthenosphere is a layer of soft, weak rock that can flow slowly; and the mesosphere is the strong, lowest layer. **3.** An intrusive rock cools from magma inside Earth, and an extrusive rock cools from lava at Earth's surface. **4.** Wegener could not explain how the continents could move through the solid rock of the ocean floor or what force could move entire continents. **5.** The P wave arrived in about 7 seconds, and the S wave arrived in about 11.9 seconds.

Using Science Skills

1. melting; volcanoes **2.** An ocean plate is being subducted beneath a continental plate. **3.** New ocean crust is being added as sea-floor spreading is occurring. **4.** New crust is being created at B, at a mid-ocean ridge. Crust is being destroyed at A and E in subduction zones. **5.** a convergent boundary

Essay

1. As the oceanic plate sinks into the mantle in the subduction zone, the plate causes melting. Magma forms and rises to the surface, where it erupts and forms volcanoes. **2.** The rock cycle is a series of processes in which rocks continuously change from one type to another. These processes include erosion,
weathering, melting, cooling, heat and pressure, and compaction and cementation. **3.** Some mountains form at convergent plate boundaries where two plates collide. Other mountains form at divergent plate boundaries along the mid-ocean ridge systems. **4.** Earthquake epicenters can occur anywhere, but most earthquakes occur at plate boundaries. Earthquake epicenters commonly follow along a plate boundary and can be used to map the location of the boundary. **5.** You could use the hardness test. Quartz would scratch glass, but calcite would not. Calcite also reacts with dilute hydrochloric acid. Place a drop of acid on both samples. The sample that bubbles is calcite.

Chapter 22 Test B Answers

Multiple Choice

1. d	**2.** b	**3.** c	**4.** c	**5.** b	**6.** b
7. a	**8.** d	**9.** c	**10.** b	**11.** b	**12.** d
13. c	**14.** b	**15.** d			

Completion

1. geology **2.** lithosphere **3.** streak **4.** extrusive **5.** subduction **6.** heat **7.** 7 **8.** seismograph **9.** crater **10.** composite

Short Answer

1. by heat, pressure, or reactions with hot water **2.** the theory of plate tectonics **3.** water content, silica content, and temperature **4.** After an eruption, the empty magma chamber or main vent of a volcano may collapse, forming a large depression at the top of the volcano. **5.** at plate boundaries and at hot spots

Using Science Skills

1. metamorphic rock **2.** heat and pressure **3.** cooling **4.** An igneous rock would undergo weathering and erosion to form sediment. The sediment would undergo compaction and cementation to form a sedimentary rock. Heat and pressure would change the sedimentary rock to a metamorphic rock. **5.** Weathering and erosion form sediment, which piles up. Over time, this sediment is squeezed and cemented together to form sedimentary rock.

Chapter 23 Test A Answers

Multiple Choice

1. c	**2.** d	**3.** b	**4.** d	**5.** b	**6.** c
7. a	**8.** a	**9.** a	**10.** b	**11.** c	**12.** d
13. b					

Completion

1. alluvial fan **2.** carbon dioxide **3.** continental shelf **4.** U-shaped **5.** hydraulic action

Short Answer

1. precipitation, evaporation, condensation, transpiration, and the return of water to the ocean via runoff or groundwater flow **2.** Weathering breaks down or chemically alters rocks, while erosion wears down and carries away rock and soil. Weathering contributes to erosion. **3.** Both occur rapidly on steep slopes. **4.** Fine particles are suspended in the air and blown about by the wind. Larger particles bounce along the ground by saltation. The largest particles are pushed along the ground by the wind. **5.** As the glacier moves, it grinds and scrapes the bedrock and soil at its base and sides.

Using Science Skills

1. Layer F **2.** younger **3.** The fault is older than the dike. The fault must be older than the dike because the fault is cut by the dike. **4.** layers A and K, layers B and J, layers C and I, layers D and H, and layers E and G **5.** The layers are older than layer F, with layer A–K being the oldest, and E–G the youngest. All of the layers are older than 200 million years because they are cut by the dike, which is 200 million years old.

Essay

1. The two types of glaciers are continental glaciers and valley glaciers. A continental glacier is a thick sheet of ice that covers a very large area. A valley glacier occurs high in a mountain valley. Valley glaciers are much smaller than continental glaciers. **2.** Fine sediment is carried in suspension. Some material is carried in solution by the water. Larger particles slide or are pushed along the bottom. Some medium-sized particles move by bouncing along the bottom. This process is called saltation. **3.** Possible answer: A molecule of water falls as precipitation; it flows as runoff along the surface; it then soaks into the soil to become groundwater. The groundwater flows toward the coast, where the water molecule flows into the ocean. It then evaporates and travels up into the atmosphere. As it travels up, it cools and condenses. It is joined by other water molecules and then falls back to the surface as precipitation. **4.** Surface currents are large streams of ocean water that move continuously over the ocean surface in about the same path. Surface currents are caused by wind blowing across the ocean's surface. Deep currents are caused by differences in the density of ocean water. These density differences can be caused by differences in water temperature or salinity. Cold temperatures or high salinity cause water to become denser. **5.** The fossil must be easy to identify so it can be identified by geologists who are not experts in that particular fossil group. In order to date rock layers over large distances, the index fossil must have occurred in a widespread area. If the fossil occurred only in a small, restricted area it will not be useful for matching up or relatively dating rock layers over large regions. If the fossil lived for a long period of time, it would not be very useful in narrowing down the relative age of a rock layer.

Chapter 23 Test B Answers

Multiple Choice

1. b	**2.** a	**3.** d	**4.** d	**5.** c	**6.** a
7. c	**8.** b	**9.** d	**10.** b	**11.** d	**12.** c
13. a	**14.** d	**15.** d	**16.** a	**17.** d	

Completion

1. permeable **2.** glaciers **3.** Weathering **4.** water **5.** creep **6.** Saltation **7.** continental **8.** loess **9.** longshore drift **10.** Cenozoic

Short Answer

1. waterfalls, rapids, and V-shaped valleys **2.** stalactites and stalagm **3.** The amount of light decreases, temperature decreases, and pressure increases. **4.** Accept any four of the following: wind, glaciers, gravity, groundwater, waves, streams, weathering. **5.** Precambrian time, Paleozoic Era, Mesozoic Era, and Cenozoic Era

Using Science Skills

1. At point D; the stream flow is faster because water moves faster on the outside of the curve in a meander. **2.** an oxbow lake **3.** deposition; erosion **4.** The flat area around stream F, between the steeper walls of the main valley, is the floodplain. **5.** tributaries

Chapter 24 Test A Answers

Multiple Choice

1. d	**2.** d	**3.** d	**4.** b	**5.** d	**6.** a
7. c	**8.** a	**9.** c	**10.** a	**11.** d	**12.** b
13. c	**14.** d	**15.** c			

Completion

1. carbon dioxide, oxygen **2.** thermosphere **3.** solstice **4.** anticyclone **5.** El Niño

Short Answer

1. During the day, temperatures would be boiling hot, and at night, they would be freezing cold. **2.** Sleet is rain that freezes as it falls. Freezing rain falls as rain and freezes after hitting the surface. **3.** A thunderstorm forms when columns of air rise within a cumulonimbus cloud. If the rising air is cooled to the dew point and the convection is strong enough, a thunderstorm results. **4.** Front A is a cold front, Front B is a warm front, Front C is an occluded front, and Front D is a stationary front. **5.** latitude, the distribution of air pressure systems and global winds, and the existence of a mountain barrier

Using Science Skills

1. Air masses are classified by whether they form over land or over water and the latitude at which they form. **2.** A is a continental polar air mass and has cold, dry air. D is a continental tropical air mass and has warm, dry air. **3.** B is a maritime tropical air mass, and C is a maritime polar air mass. They both form over water and contain moist air. B has warm air and C has cool air. **4.** Possible answer: The weather is warm and humid because a maritime tropical air mass, which has warm, moist air, is moving into the area. **5.** L represents a center of low pressure or a low. A weather system with an area of low pressure at its center is called a cyclone. This weather system is associated with clouds, precipitation, and stormy weather.

Essay

1. As Earth revolves around the sun, the north end of Earth's axis points in the same direction, which is toward the North Star. But the orientation of the axis changes relative to the sun over the course of a year. When the north end of Earth's axis is tilted toward the sun, the south end is tilted away from the sun. At this time, the temperate zone in the Northern Hemisphere has summer, and the temperate zone in the Southern Hemisphere has winter. Six months later, Earth has reached the opposite side of its orbit, and the north end of its axis tilts away from the sun. The temperate zone in the Northern Hemisphere has winter, and the temperate zone in the Southern Hemisphere has summer.

2. Trade winds are wind belts or convection cells just north and south of the equator. They are caused by temperature variations across Earth's surface. At the equator, temperatures tend to be warmer than at other latitudes. Warm air rises at the equator, creating a low-pressure region. This warm air is replaced by cooler air brought by global winds blowing near the surface. Higher in the atmosphere, the air blows away from the equator toward the poles. The winds curve because of the Coriolis effect caused by Earth's rotation. Trade winds in the Northern Hemisphere curve to the right and blow from the northeast to the southwest. Trade winds in the Southern Hemisphere curve to the left and blow from the southeast to the northwest. **3.** Humidity is the amount of water vapor in the air. The humidity stays the same if the temperature decreases. Relative humidity is a ratio of the amount of water vapor in the air compared to the maximum amount of water vapor that can exist at that temperature. The maximum amount of water vapor that can exist in air is greater at high temperatures than at low temperatures. If the temperature decreases, the relative humidity increases even though the amount of water vapor stays the same. The temperature at which air becomes saturated, which is when the relative humidity is 100 percent, is the dew point. If the temperature decreases to the dew point, water vapor will condense. **4.** As a warm front passes through, the area might have stratus clouds, steady rain, and occasionally heavy showers or thunderstorms. After the warm front passes through, the skies are mostly clear, there may be some cumulus clouds, and temperatures rise. As a cold front passes through, the area might have cumulus or cumulonimbus clouds, strong winds, severe thunderstorms, and large amounts of precipitation, which usually lasts for only a short time. After the cold front passes through, the skies clear and temperatures drop. **5.** Meteorologists use Doppler radar to obtain information about the speed of storms and to track the path of storms. Automated weather stations gather data such as temperature, precipitation, and wind speed and direction. Weather satellites provide information such as cloud cover, humidity, temperature, and wind speed. High-speed computers help meteorologists compile and analyze the large amount of weather data and make forecasts.

Chapter 24 Test B Answers
Multiple Choice

1. b   **2.** c   **3.** a   **4.** d   **5.** c   **6.** d
7. d   **8.** d   **9.** a   **10.** c   **11.** a   **12.** d
13. b   **14.** c   **15.** a

Completion

1. atmosphere **2.** tilt, axis **3.** 0°, 90° **4.** high, low **5.** stratus, cumulus, cirrus **6.** precipitation **7.** front **8.** thunderstorm **9.** Doppler radar **10.** temperature, precipitation

Short Answer

1. troposphere, stratosphere, mesosphere, thermosphere **2.** Regions near the equator receive more direct sunlight than regions near the poles receive. **3.** the process by which gases, including water vapor and carbon dioxide, absorb energy, radiate energy, and warm the lower atmosphere **4.** clouds, precipitation, and stormy weather **5.** Conserving energy and a greater reliance on solar, nuclear, or geothermal power could limit the effects of global warming because they would reduce the amount of carbon dioxide released.

Using Science Skills

1. Because cold, dry air is denser than warm, moist air, the cold air pushes the warm air up. As warm air rises, it cools, and water vapor in the air condenses and forms clouds. **2.** A cold, dry air mass is overtaking a warm, moist air mass, and the warm air mass is being lifted up by the cold air. **3.** Both a cold front and a warm front have a cold, dry air mass and a warm, moist air mass colliding. In both fronts, the cold air is under the warm air, and in both fronts, precipitation can occur. **4.** At a cold front, a cold air mass is overtaking a warm air mass and lifting it up. At a warm front, a warm air mass is overtaking a cold air mass and rising over the cold air. **5.** The warm air mass has been trapped between two cold air masses, which have forced it to rise, cutting it off from the ground.

Chapter 25 Test A Answers
Multiple Choice

1. c   **2.** d   **3.** a   **4.** b   **5.** c   **6.** a
7. b   **8.** c   **9.** d   **10.** b   **11.** d   **12.** c
13. d   **14.** c   **15.** c

Completion

1. average **2.** moons **3.** 100 **4.** Kuiper **5.** temperatures

Short Answer

1. Ptolemy's view was geocentric. Aristarchus' view was heliocentric. **2.** the plane of Earth's orbit **3.** A full moon occurs when the side of the moon facing Earth is fully lit by the sun, and Earth is between the sun and the moon. A new moon occurs when the moon is between the sun and Earth, and the moon's dark side faces Earth.

4. Mars is most similar to Earth of all the planets in size, mass, and density. It has distinct seasons and shows evidence of once having a great deal of water. **5.** The weak gravity of small asteroids and impacts with other objects caused these shapes. **6.** Planetesimals grew larger because more gas condensed in the outer solar system. The gravity of these larger planetesimals could attract and capture hydrogen and helium, which were abundant.

Using Science Skills

1. Newton's first law of motion states that an object in motion will continue to move in a straight line unless acted upon by a force. A planet in orbit C would move approximately along path A if another force—gravity—was not acting on it. The planet has inertia, which carries it in direction A, but force B pulls the planet in a curved path C. The planet stays in orbit because of the balance between inertia and the gravitational pull of the sun. **2.** The planet's inertia would carry it forward in a straight-line path, such as A. Because there would be no gravitational force on the planet from the sun, the net force on the planet would be zero. As a result, there would be no change in the planet's speed or direction. **3.** Arrow B represents the gravitational force between the planet and the sun. The force acts between the center of the planet and the center of the sun, and both the center of the planet and the center of the sun lie in the orbital plane. Therefore, the force of attraction between the centers must also lie in the same plane. **4.** Saturn is not dense, but it still has mass, so inertia and gravity balance to keep Saturn in orbit. **5.** Mars; the period of the asteroid would be greater than 1.88 years because the asteroid belt is beyond the orbit of Mars, and orbital periods increase as distance from the sun increases.

Essay

1. Possible answers: Space probes, or unpiloted vehicles, are being used to photograph and measure parameters of the planets, moons, and other objects, and then transmit information back to Earth. The Hubble telescope in orbit around Earth and others telescopes provide views and information about the solar system and beyond. The space shuttle is a reusable vehicle that sends humans into orbit around Earth to do scientific research. The International Space Station is a permanent laboratory designed for research in space. **2.** Most of that material of this mass has already joined a solar-system component, such as a planet, or is already in orbit. **3.** Two moons, Ganymede and Callisto, are about the size of Mercury. Io and Europa are about the size of Earth's moon. Unlike Jupiter, Ganymede, Io, and Europa have metal cores and rocky mantles. Io is the most volcanically active body in the solar system. Europa has an icy crust that appears to rest on a liquid-water ocean. Ganymede and

Callisto are covered with ice. **4.** Comets are dusty pieces of ice and rock that have no tails in the regions of space far from the sun. Comets travel in highly elliptical orbits around the sun. A comet develops two tails as it approaches the sun. The bluish tail is an ion tail comprised of charged gas particles pushed away from the comet by the solar wind. The dust tail is white and is produced by dust that is pushed away from the sun by photons. The ion tail of a comet can be millions of kilometers long and always faces away from the sun. **5.** Any theory must explain the following: 1) why the planets lie in a single plane, 2) why all the planets orbit the sun in a single direction, and 3) the difference in size and composition between the terrestrial planets and the gas giants. The nebular theory satisfies all three criteria.

Chapter 25 Test B Answers

Multiple Choice

1. b	**2.** a	**3.** c	**4.** b	**5.** d	**6.** b
7. a	**8.** d	**9.** c	**10.** a	**11.** a	**12.** b
13. c	**14.** d	**15.** d			

Completion

1. toward the sun **2.** Soviet Union **3.** atmosphere **4.** geocentric **5.** full moon **6.** period of rotation **7.** asteroids **8.** comets **9.** Oort cloud **10.** nebula

Short Answer

1. the sun, planets and their moons, and a variety of smaller objects, such as asteroids, meteoroids, and comets **2.** Neil Armstrong **3.** the impact of high speed meteoroids **4.** tens of thousands of objects, mostly made of ice, dust, and rock **5.** remnants of previous stars

Using Science Skills

1. Heliocentric; the sun is shown at the center, and other bodies are indicated in orbit around the sun. **2.** Planets; 1. Mercury, terrestrial; 2. Venus, terrestrial; 3. Earth, terrestrial; 4. Mars, terrestrial; 5. Jupiter, gas giant; 6. Saturn, gas giant; 7. Uranus, gas giant; 8. Neptune, gas giant; 9. Pluto, neither (can't be classified as either terrestrial or gas giant) **3.** The asteroid belt lies mostly between Mars and Jupiter, so the diagram could be marked anywhere between 4 and 5. **4.** Sufficiently cool temperatures for ice-forming compounds to condense must occur beyond Mars (4). Mars is the last terrestrial planet before the first of the gas giants, Jupiter. Cool temperatures had to exist in this region for the gas giants to form. **5.** The Kuiper belt would have to be drawn extending from Pluto (9) to a little more than twice the distance of Pluto from the sun. The Oort cloud could not be drawn on this scale because it extends out to 50,000 AU.

Chapter 26 Test A Answers

Multiple Choice

1. b	**2.** c	**3.** d	**4.** d	**5.** a	**6.** c
7. a	**8.** b	**9.** b	**10.** b	**11.** c	**12.** d
13. d					

Completion
1. core 2. parallax 3. mass 4. eclipsing 5. expanding

Short Answer
1. Area C is the radiation zone of the sun. Area B is the convection zone. The radiation zone transfers energy primarily by electromagnetic waves. The convection zone transfers energy primarily by moving gases in convection currents. 2. absorption lines 3. supergiants 4. gravity and heat from contraction 5. When hydrogen is gone, helium fusion begins, producing carbon, oxygen, and certain heavier elements. Elements heavier than iron are created in a supernova. 6. a mysterious force called dark energy

Using Science Skills
1. By the placement on the H-R diagram, we know that both stars are of roughly equal absolute brightness and surface temperature, and that both are white dwarfs. Because star X appears dimmer, it must be farther from Earth. 2. The hottest stars are blue and very bright. The coolest stars are red and have a much lower absolute brightness. They are found in the lower right of the main sequence. 3. region B, the main sequence, near the center (surface temperature of 5800 K) 4. The sun is a yellow star located in about the middle of region B, the main sequence. It will remain stable there for at least another 5 billion years. In its next stage, the sun will be classified as a red giant (region D). It will then become a white dwarf (region A). 5. As a star begins to fuse helium nuclei, its outer shell expands greatly. The outer shell then cools as it expands. The star is then classified as a red giant or a supergiant, depending on its original mass. Red giants are located in region D, and supergiants are located in region C.

Essay
1. The sun's core has a high enough temperature and pressure for fusion to take place. Less massive hydrogen nuclei combine into more massive helium nuclei, releasing enormous amounts of energy. 2. The apparent brightness is how bright a star appears and varies with the distance from which the star is viewed. Absolute brightness is a characteristic of the star and does not depend on how far it is from Earth.
3. As high-mass stars evolve to the fusion of elements other than hydrogen, they create other elements, including iron. The stars eventually run out of elements to fuse. Gravity overcomes the lower thermal pressure, and the star collapses, producing a violent explosion called a supernova. The heavier elements in our solar system, including the atoms in our bodies, come from a supernova that occurred billions of years ago.
4. New stars are not forming in older elliptical galaxies because there is little gas or dust between the stars. Irregular galaxies have many young stars and large amounts of gas and dust from which to produce new stars. 5. Dark matter seems to supply most of the gravitational attraction that keeps the galaxies from flying apart. The amount of dark matter in the universe will determine if the universe will continue to expand, stop expanding, or, perhaps, increase in the rate at which it is expanding. The amount of dark energy will determine if the universe will continue to expand forever.

Chapter 26 Test B Answers
Multiple Choice
1. d	2. a	3. b	4. a	5. b	6. d
7. c	8. a	9. b	10. d	11. c	12. a
13. c	14. a	15. c	16. a	17. c	

Completion
1. hydrogen 2. gravity 3. elements 4. main sequence 5. protostar 6. fusion 7. white dwarf; black dwarf 8. star system 9. globular cluster 10. big bang 11. dark matter

Short Answer
1. 5 billion years 2. the photosphere 3. to determine the stars' distances from Earth 4. The larger the observed shift is, the faster is the speed. 5. Scientists know how fast the universe is expanding and can infer how long it has been expanding since the big bang.

Using Science Skills
1. Helium fusion would be occurring in stage G. In stage F, the star is a main-sequence star, and its energy is supplied by the fusion of hydrogen. Stage G represents the star as a red giant. As the core of the red giant collapses, it becomes hot enough to cause helium to undergo fusion. 2. Figure 26-2A; the subsequent stages of the model indicate a supernova at stage C and two possible fates at stages D and E. Low-mass stars have only one ultimate fate as a black dwarf at stage I from the white dwarf at stage H. Also, Figure 26-2A shows a supergiant, which is not a stage for a low mass star. 3. Figure 26-2B; small nebulas most likely produce low-mass to medium-mass stars because of the lower available mass in the nebula. 4. A high-mass star; a supernova results in one of two fates, depending on the star's mass. It could become a neutron star (stage D) or, for more massive stars, a black hole (stage E). 5. Figure 26-2B is a low-mass star, and Figure 26-2A represents a high-mass star. Figure 26-2A depicts the fate of the star as either a neutron star or a black hole. High-mass stars are shorter lived than low-mass stars because high-mass stars burn brighter, use up their hydrogen fuel in the core sooner, and therefore leave the main sequence sooner.

Unit 3 Test A Answers
Multiple Choice
1. d	2. b	3. a	4. b	5. a	6. d
7. b	8. a	9. b	10. c	11. d	12. b
13. b	14. d	15. a	16. b	17. c	18. d
19. c	20. d	21. a	22. b	23. c	24. a
25. b	26. b	27. b	28. c	29. d	30. d

Completion
1. clastic **2.** Pangaea **3.** mid-ocean ridge **4.** P
5. alluvial fan **6.** carbon dioxide **7.** continental shelf
8. U-shaped **9.** thermosphere **10.** solstice
11. anticyclone **12.** El Niño **13.** average **14.** moons
15. 100 **16.** Kuiper **17.** core **18.** parallax **19.** mass
20. eclipsing

Short Answer
1. by scraping the mineral on a piece of unglazed
porcelain called a streak plate **2.** The lithosphere is cool
and rigid; the aesthenosphere is a layer of soft, weak
rock that can flow slowly; and the mesosphere is the
strong, lowest layer. **3.** Both occur rapidly on steep
slopes. **4.** Fine particles are suspended in the air and
blown about by the wind. Larger particles bounce along
the ground by saltation. The largest particles are
pushed along the ground by the wind. **5.** Sleet is rain
that freezes as it falls. Freezing rain falls as rain and
freezes after hitting the surface. **6.** A thunderstorm
forms when columns of air rise within a cumulonimbus
cloud. If the rising air is cooled to the dew point and the
convection is strong enough, a thunderstorm results.
7. the plane of Earth's orbit **8.** A full moon occurs when
the side of the moon facing Earth is fully lit by the sun,
and Earth is between the sun and the moon. A new
moon occurs when the moon is between the sun and
Earth, and the moon's dark side faces Earth.
9. supergiants **10.** gravity and heat from contraction

Using Science Skills
1. melting; volcanoes **2.** An ocean plate is being
subducted beneath a continental plate. **3.** Layer F
4. younger **5.** Air masses are classified by whether they
form over land or over water and the latitude at which
they form. **6.** A is a continental polar air mass and has
cold, dry air. D is a continental tropical air **7.** Arrow B
represents the gravitational force between the planet
and the sun. The force acts between the center of the
planet and the center of the sun, and both the center of
the planet and the center of the sun lie in the orbital
plane. Therefore, the force of attraction between the
centers must also lie in the same plane. **8.** Saturn is not
dense, but it still has mass, so inertia and gravity
balance to keep Saturn in orbit. **9.** By the placement on
the H-R diagram, we know that both stars are of
roughly equal absolute brightness and surface
temperature, and that both are white dwarfs. Because
star X appears dimmer, it must be farther from Earth.
10. The hottest stars are blue and very bright. The
coolest stars are red and have a much lower absolute
brightness. They are found in the lower right of the main
sequence.

Essay
1. As the oceanic plate sinks into the mantle in the
subduction zone, the plate causes melting. Magma
forms and rises to the surface, where it erupts and

forms volcanoes. **2.** Possible answer: A molecule of
water falls as precipitation; it flows as runoff along the
surface; it then soaks into the soil to become
groundwater. The groundwater flows toward the coast,
where the water molecule flows into the ocean. It then
evaporates and travels up into the atmosphere. As it
travels up, it cools and condenses. It is joined by other
water molecules and then falls back to the surface as
precipitation. **3.** As a warm front passes through, the
area might have stratus clouds, steady rain, and
occasionally heavy showers or thunderstorms. After the
warm front passes through, the skies are mostly clear,
there may be some cumulus clouds, and temperatures
rise. As a cold front passes through, the area might
have cumulus or cumulonimbus clouds, strong winds,
severe thunderstorms, and large amounts of
precipitation, which usually lasts for only a short time.
After the cold front passes through, the skies clear and
temperatures drop. **4.** Mars; the period of the asteroid
would be greater than 1.88 years because the asteroid
belt is beyond the orbit of Mars, and orbital periods
increase as distance from the sun increases. **5.** As
high-mass stars evolve to the fusion of elements other
than hydrogen, they create other elements, including
iron. The stars eventually run out of elements to fuse.
Gravity overcomes the lower thermal pressure, and the
star collapses, producing a violent explosion called a
supernova. The heavier elements in our solar system,
including the atoms in our bodies, come from a
supernova that occurred billions of years ago.

Unit 3 Test B Answers
Multiple Choice

1. d	**2.** b	**3.** c	**4.** d	**5.** c	**6.** b
7. c	**8.** a	**9.** c	**10.** b	**11.** d	**12.** b
13. d	**14.** c	**15.** d	**16.** c	**17.** a	**18.** d
19. d	**20.** c	**21.** a	**22.** a	**23.** b	**24.** c
25. b	**26.** d	**27.** c	**28.** a	**29.** b	**30.** d

Completion
1. geology **2.** lithosphere **3.** streak **4.** continental
5. loess **6.** longshore drift **7.** thunderstorm **8.** Doppler
radar **9.** temperature, precipitation **10.** toward the sun
11. Soviet Union **12.** atmosphere **13.** main sequence
14. star system **15.** big bang

Short Answer
1. by heat, pressure, or reactions with hot water **2.** the
theory of plate tectonics **3.** water content, silica
content, and temperature **4.** The amount of light
decreases, temperature decreases, and pressure
increases. **5.** Accept any four of the following: wind,
glaciers, gravity, groundwater, waves, streams,
weathering. **6.** Precambrian time, Paleozoic Era,
Mesozoic Era, and Cenozoic Era **7.** Regions near the
equator receive more direct sunlight than regions near
the poles receive. **8.** the process by which gases,
including water vapor and carbon dioxide, absorb

energy, radiate energy, and warm the lower atmosphere
9. clouds, precipitation, and stormy weather **10.** Neil
Armstrong **11.** the impact of high speed meteoroids
12. tens of thousands of objects, mostly made of ice,
dust, and rock **13.** to determine the stars' distances
from Earth **14.** The larger the observed shift is, the
faster is the speed. **15.** Scientists know how fast the
universe is expanding and can infer how long it has
been expanding since the big bang.
Using Science Skills
1. metamorphic rock **2.** heat and pressure **3.** At point
D; the stream flow is faster because water moves faster
on the outside of the curve in a meander. **4.** an oxbow
lake **5.** A cold, dry air mass is overtaking a warm, moist
air mass, and the warm air mass is being lifted up by
the cold air. **6.** Both a cold front and a warm front have
a cold, dry air mass and a warm, moist air mass
colliding. In both fronts, the cold air is under the
warm air, and in both fronts, precipitation can occur.

7. Heliocentric; the sun is shown at the center, and
other bodies are indicated in orbit around the sun. **8.**
Planets; 1. Mercury, terrestrial; 2. Venus, terrestrial; 3.
Earth, terrestrial; 4. Mars, terrestrial; 5. Jupiter, gas giant;
6. Saturn, gas giant; 7. Uranus, gas giant; 8. Neptune,
gas giant; 9. Pluto, neither (can't be classified as either
terrestrial or gas giant) **9.** Helium fusion would be
occurring in stage G. In stage F, the star is a main-
sequence star, and its energy is supplied by the fusion
of hydrogen. Stage G represents the star as a red giant.
As the core of the red giant collapses, it becomes hot
enough to cause helium to undergo fusion. **10.** Figure
26-2A; the subsequent stages of the model indicate a
supernova at stage C and two possible fates at stages
D and E. Low-mass stars have only one ultimate fate as
a black dwarf at stage I from the white dwarf at stage H.
Also, Figure 26-2A shows a supergiant, which is not a
stage for a low mass star.